PERIL AT END HOUSE

" Agatha is a British institution."
Beverley Baxter, SUNDAY EXPRESS

" In the school of detective fiction, Agatha Christie is to-day the undisputed Head Girl."
Margery Allingham, NEW YORK TIMES

" Agatha Christie I would call a Beta plus plus in the detective field."
C. A. Lejeune, BBC CRITICS

Famous Books and Authors in the Fontana Series

Fontana books make available, in attractive, readable yet inexpensive editions, the best books, both fiction and non-fiction, of famous contemporary authors. These include books up to 832 pages, complete and unabridged.

If you would like to be kept informed of new and forthcoming titles please apply to your local bookseller or write to :

WILLIAM COLLINS SONS & CO. LTD.
144 Cathedral Street, Glasgow, C.4

Peril
at End House

AGATHA CHRISTIE

COLLINS

fontana books

First published by Collins for the Crime Club 1932
First issued in Fontana Books 1961

To
EDEN PHILLPOTTS

To whom I shall always be grateful for his
friendship and the encouragement he gave me
many years ago

Printed in Great Britain
Collins Clear-Type Press : London & Glasgow

CONTENTS

CHAPTER ONE

THE MAJESTIC HOTEL

No seaside town in the south of England is, I think, as attractive as St. Loo. It is well named the Queen of Watering Places and reminds one forcibly of the Riviera. The Cornish coast is to my mind every bit as fascinating as that of the south of France.

I remarked as much to my friend, Hercule Poirot.

"So it said on our menu in the restaurant car yesterday, *mon ami*. Your remark is not original."

"But don't you agree?"

He was smiling to himself and did not at once answer my question. I repeated it.

"A thousand pardons, Hastings. My thoughts were wandering. Wandering indeed to that part of the world you mentioned just now."

"The south of France?"

"Yes. I was thinking of that last winter that I spent there and of the events which occurred."

I remembered. A murder had been committed on the Blue Train, and the mystery—a complicated and baffling one—had been solved by Poirot with his usual unerring acumen.

"How I wish I had been with you," I said with deep regret.

"I too," said Poirot. "Your experience would have been invaluable to me."

I looked at him sideways. As a result of long habit, I distrust his compliments, but he appeared perfectly serious. And after all, why not? I have a very long experience of the methods he employs.

"What I particularly missed was your vivid imagination,

Hastings," he went on dreamily. "One needs a certain amount of light relief. My valet, Georges, an admirable man with whom I sometimes permitted myself to discuss a point, has no imagination whatever."

This remark seemed to me quite irrelevant.

"Tell me, Poirot," I said. "Are you never tempted to renew your activities? This passive life——"

"Suits me admirably, my friend. To sit in the sun—what could be more charming? To step from your pedestal at the zenith of your fame—what could be a grander gesture? They say of me : '*That is Hercule Poirot!—The great—the unique!—There was never any one like him, there never will be!*' *Eh bien*—I am satisfied. I ask no more. I am modest."

I should not myself have used the word *modest*. It seemed to me that my little friend's egotism had certainly not declined with his years. He leaned back in his chair, caressing his moustache and almost purring with self-satisfaction.

We were sitting on one of the terraces of the Majestic Hotel. It is the biggest hotel in St. Loo and stands in its own grounds on a headland overlooking the sea. The gardens of the hotel lay below us freely interspersed with palm trees. The sea was of a deep and lovely blue, the sky clear and the sun shining with all the single-hearted fervour an August sun should (but in England so often does not) have. There was a vigorous humming of bees, a pleasant sound—and altogether nothing could have been more ideal.

We had only arrived last night, and this was the first morning of what we proposed should be a week's stay. If only these weather conditions continued, we should indeed have a perfect holiday.

I picked up the morning paper which had fallen from my hand and resumed my perusal of the morning's news. The political situation seemed unsatisfactory, but uninteresting, there was trouble in China, there was a long account of a rumoured City swindle, but on the whole there was no news of a very thrilling order.

"Curious thing this parrot disease," I remarked, as I turned the sheet.

"Very curious."

"Two more deaths at Leeds, I see."

"Most regrettable."

I turned a page.

"Still no news of that flying fellow, Seton, in his round-the-world flight. Pretty plucky, these fellows. That amphibian machine of his, the *Albatross*, must be a great invention. Too bad if he's gone west. Not that they've given up hope yet. He may have made one of the Pacific islands."

"The Solomon islanders are still cannibals, are they not?" inquired Poirot pleasantly.

"Must be a fine fellow. That sort of thing makes one feel it's a good thing to be an Englishman after all."

"It consoles for the defeats at Wimbledon," said Poirot.

"I—I didn't mean," I began.

My friend waved my attempted apology aside gracefully.

"Me," he announced. "I am not amphibian, like the machine of the poor Captain Seton, but I am cosmopolitan. And for the English I have always had, as you know, a great admiration. The thorough way, for instance, in which they read the daily paper."

My attention had strayed to political news.

"They seem to be giving the Home Secretary a pretty bad time of it," I remarked with a chuckle.

"The poor man. He has his troubles, that one. Ah! yes. So much so that he seeks for help in the most improbable quarters."

I stared at him.

With a slight smile, Poirot drew from his pocket his morning's correspondence, neatly secured by a rubber band. From this he selected one letter which he tossed across to me.

"It must have missed us yesterday," he said.

I read the letter with a pleasurable feeling of excitement.

"But, Poirot," I cried. "This is most flattering!"

"You think so, my friend?"

"He speaks in the warmest terms of your ability."

"He is right," said Poirot, modestly averting his eyes.

"He begs you to investigate this matter for him—puts it as a personal favour."

"Quite so. It is unnecessary to repeat all this to me. You understand, my dear Hastings. I have read the letter myself."

"It is too bad," I cried. "This will put an end to our holiday."

"No, no, *calmez vous*—there is no question of that."

"But the Home Secretary says the matter is urgent."

"He may be right—or again he may not. These politicians, they are easily excited. I have seen myself, in the Chambre des Deputés in Paris——"

"Yes, yes, but Poirot, surely we ought to be making arrangements? The express to London has gone—it leaves at twelve o'clock. The next——"

"Calm yourself, Hastings, calm yourself, I pray of you! Always the excitement, the agitation. We are not going to London to-day—nor yet to-morrow."

"But this summons——"

"Does not concern me. I do not belong to your police force, Hastings. I am asked to undertake a case as a private investigator. I refuse."

"You *refuse*?"

"Certainly. I write with perfect politeness, tender my regrets, my apologies, explain that I am completely desolated —but what will you? I have retired—I am finished."

"You are not finished," I exclaimed warmly.

Poirot patted my knee.

"There speaks the good friend—the faithful dog. And you have reason, too. The grey cells, they still function—the order, the method—it is still there. But when I have retired, my friend, I have retired! It is finished! I am not a stage favourite who gives the world a dozen farewells. In all generosity I say: let the young men have a chance. They may possibly do something creditable. I doubt it, but they may. Anyway they will do well enough for this doubtless tiresome affair of the Home Secretary's."

"But, Poirot, the compliment!"

"Me, I am above compliments. The Home Secretary, being a man of sense, realises that if he can only obtain my services all will be successful. What will you? He is unlucky. Hercule Poirot has solved his last case."

I looked at him. In my heart of hearts I deplored his obstinacy. The solving of such a case as was indicated might add still further lustre to his already world-wide reputation. Nevertheless I could not but admire his unyielding attitude.

Suddenly a thought struck me and I smiled.

"I wonder," I said, "that you are not afraid. Such an emphatic pronouncement will surely tempt the gods."

"Impossible," he replied, "that anyone should shake the decision of Hercule Poirot."

"*Impossible*, Poirot?"

"You are right, *mon ami*, one should not use such a word. *Eh, ma foi*, I do not say that if a bullet should strike the wall by my head, I would not investigate the matter! One is human after all!"

I smiled. A little pebble had just struck the terrace beside us, and Poirot's fanciful analogy from it tickled my fancy. He stooped now and picked up the pebble as he went on.

"Yes—one is human. One is the sleeping dog—well and good, but the sleeping dog can be roused. There is a proverb in your language that says so."

"In fact," I said, "if you find a dagger planted by your pillow to-morrow morning—let the criminal who put it there beware!"

He nodded, but rather absently.

Suddenly, to my surprise, he rose and descended the couple of steps that led from the terrace to the garden. As he did so, a girl came into sight hurrying up towards us.

I had just registered the impression that she was a decidedly pretty girl when my attention was drawn to

Poirot who, not looking where he was going, had stumbled over a root and fallen heavily. He was just abreast of the girl at the time and she and I between us helped him to his feet. My attention was naturally on my friend, but I was conscious of an impression of dark hair, an impish face and big dark blue eyes.

" A thousand pardons," stammered Poirot. " Mademoiselle, you are most kind. I regret exceedingly—ouch!— my foot he pains me considerably. No, no, it is nothing really—the turned ankle, that is all. In a few minutes all will be well. But if you could help me, Hastings—you and Mademoiselle between you, if she will be so very kind. I am ashamed to ask it of her."

With me on the one side and the girl on the other we soon got Poirot on to a chair on the terrace. I then suggested fetching a doctor, but this my friend negatived sharply.

" It is nothing, I tell you. The ankle turned, that is all. Painful for the moment, but soon over." He made a grimace. " See, in a little minute I shall have forgotten. Mademoiselle, I thank you a thousand times. You were most kind. Sit down, I beg of you."

The girl took a chair.

" It's nothing," she said. " But I wish you would let it be seen to."

" Mademoiselle, I assure you, it is a *bagatelle*! In the pleasure of your society the pain passes already."

The girl laughed.

" That's good."

" What about a cocktail?" I suggested. " It's just about the time."

" Well——" She hesitated. " Thanks very much."

" Martini?"

" Yes, please—dry Martini."

I went off. On my return, after having ordered the drinks, I found Poirot and the girl engaged in animated conversation.

" Imagine, Hastings," he said, " that house there—the

one on the point—that we have admired so much, it belongs to Mademoiselle here."

"Indeed?" I said, though I was unable to recall having expressed any admiration. In fact I had hardly noticed the house. "It looks rather eerie and imposing standing there by itself far from anything."

"It's called End House," said the girl. "I love it—but it's a tumble-down old place. Going to rack and ruin."

"You are the last of an old family, Mademoiselle?"

"Oh! we're nothing important. But there have been Buckleys here for two or three hundred years. My brother died three years ago, so I'm the last of the family."

"That is sad. You live there alone, Mademoiselle?"

"Oh! I'm away a good deal and when I'm at home there's usually a cheery crowd coming and going."

"That is so modern. Me, I was picturing you in a dark mysterious mansion, haunted by a family curse."

"How marvellous! What a picturesque imagination you must have. No, it's not haunted. Or if so, the ghost is a beneficent one. I've had three escapes from sudden death in as many days, so I must bear a charmed life."

Poirot sat up alertly.

"Escapes from death? That sounds interesting, Mademoiselle."

"Oh! they weren't very thrilling. Just accidents you know." She jerked her head sharply as a wasp flew past. "Curse these wasps. There must be a nest of them round here."

"The bees and the wasps—you do not like them, Mademoiselle? You have been stung—yes?"

"No—but I hate the way they come right past your face."

"The bee in the bonnet," said Poirot. "Your English phrase."

At that moment the cocktails arrived. We all held up our glasses and made the usual inane observations.

"I'm due in the hotel for cocktails, really," said Miss

Buckley. " I expect they're wondering what has become of me."

Poirot cleared his throat and set down his glass.

" Ah! for a cup of good rich chocolate," he murmured. " But in England they make it not. Still, in England you have some very pleasing customs. The young girls, their hats they come on and off—so prettily—so easily——"

The girl stared at him.

" What do you mean? Why shouldn't they?"

" You ask that because you are young—so young, Mademoiselle. But to me the natural thing seems to have a coiffure high and rigid—so—and the hat attached with many hatpins —là—là—là—et là."

He executed four vicious jabs in the air.

" But how frightfully uncomfortable!"

" Ah! I should think so," said Poirot. No martyred lady could have spoken with more feeling. " When the wind blew it was the agony—it gave you the *migraine*."

Miss Buckley dragged off the simple wide-brimmed felt she was wearing and cast it down beside her.

" And now we do this," she laughed.

" Which is sensible and charming," said Poirot, with a little bow.

I looked at her with interest. Her dark hair was ruffled and gave her an elfin look. There was something elfin about her altogether. The small, vivid face, pansy-shaped, the enormous dark blue eyes, and something else—something haunting and arresting. Was it a hint of recklessness? There were dark shadows under the eyes.

The terrace on which we were sitting was a little used one. The main terrace where most people sat was just round the corner at a point where the cliff shelved directly down to the sea.

From round this corner now there appeared a man, a red-faced man with a rolling carriage who carried his hands half clenched by his side. There was something breezy and carefree about him—a typical sailor.

"I can't think where the girl's got to," he was saying in tones that easily carried to where we sat. "Nick—Nick."

Miss Buckley rose.

"I knew they'd be getting in a state. Attaboy—George—here I am."

"Freddie's frantic for a drink. Come on, girl."

He cast a glance of frank curiosity at Poirot, who must have differed considerably from most of Nick's friends.

The girl performed a wave of introduction.

"This is Commander Challenger—er——"

But to my surprise Poirot did not supply the name for which she was waiting. Instead he rose, bowed very ceremoniously and murmured.

"Of the English Navy. I have a great regard for the English Navy."

This type of remark is not one that an Englishman acclaims most readily. Commander Challenger flushed and Nick Buckley took command of the situation.

"Come on, George. Don't gape. Let's find Freddie and Jim."

She smiled at Poirot.

"Thanks for the cocktail. I hope the ankle will be all right."

With a nod to me she slipped her hand through the sailor's arm and they disappeared round the corner together.

"So that is one of Mademoiselle's friends," murmured Poirot thoughtfully. "One of her cheery crowd. What about him? Give me your expert judgment, Hastings. Is he what you call a good fellow—yes?"

Pausing for a moment to try and decide exactly what Poirot thought I should mean by a "good fellow," I gave a doubtful assent.

"He seems all right—yes," I said. "So far as one can tell by a cursory glance."

"I wonder," said Poirot.

The girl had left her hat behind. Poirot stooped to pick it up and twirled it round absent-mindedly on his finger.

"Has he a *tendresse* for her? What do you think, Hastings?"

"My dear Poirot! How *can* I tell? Here—give me that hat. The lady will want it. I'll take it to her."

Poirot paid no attention to my request. He continued to revolve the hat slowly on his finger.

"*Pas encore. Ca m'amuse.*"

"Really, Poirot!"

"Yes, my friend, I grow old and childish, do I not?"

This was so exactly what I was feeling that I was somewhat disconcerted to have it put into words. Poirot gave a little chuckle, then leaning forward he laid a finger against the side of his nose.

"But no—I am not so completely imbecile as you think! We will return the hat—but assuredly—but later! We will return it to End House and thus we shall have the opportunity of seeing the charming Miss Nick again."

"Poirot," I said. "I believe you have fallen in love."

"She is a pretty girl—eh?"

"Well—you saw for yourself. Why ask me?"

"Because, alas! I cannot judge. To me, nowadays, anything young is beautiful. *Jeunesse—jeunesse.* . . . It is the tragedy of my years. But you—I appeal to you! Your judgment is not up-to-date, naturally, having lived in the Argentine so long. You admire the figure of five years ago, but you are at any rate more modern than I am. She is pretty—yes? She has the appeal to the sexes?"

"One sex is sufficient, Poirot. The answer, I should say, is very much in the affirmative. Why are you so interested in the lady?"

"Am I interested?"

"Well—look at what you've just been saying."

"You are under a misapprehension, *mon ami*. I may be interested in the lady—yes—but I am much more interested in her hat."

I stared at him, but he appeared perfectly serious.

He nodded his head at me

"Yes, Hastings, this very hat." He held it towards me. "You see the reason for my interest?"

"It's a nice hat," I said, bewildered. "But quite an ordinary hat. Lots of girls have hats like it."

"Not like this one."

I looked at it more closely.

"You see, Hastings?"

"A perfectly plain fawn felt. Good style——"

"I did not ask you to describe the hat. It is plain that you do *not* see. Almost incredible, my poor Hastings, how you hardly ever *do* see! It amazes me every time anew! But regard, my dear old imbecile—it is not necessary to employ the grey cells—the eyes will do. Regard—regard——"

And then at last I saw to what he had been trying to draw my attention. The slowly turning hat was revolving on his finger, and that finger was stuck neatly through a hole in the brim of the hat. When he saw that I had realised his meaning, he drew his finger out and held the hat towards me. It was a small neat hole, quite round, and I could not imagine its purpose, if purpose it had.

"Did you observe the way Mademoiselle Nick flinched when a bee flew past? The bee in the bonnet—the hole in the hat."

"But a bee couldn't make a hole like that."

"Exactly, Hastings! What acumen! It could not. *But a bullet could, mon cher!*"

"*A bullet?*"

"*Mais oui!* A bullet like *this*."

He held out his hand with a small object in the palm of it.

"A spent bullet, *mon ami*. It was that which hit the terrace just now when we were talking. A spent bullet!"

"You mean——?"

"*I mean that one inch of difference and that hole would not be through the hat but through the head.* Now do you see why I am interested, Hastings? You were right, my friend, when you told me not to use the word 'impossible.' Yes—one is human! Ah! but he made a grave mistake, that would-be murderer, when he shot at his victim within a dozen yards of Hercule Poirot! For him, it is indeed *la mauvaise chance*. But you see now why we must make our entry into End House and get into touch with Mademoiselle? *Three near escapes from death in three days.* That is what she said. We must act quickly, Hastings. The peril is very close at hand."

CHAPTER TWO

END HOUSE

"POIROT," I said. "I have been thinking."

"An admirable exercise, my friend. Continue it."

We were sitting facing each other at lunch at a small table in the window.

"This shot must have been fired quite close to us. And yet we did not hear it."

"And you think that in the peaceful stillness, with the rippling waves the only sound, we should have done so?"

"Well, it's odd."

"No, it is not odd. Some sounds—you get used to them so soon that you hardly notice they are there. All this morning, my friend, speedboats have been making trips in the bay. You complained at first—soon, you did not even notice. But, *ma foi*, you could fire a machine gun almost and not notice it when one of those boats is on the sea."

"Yes, that's true."

"Ah! *voilà*," murmured Poirot. "Mademoiselle and her friends. They are to lunch here, it seems. And therefore I must return the hat. But no matter. The affair is sufficiently serious to warrant a visit all on its own."

He leaped up nimbly from his seat, hurried across the room, and presented the hat with a bow just as Miss Buckley and her companions were seating themselves at table.

They were a party of four, Nick Buckley, Commander Challenger, another man and another girl. From where we sat we had a very imperfect view of them. From time to time the naval man's laugh boomed out. He seemed a simple, likeable soul, and I had already taken a fancy to him.

My friend was silent and distrait during our meal. He crumbled his bread, made strange little ejaculations to himself and straightened everything on the table. I tried to talk, but meeting with no encouragement soon gave it up.

He continued to sit on at the table long after he had finished his cheese. As soon as the other party had left the room, however, he too rose to his feet. They were just settling themselves at a table in the lounge when Poirot marched up to them in his most military fashion, and addressed Nick directly.

"Mademoiselle, may I crave one little word with you."

The girl frowned. I realised her feelings clearly enough. She was afraid that this queer little foreigner was going to be a nuisance. I could not but sympathise with her, knowing how it must appear in her eyes. Rather unwillingly, she moved a few steps aside.

Almost immediately I saw an expression of surprise pass over her face at the low hurried words Poirot was uttering.

In the meantime, I was feeling rather awkward and ill at ease. Challenger with ready tact came to my rescue, offering me a cigarette and making some commonplace observation. We had taken each other's measure and were inclined to be sympathetic to each other. I fancied that I was more his own kind than the man with whom he had been lunching. I now had the opportunity of observing the latter. A tall, fair, rather exquisite young man, with a rather fleshy nose and over-emphasised good-looks. He had a supercilious manner and a tired drawl. There was a sleekness about him that I especially disliked.

Then I looked at the woman. She was sitting straight opposite me in a big chair and had just thrown off her hat. She was an unusual type—a weary Madonna describes it best. She had fair, almost colourless hair, parted in the middle and drawn straight down over her ears to a knot in the neck. Her face was dead white and emaciated—yet curiously attractive. Her eyes were very light grey with large pupils. She had a curious look of detachment. She was staring at me. Suddenly she spoke.

"Sit down—till your friend has finished with Nick."

She had an affected voice, languid and artificial—yet which had a curious attraction—a kind of resonant lingering beauty. She impressed me, I think, as the most tired person I had ever met. Tired in mind, not in body, as though she had found everything in the world to be empty and value-less.

"Miss Buckley very kindly helped my friend when he twisted his ankle this morning," I explained, as I accepted her offer.

"So Nick said." Her eyes considered me, still detachedly. "Nothing wrong with his ankle now, is there?"

I felt myself blushing.

"Just a momentary sprain," I explained.

"Oh! well—I'm glad to hear Nick didn't invent the whole thing. She's the most heaven-sent little liar that ever existed, you know. Amazing—it's quite a gift."

I hardly knew what to say. My discomfiture seemed to amuse her.

"She's one of my oldest friends," she said, "and I always think loyalty's such a tiresome virtue, don't you? Principally practised by the Scots—like thrift and keeping the Sabbath. But Nick is a liar, isn't she, Jim? That marvellous story about the brakes of the car—and Jim says there was nothing in it at all."

The fair man said in a soft rich voice:

"I know something about cars."

He half turned his head. Outside amongst other cars was a long, red car. It seemed longer and redder than any car could be. It had a long gleaming bonnet of polished metal. A super car!

" Is that your car?" I asked on a sudden impulse.

He nodded.

" Yes."

I had an insane desire to say, " It would be!"

Poirot rejoined us at that moment. I rose, he took me by the arm, gave a quick bow to the party, and drew me rapidly away.

" It is arranged, my friend. We are to call on Mademoiselle at End House at half-past six. She will be returned from the motoring by then. Yes, yes, surely she will have returned—in safety."

His face was anxious and his tone was worried.

" What did you say to her?"

" I asked her to accord me an interview—as soon as possible. She was a little unwilling—naturally. She thinks—I can see the thoughts passing through her mind : ' Who is he—this little man? Is he the bounder, the upstart, the Moving Picture director?' If she could have refused she would—but it is difficult—asked like that on the spur of the moment it is easier to consent. She admits that she will be back by six-thirty. *Ca y est!*"

I remarked that that seemed to be all right then, but my remark met with little favour. Indeed Poirot was as jumpy as the proverbial cat. He walked about our sitting-room all the afternoon, murmuring to himself and ceaselessly rearranging and straightening the ornaments. When I spoke to him, he waved his hands and shook his head.

In the end we started out from the hotel at barely six o'clock.

" It seems incredible," I remarked, as we descended the steps of the terrace. " To attempt to shoot anyone in a hotel garden. Only a madman would do such a thing."

" I disagree with you. Given one condition, it would be quite a reasonably safe affair. To begin with the garden is deserted. The people who come to hotels are like a flock of sheep. It is customary to sit on the terrace overlooking the bay—*eh bien*, so everyone sits on the terrace. Only, I who am an original, sit overlooking the garden. And even then, I *saw* nothing. There is plenty of cover, you observe— trees, groups of palms, flowering shrubs. Anyone could hide himself comfortably and be unobserved whilst he waited for Mademoiselle to pass this way. And she would come this way. To come round by the road from End House would be much longer. Mademoiselle Nick Buckley, she would be of those who are always late and taking the short cut!"

"All the same, the risk was enormous. He might have been seen—and you can't make shooting look like an accident."

"Not like an *accident*—no."

"What do you mean?"

"Nothing—a little idea. I may or may not be justified. Leaving it aside for a moment, there is what I mentioned just now—an essential *condition*."

"Which is?"

"Surely you can tell me, Hastings."

"I wouldn't like to deprive you of the pleasure of being clever at my expense!"

"Oh! the sarcasm! The irony! Well, what leaps to the eye is this : *the motive cannot be obvious*. If it *were*—why, then, truly the risk would indeed be too great to be taken! People would say : 'I wonder if it were So-and-So. Where was So-and-So when the shot was fired?' No, the murderer —the would-be murderer, I should say—cannot be obvious. And that, Hastings, is why I am afraid! Yes, at this minute I am afraid. I reassure myself. I say : 'There are four of them.' I say : 'Nothing can happen when they are all to- gether.' I say : 'It would be madness!' And all the time I am afraid. These 'accidents'—I want to hear about them!"

He turned back abruptly.

"It is still early. We will go the other way by the road. The garden has nothing to tell us. Let us inspect the ortho- dox approach to End House."

Our way led out of the front gate of the hotel and up a

sharp hill to the right. At the top of it was a small lane with a notice on the wall : " TO END HOUSE ONLY."

We followed it and after a few hundred yards the lane gave an abrupt turn and ended in a pair of dilapidated entrance gates, which would have been the better for a coat of paint.

Inside the gates, to the right, was a small lodge. This lodge presented a piquant contrast to the gates and to the condition of the grass-grown drive. The small garden round it was spick and span, the window frames and sashes had been lately painted and there were clean bright curtains at the windows.

Bending over a flower-bed was a man in a faded Norfolk jacket. He straightened up as the gate creaked and turned to look at us. He was a man of about sixty, six foot at least, with a powerful frame and a weather-beaten face. His head was almost completely bald. His eyes were a vivid blue and twinkled. He seemed a genial soul.

" Good-afternoon," he observed as we passed.

I responded in kind, and as we went on up the drive I was conscious of those blue eyes raking our backs inquisitively.

" I wonder," said Poirot, thoughtfully.

He left it at that without vouchsafing any explanation of what it was that he wondered.

The house itself was large and rather dreary-looking. It was shut in by trees, the branches of which actually touched the roof. It was clearly in bad repair. Poirot swept it with an appraising glance before ringing the bell—an old-fashioned bell that needed a Herculean pull to produce any effect and which once started, echoed mournfully on and on.

The door was opened by a middle-aged woman—" a decent woman in black "—so I felt she should be described. Very respectable, rather mournful, completely uninterested.

Miss Buckley, she said, had not yet returned. Poirot explained that we had an appointment. He had some little difficulty in gaining his point, she was the type that is apt to be suspicious of foreigners. Indeed I flatter myself that it was *my* appearance which turned the scale. We were admitted and ushered into the drawing-room to await Miss Buckley's return.

There was no mournful note here. The room gave on the sea and was full of sunshine. It was shabby and betrayed conflicting styles—ultra modern of a cheap variety superimposed on solid Victorian. The curtains were of faded brocade, but the covers were new and gay and the cushions were positively hectic. On the walls were hung family portraits. Some of them, I thought, looked remarkably good. There was a gramophone and some records lying idly about. There was a portable wireless, practically no books, and one newspaper flung open on the end of the sofa. Poirot picked it up—then laid it down with a grimace. It was the St. Loo *Weekly Herald and Directory*. Something impelled him to pick it up a second time, and he was glancing at a column when the door opened and Nick Buckley came into the room.

"Bring the ice, Ellen," she called over her shoulder, then addressed herself to us.

"Well, here I am—and I've shaken off the others. I'm devoured with curiosity. Am I the long-lost heroine that is badly wanted for the Talkies? You were so very solemn"—she addressed herself to Poirot—"that I feel it can't be anything else. Do make me a handsome offer."

"Alas! Mademoiselle——" began Poirot.

"Don't say it's the opposite," she begged him. "Don't say you paint miniatures and want me to buy one. But no—with that moustache and staying at the Majestic, which has the nastiest food and the highest prices in England—no, it simply can't be."

The woman who had opened the door to us came into the room with ice and a tray of bottles. Nick mixed cocktails expertly, continuing to talk. I think at last Poirot's silence (so unlike him) impressed itself upon her. She stopped in the very act of filling the glasses and said sharply :

"Well?"

"That is what I wish it to be—well, Mademoiselle." He took the cocktail from her hand. "To your good health, Mademoiselle—to your continued good health."

The girl was no fool. The significance of his tone was not lost on her.

"Is—anything the matter?"

"Yes, Mademoiselle. This . . ."

He held out his hand to her with the bullet on the palm of it. She picked it up with a puzzled frown.

"You know what that is?"

"Yes, of course I know. It's a bullet."

"Exactly. Mademoiselle—it was not a wasp that flew past your face this morning—it was this bullet."

"Do you mean—was some criminal idiot shooting bullets in a hotel garden?"

"It would seem so."

"Well, I'm damned," said Nick frankly. "I do seem to bear a charmed life. That's number four."

"Yes," said Poirot. "That is number four. I want, Mademoiselle, to hear about the other three—accidents."

She stared at him.

"I want to be very sure, Mademoiselle, that they were—*accidents.*"

"Why, of course! What else could they be?"

"Mademoiselle, prepare yourself, I beg, for a great shock. What if someone is attempting your life?"

All Nick's response to this was a burst of laughter. The idea seemed to amuse her hugely.

"What a marvellous idea! My dear man, who on earth do you think would attempt my life? I'm not the beautiful young heiress whose death releases millions. I wish somebody *was* trying to kill me—that *would* be a thrill, if you like —but I'm afraid there's not a hope!"

"Will you tell me, Mademoiselle, about those accidents?"

"Of course—but there's nothing in it. They were just stupid things. There's a heavy picture hangs over my bed. It fell in the night. Just by pure chance I had happened to hear a door banging somewhere in the house and went down to find it and shut it—and so I escaped. It would probably have bashed my head in. That's No. 1."

Poirot did not smile.

"Continue, Mademoiselle. Let us pass to No. 2."

"Oh, that's weaker still. There's a scrambly cliff path down to the sea. I go down that way to bathe. There's a rock you can dive off. A boulder got dislodged somehow and came roaring down just missing me. The third thing was quite different. Something went wrong with the brakes of the car—I don't know quite what—the garage man explained, but I didn't follow it. Anyway if I'd gone through the gate and down the hill, they wouldn't have held and I suppose I'd have gone slap into the Town Hall and there would have been the devil of a smash. Slight defacement of the Town Hall, complete obliteration of Me. But owing to my *always* leaving something behind, I turned back and merely ran into the laurel hedge."

"And you cannot tell me what the trouble was?"

"You can go and ask them at Mott's Garage. They'll know. It was something quite simple and mechanical that had been unscrewed, I think. I wondered if Ellen's boy (my stand-by who opened the door to you, has got a small boy) had tinkered with it. Boys do like messing about with cars. Of course Ellen swore he'd never been near the car. I think something must just have worked loose in spite of what Mott said."

"Where is your garage, Mademoiselle?"

"Round the other side of the house."

"Is it kept locked?"

Nick's eyes widened in surprise.

"Oh! *no*. Of course not."

"Anyone could tamper with the car unobserved?"

"Well—yes—I suppose so. But it's so silly."

"No, Mademoiselle. It is not silly. You do not understand. You are in danger—grave danger. I tell it to you. I! And you do not know who I am?"

"No?" said Nick, breathlessly.

"I am Hercule Poirot."

"Oh!" said Nick, in rather a flat tone. "Oh, yes."

"You know my name, eh?"

"Oh, yes."

She wriggled uncomfortably. A hunted look came into her eyes. Poirot observed her keenly.

"You are not at ease. That means, I suppose, that you have not read my books."

"Well—no—not all of them. But I know the name, of course."

"Mademoiselle, you are a polite little liar." (I started, remembering the words spoken at the Majestic Hotel that day after lunch.) "I forget—you are only a child—you would not have heard. So quickly does fame pass. My friend there—he will tell you."

Nick looked at me. I cleared my throat, somewhat embarrassed.

"Monsieur Poirot is—er—was—a great detective," I explained.

"Ah! my friend," cried Poirot. "Is that all you can find to say? Mais dis donc! Say then to Mademoiselle that I am a detective unique, unsurpassed, the greatest that ever lived!"

"That is now unnecessary," I said coldly. "You have told her yourself."

"Ah, yes, but it is more agreeable to have been able to preserve the modesty. One should not sing one's own praises."

"One should not keep a dog and have to bark oneself," agreed Nick, with mock sympathy. "Who is the dog, by the way? Dr. Watson, I presume."

"My name is Hastings," I said coldly.

"Battle of—1066," said Nick. "Who said I wasn't educated? Well, this is all too, *too* marvellous! Do you think someone really wants to do away with me? It would be thrilling. But, of course, that sort of thing doesn't really happen. Only in books. I expect Monsieur Poirot is like a surgeon who's invented an operation or a doctor who's found an obscure disease and wants everyone to have it."

"*Sacré tonnerre!*" thundered Poirot. "Will you be serious? You young people of to-day, will nothing make you serious? It would not have been a joke, Mademoiselle, if you had been lying in the hotel garden a pretty little corpse with a nice little hole through your head instead of your hat. You would not have laughed then—eh?"

"Unearthly laughter heard at a *séance*," said Nick. "But seriously, M. Poirot—it's very kind of you and all that—but the whole thing *must* be an accident."

"You are as obstinate as the devil!"

"That's where I got my name from. My grandfather was popularly supposed to have sold his soul to the devil. Everyone round here called him Old Nick. He was a wicked old man—but great fun. I adored him. I went everywhere with him and so they called us Old Nick and Young Nick. My real name is Magdala."

"That is an uncommon name."

"Yes, it's a kind of family one. There have been lots of Magdalas in the Buckley family. There's one up there." She nodded at a picture on the wall.

"Ah!" said Poirot. Then looking at a portrait hanging over the mantelpiece, he said :

"Is that your grandfather, Mademoiselle?"

"Yes, rather an arresting portrait, isn't it? Jim Lazarus offered to buy it, but I wouldn't sell. I've got an affection for Old Nick."

"Ah!" Poirot was silent for a minute, then he said very earnestly :

"*Revenons à nos moutons.* Listen, Mademoiselle. I implore you to be serious. You are in danger. To-day, somebody shot at you with a Mauser pistol——"

"A Mauser pistol?"

For a moment she was startled.

"Yes, why? Do you know of anyone who has a Mauser pistol?"

She smiled.

"I've got one myself."

"You have?"

"Yes—it was Dad's. He brought it back from the War. It's been knocking round here ever since. I saw it only the other day in that drawer."

She indicated an old-fashioned bureau. Now, as though suddenly struck by an idea, she crossed to it and pulled the drawer open. She turned rather blankly. Her voice held a new note.

"Oh!" she said. "It's—it's gone."

CHAPTER THREE

ACCIDENTS?

It was from that moment that the conversation took on a different tone. Up to now, Poirot and the girl had been at cross-purposes. They were separated by a gulf of years. His fame and reputation meant nothing to her—she was of the generation that knows only the great names of the immediate moment. She was, therefore, unimpressed by his warnings. He was to her only a rather comic elderly foreigner with an amusingly melodramatic mind.

And this attitude baffled Poirot. To begin with, his vanity suffered. It was his constant dictum that all the world knew Hercule Poirot. Here was someone who did not. Very good for him, I could not but feel—but not precisely helpful to the object in view!

With the discovery of the missing pistol, however, the affair took on a new phase. Nick ceased to treat it as a mildly amusing joke. She still treated the matter lightly, because it was her habit and her creed to treat all occurrences lightly, but there was a distinct difference in her manner.

She came back and sat down on the arm of a chair, frowning thoughtfully.

"That's odd," she said.

Poirot whirled round on me.

"You remember, Hastings, the little idea I mentioned? Well, it was correct, my little idea! Supposing Mademoiselle had been found shot lying in the hotel garden? She might not have been found for some hours—few people pass that way. And *beside her hand*—just fallen from it—*is her own pistol*. Doubtless the good Madame Ellen would identify it. There would be suggestions, no doubt, of worry or of sleeplessness——"

Nick moved uneasily.

"That's true. I have been worried to death. Everybody's been telling me I'm nervy. Yes—they'd say all that. . . ."

"And bring in a verdict of suicide. Mademoiselle's finger-prints conveniently on the pistol and nobody else's—but yes, it would be very simple and convincing."

"How terribly amusing!" said Nick, but not, I was glad to note, as though she were terribly amused.

Poirot accepted her words in the conventional sense in which they were uttered.

"*N'est ce pas?* But you understand, Mademoiselle, there must be no more of this. Four failures—yes—but the fifth time there may be a success."

"Bring out your rubber-tyred hearses," murmured Nick.

"But we are here, my friend and I, to obviate all that!"

I felt grateful for the "we." Poirot has a habit of sometimes ignoring my existence.

"Yes," I put in. "You mustn't be alarmed, Miss Buckley. We will protect you."

"How frightfully nice of you," said Nick. "I think the whole thing is perfectly marvellous. Too, too thrilling."

She still preserved her airy detached manner, but her eyes, I thought, looked troubled.

"And the first thing to do," said Poirot, "is to have the consultation."

He sat down and beamed upon her in a friendly manner.

"To begin with, Mademoiselle, a conventional question —but—have you any enemies?"

Nick shook her head rather regretfully.

"I'm afraid not," she said, apologetically.

"*Bon*. We will dismiss that possibility then. And now we ask the question of the cinema, of the detective novel— Who profits by your death, Mademoiselle?"

"I can't imagine," said Nick. "That's why it all seems such nonsense. There's this beastly old barn, of course, but it's mortgaged up to the hilt, the roof leaks and there can't be a coal mine or anything exciting like that hidden in the cliff."

"It is mortgaged—*hein*?"

"Yes. I had to mortgage it. You see there were two lots of death duties—quite soon after each other. First my grandfather died—just six years ago, and then my brother. That just about put the lid on the financial position."

"And your father?"

"He was invalided home from the War, then got pneumonia and died in 1919. My mother died when I was a baby. I lived here with grandfather. He and Dad didn't get on (I don't wonder), so Dad found it convenient to park me and go roaming the world on his own account. Gerald— that was my brother—didn't get on with grandfather either. I dare say I shouldn't have got on with him if I'd been a boy. Being a girl saved me. Grandfather used to say I was a chip of the old block and had inherited his spirit." She laughed. "He was an awful old rip, I believe. But frightfully lucky. There was a saying round here that everything he touched turned to gold. He was a gambler, though, and gambled it away again. When he died he left hardly anything beside the house and land. I was sixteen when he died and Gerald was twenty-two. Gerald was killed in a motor accident just three years ago and the place came to me."

"And after you, Mademoiselle? Who is your nearest relation?"

" My cousin, Charles. Charles Vyse. He's a lawyer down here. Quite good and worthy but very dull. He gives me good advice and tries to restrain my extravagant tastes."

" He manages your affairs for you—eh?"

" Well—yes, if you like to put it that way. I haven't many affairs to manage. He arranged the mortgage for me and made me let the lodge."

" Ah!—the lodge. I was going to ask you about that. It is let?"

" Yes—to some Australians. Croft their name is. Very hearty, you know—and all that sort of thing. Simply oppressively kind. Always bringing up sticks of celery and early peas and things like that. They're shocked at the way I let the garden go. They're rather a nuisance, really—at least he is. Too terribly friendly for words. She's a cripple, poor thing, and lies on a sofa all day. Anyway they pay the rent and that's the great thing."

" How long have they been here?"

" Oh! about six months."

" I see. Now, beyond this cousin of yours—on your father's side or your mother's, by the way?"

" Mother's. My mother was Amy Vyse."

" *Bien!* Now, beyond this cousin, as I was saying, have you any other relatives?"

" Some very distant cousins in Yorkshire—Buckleys."

" No one else?"

" No."

" That is lonely."

Nick stared at him.

" Lonely? What a funny idea. I'm not down here much, you know. I'm usually in London. Relations are too devastating as a rule. They fuss and interfere. It's much more fun to be on one's own."

" I will not waste the sympathy. You are a modern, I see, Mademoiselle. Now—your household."

" How grand that sounds! Ellen's the household. And her husband, who's a sort of gardener—not a very good one.

I pay them frightfully little because I let them have the child here. Ellen does for me when I'm down here and if I have a party we get in who and what we can to help. I'm giving a party on Monday. It's Regatta week, you know."

"Monday—and to-day is Saturday. Yes. Yes. And now, Mademoiselle, your friends—the ones with whom you were lunching to-day, for instance?"

"Well, Freddie Rice—the fair girl—is practically my greatest friend. She's had a rotten life. Married to a beast—a man who drank and drugged and was altogether a queer of the worst description. She had to leave him a year or two ago. Since then she's drifted round. I wish to goodness she'd get a divorce and marry Jim Lazarus."

"Lazarus? The art dealer in Bond Street?"

"Yes. Jim's the only son. Rolling in money, of course. Did you see that car of his? He's a Jew, of course, but a frightfully decent one. And he's devoted to Freddie. They go about everywhere together. They are staying at the Majestic over the week-end and are coming to me on Monday."

"And Mrs. Rice's husband?"

"The mess? Oh! he's dropped out of everything. Nobody knows where he is. It makes it horribly awkward for Freddie. You can't divorce a man when you don't know where he is."

"*Evidemment !* "

"Poor Freddie," said Nick, pensively. "She's had rotten luck. The thing was all fixed once. She got hold of him and put it to him, and he said he was perfectly willing, but he simply hadn't got the cash to take a woman to a hotel. So the end of it all was she forked out—and he took it and off he went and has never been heard of from that day to this. Pretty mean, I call it."

"Good heavens," I exclaimed.

"My friend Hastings is shocked," remarked Poirot. "You must be more careful, Mademoiselle. He is out of date, you comprehend. He has just returned from those great clear open spaces, etc., and he has yet to learn the language of nowadays."

"Well, there's nothing to get shocked about," said Nick, opening her eyes very wide. "I mean, everybody knows, don't they, that there are such people. But I call it a low-down trick all the same. Poor old Freddie was so damned hard up at the time that she didn't know where to turn."

"Yes, yes, not a very pretty affair. And your other friend, Mademoiselle. The good Commander Challenger?"

"George? I've known George all my life—well, for the last five years anyway. He's a good scout, George."

"He wishes you to marry him—eh?"

"He does mention it now and again. In the small hours of the morning or after the second glass of port."

"But you remain hard-hearted."

"What would be the use of George and me marrying one another? We've neither of us got a bean. And one would get terribly bored with George. That 'playing for one's side,' 'good old school' manner. After all, he's forty if he's a day."

The remark made me wince slightly.

"In fact he has one foot in the grave," said Poirot. "Oh! do not mind me, Mademoiselle. I am a grandpapa—a no-body. And now, tell me more about these accidents. The picture, for instance?"

"It's been hung up again—on a new cord. You can come and see it if you like."

She led the way out of the room and we followed her. The picture in question was an oil painting in a heavy frame. It hung directly over the bed-head.

With a murmured, "You permit, Mademoiselle," Poirot removed his shoes and mounted upon the bed. He examined the picture and the cord, and gingerly tested the weight of the painting. With an elegant grimace he descended.

"To have that descend on one's head—no, it would not be pretty. The cord by which it was hung, Mademoiselle, was it, like this one, a wire cable?"

" Yes, but not so thick. I got a thicker one this time."

" That is comprehensible. And you examined the break —the edges were frayed?"

" I think so—but I didn't notice particularly. Why should I?"

" Exactly. As you say, why should you? All the same, I should much like to look at that piece of wire. Is it about the house anywhere?"

" It was still on the picture. I expect the man who put the new wire on just threw the old one away."

" A pity. I should like to have seen it."

" You don't think it was just an accident after all? Surely it couldn't have been anything else."

" It may have been an accident. It is impossible to say. But the damage to the brakes of your car—that was not an accident. And the stone that rolled down the cliff—I should like to see the spot where that accident occurred."

Nick took us out in the garden and led us to the cliff edge. The sea glittered blue below us. A rough path led down the face of the rock. Nick described just where the accident occurred and Poirot nodded thoughtfully. Then he asked :

" How many ways are there into your garden, Mademoiselle?"

" There's the front way—past the lodge. And a trades-man's entrance—a door in the wall half-way up that lane. Then there's a gate just along here on the cliff edge. It leads out on to a zig zag path that leads up from that beach to the Majestic Hotel. And then, of course, you can go straight through a gap in the hedge into the Majestic garden—that's the way I went this morning. To go through the Majestic garden is a short cut to the town anyway."

" And your gardener—where does he usually work?"

" Well, he usually potters round the kitchen garden, or else he sits in the potting-shed and pretends to be sharpening the shears."

" Round the other side of the house, that is to say?"

"So that if anyone were to come in here and dislodge a boulder he would be very unlikely to be noticed."

Nick gave a sudden little shiver.

"Do you—do you really think that is what happened?" she asked, "I can't believe it somehow. It seems so perfectly futile."

Poirot drew the bullet from his pocket again and looked at it.

"That was not futile, Mademoiselle," he said gently.

"It must have been some madman."

"Possibly. It is an interesting subject of after-dinner conversation—are all criminals really madmen? There may be a malformation in their little grey cells—yes, it is very likely. That, it is the affair of the doctor. For me—I have different work to perform. I have the innocent to think of, not the guilty—the victim, not the criminal. It is you I am considering now, Mademoiselle, not your unknown assailant. You are young and beautiful, and the sun shines and the world is pleasant, and there is life and love ahead of you. It is all that of which I think, Mademoiselle. Tell me, these friends of yours, Mrs. Rice and Mr. Lazarus—they have been down here, how long?"

"Freddie came down on Wednesday to this part of the world. She stopped with some people near Tavistock for a couple of nights. She came on here yesterday. Jim has been touring round about, I believe."

"And Commander Challenger?"

"He's at Devonport. He comes over in his car whenever he can—week-ends mostly."

Poirot nodded. We were walking back to the house. There was a silence, and then he said suddenly:

"Have you a friend whom you can trust, Mademoiselle?"

"There's Freddie."

"Other than Mrs. Rice."

"Well, I don't know. I suppose I have. Why?"

"Because I want you to have a friend to stay with you—immediately."

" Oh ! "

Nick seemed rather taken aback. She was silent a moment or two, thinking. Then she said doubtfully :

" There's Maggie. I could get hold of her, I expect."

" Who is Maggie ? "

" One of my Yorkshire cousins. There's a large family of them. He's a clergyman, you know. Maggie's about my age, and I usually have her to stay sometime or other in the summer. She's no fun, though—one of those painfully pure girls, with the kind of hair that has just become fashionable by accident. I was hoping to get out of having her this year."

" Not at all. Your cousin, Mademoiselle, will do admirably. Just the type of person I had in mind."

" All right," said Nick, with a sigh. " I'll wire her. I certainly don't know who else I could get hold of just now. Everyone's fixed up. But if it isn't the Choirboys' Outing or the Mothers' Beanfeast she'll come all right. Though what you expect her to *do*. . . ."

" Could you arrange for her to sleep in your room ? "

" I suppose so."

" She would not think that an odd request ? "

" Oh, no, Maggie never thinks. She just *does*—earnestly, you know. Christian works—with faith and perseverance. All right, I'll wire her to come on Monday."

" Why not to-morrow ? "

" With Sunday trains ? She'll think I'm dying if I suggest that. No, I'll say Monday. Are you going to tell her about the awful fate hanging over me ? "

" *Nous verrons*. You still make a jest of it ? You have courage, I am glad to see."

" It makes a diversion anyway," said Nick.

Something in her tone struck me and I glanced at her curiously. I had a feeling that there was something she had left untold. We had re-entered the drawing-room. Poirot was fingering the newspaper on the sofa.

" You read this, Mademoiselle ? " he asked, suddenly.

" The St. Loo *Herald*? Not seriously. I opened it to see the tides. It gives them every week."

" I see. By the way, Mademoiselle, have you ever made a will?"

" Yes, I did. About six months ago. Just before my op."

" *Qu'est ce que vous dites?* Your *op*?"

" Operation. For appendicitis. Someone said I ought to make a will, so I did. It made me feel quite important."

" And the terms of that will?"

" I left End House to Charles. I hadn't much else to leave, but what there was I left to Freddie. I should think probably the—what do you call them—liabilities would have exceeded the assets, really."

Poirot nodded absently.

" I will take my leave now. *Au revoir, Mademoiselle.* Be careful."

" What of?" asked Nick.

" You are intelligent. Yes, that is the weak point—in which direction are you to be careful? Who can say? But have confidence, Mademoiselle. In a few days I shall have discovered the truth."

" Until then beware of poison, bombs, revolver shots, motor accidents and arrows dipped in the secret poison of the South American Indians," finished Nick glibly.

" Do not mock yourself, Mademoiselle," said Poirot gravely.

He paused as he reached the door.

" By the way," he said. " What price did M. Lazarus offer you for the portrait of your grandfather?"

" Fifty pounds."

" Ah!" said Poirot.

He looked earnestly back at the dark saturnine face above the mantelpiece.

" But, as I told you, I don't want to sell the old boy."

" No," said Poirot, thoughtfully. " No, I understand."

CHAPTER FOUR

THERE MUST BE SOMETHING!

"Poirot," I said, as soon as we were out upon the road. "There is one thing I think you ought to know."

"And what is that, *mon ami*?"

I told him of Mrs. Rice's version of the trouble with the motor.

"*Tiens! C'est interessant, ça.* There is, of course, a type, vain, hysterical, that seeks to make itself interesting by having marvellous escapes from death and which will recount to you surprising histories that never happened! Yes, it is well known, that type there. Such people will even do themselves grave bodily injury to sustain the fiction."

"You don't think that——"

"That Mademoiselle Nick is of that type? No, indeed. You observed, Hastings, that we had great difficulty in convincing her of her danger. And right to the end she kept up the farce of a half-mocking disbelief. She is of her generation, that little one. All the same, it is interesting—what Madame Rice said. Why should she say it? Why say it even if it were true? It was unnecessary—almost *gauche*."

"Yes," I said. "That's true. She dragged it into the conversation neck and crop—for no earthly reason that I could see."

"That is curious. Yes, that is curious. The little facts that are curious, I like to see them appear. They are significant. They point the way."

"The way—where?"

"You put your finger on the weak spot, my excellent Hastings. Where? Where indeed! Alas, we shall not know till we get there."

"Tell me, Poirot," I said. "Why did you insist on her getting this cousin to stay?"

Poirot stopped and waved an excited forefinger at me.

" Consider," he cried. " Consider for one little moment, Hastings. How are we handicapped! How are our hands tied! To hunt down a murderer after a crime has been committed—*c'est tout simple!* Or at least it is simple to one of my ability. The murderer has, so to speak, signed his name by committing the crime. But here there is no crime—and what is more we do not want a crime. To detect a crime before it has been committed—that is indeed of a rare difficulty.

" What is our first aim? The safety of Mademoiselle. And that is not easy. No, it is not easy, Hastings. We cannot watch over her day and night—we cannot even send a policeman in big boots to watch over her. We cannot pass the night in a young lady's sleeping chamber. The affair bristles with difficulties.

" But we can do one thing. We can make it more difficult for our assassin. We can put Mademoiselle upon her guard and we can introduce a perfectly impartial witness. It will take a very clever man to get round those two circumstances."

He paused, and then said in an entirely different tone of voice :

" But what I am afraid of, Hastings——"

" Yes?"

" What I am afraid of is—that he *is* a very clever man. And I am not easy in my mind. No, I am not easy at all."

" Poirot," I said. " You're making me feel quite nervous."

" So am I nervous. Listen, my friend, that paper, the St. Loo *Weekly Herald*. It was open and folded back at— where do you think? A little paragraph which said, *' Among the guests staying at the Majestic Hotel are M. Hercule Poirot and Captain Hastings.'* Supposing—just supposing that someone had read that paragraph. They know my name—everyone knows my name——"

" Miss Buckley didn't," I said, with a grin.

" She is a scatterbrain—she does not count. A serious man

—a criminal—would know my name. And he would be afraid! He would wonder! He would ask himself questions. Three times he has attempted the life of Mademoiselle and now Hercule Poirot arrives in the neighbourhood. ' Is that coincidence?' he would ask himself. And he would fear that it might *not* be coincidence. What would he do then?"

"Lie low and hide his tracks," I suggested.

"Yes—yes—or else—if he had real audacity, he would strike *quickly*—without loss of time. Before I had time to make inquiries—*pouf*, Mademoiselle is dead. That is what a man of audacity would do."

"But why do you think that somebody read that paragraph other than Miss Buckley?"

"It was not Miss Buckley who read that paragraph. When I mentioned my name it meant nothing to her. It was not even familiar. Her face did not change. Besides she told us—she opened the paper to look at the tides—nothing else. Well, there was no tide table on that page."

"You think someone in the house——"

"Someone in the house or who had access to it. And that last is easy—the window stands open. Without doubt Miss Buckley's friends pass in and out."

"Have you any idea? Any suspicion?"

Poirot flung out his hands.

"Nothing. Whatever the motive, it is, as I predicted, not an obvious one. That is the would-be murderer's security—that is why he could act so daringly this morning. On the face of it, no one seems to have any reason for desiring the little Nick's death. The property? End House? That passes to the cousin—but does he particularly want a heavily mortgaged and very dilapidated old house? It is not even a family place so far as he is concerned. He is not a Buckley, remember. We must see this Charles Vyse, certainly, but the idea seems fantastic.

"Then there is Madame—the bosom friend—with her strange eyes and her air of a lost Madonna——"

"You felt that too?" I asked, startled.

"What is her concern in the business? She tells you that her friend is a liar. *C'est gentille, ça!* Why does she tell you? Is she afraid of something that Nick may say? Is that something connected with the car? Or did she use that as an instance, and was her real fear of something else? Did anyone tamper with the car, and if so, who? And does she know about it?

"Then the handsome blond, M. Lazarus. Where does he fit in? With his marvellous automobile and his money. Can he possibly be concerned in any way? Commander Challenger——"

"He's all right," I put in quickly. "I'm sure of that. A real pukka sahib."

"Doubtless he has been to what you consider the right school. Happily, being a foreigner, I am free from these prejudices, and can make investigations unhampered by them. But I will admit that I find it hard to connect Commander Challenger with the case. In fact, I do not see that he can be so connected."

"Of course he can't," I said, warmly.

Poirot looked at me meditatively.

"You have an extraordinary effect on me, Hastings. You have so strongly the *flair* in the wrong direction that I am almost tempted to go by it! You are that wholly admirable type of man, honest, credulous, honourable, who is invariably taken in by any scoundrel. You are the type of man who invests in doubtful oil fields, and non-existent gold mines. From hundreds like you, the swindler makes his daily bread. Ah, well—I shall study this Commander Challenger. You have awakened my doubts."

"My dear Poirot," I cried, angrily. "You are perfectly absurd. A man who has knocked about the world like I have——"

"Never learns," said Poirot, sadly. "It is amazing—but there it is."

"Do you suppose I'd have made a success of my ranch out

in the Argentine if I were the kind of credulous fool you make out?"

"Do not enrage yourself, *mon ami*. You have made a great success of it—you and your wife."

"Bella," I said, "always goes by my judgment."

"She is as wise as she is charming," said Poirot. "Let us not quarrel, my friend. See, there ahead of us, it says Mott's Garage. That, I think, is the garage mentioned by Mademoiselle Buckley. A few inquiries will soon give us the truth of that little matter."

We duly entered the place and Poirot introduced himself by explaining that he had been recommended there by Miss Buckley. He made some inquiries about hiring a car for some afternoon drives and from there slid easily into the topic of the damage sustained by Miss Buckley's car not long ago.

Immediately the garage proprietor waxed voluble. Most extraordinary thing he'd ever seen. He proceeded to be technical. I, alas, am not mechanically minded. Poirot, I should imagine, is even less so. But certain facts did emerge unmistakably. The car had been tampered with. And the damage had been something quite easily done, occupying very little time.

"So that is that," said Poirot, as we strolled away. "The little Nick was right, and the rich M. Lazarus was wrong. Hastings, my friend, all this is very interesting."

"What do we do now?"

"We visit the post office and send off a telegram if it is not too late."

"A telegram?" I said hopefully.

"Yes," said Poirot thoughtfully. "A telegram."

The post office was still open. Poirot wrote out his telegram and despatched it. He vouchsafed me no information as to its contents. Feeling that he wanted me to ask him, I carefully refrained from doing so.

"It is annoying that to-morrow is Sunday," he remarked,

as we strolled back to the hotel. " We cannot now call upon
M. Vyse till Monday morning."

" You could get hold of him at his private address."

" Naturally. But that is just what I am anxious not to do.
I would prefer, in the first place, to consult him profession-
ally and to form my judgment of him from that aspect."

" Yes," I said thoughtfully. " I suppose that would be
best."

" The answer to one simple little question, for instance,
might make a great difference. If M. Charles Vyse was in
his office at twelve-thirty this morning, then it was not he
who fired that shot in the garden of the Majestic Hotel."

" Ought we not to examine the *alibis* of the three at the
hotel?"

" That is much more difficult. It would be easy enough
for one of them to leave the others for a few minutes, a hasty
egress from one of the innumerable windows—lounge,
smoking-room, drawing-room, writing-room, quickly under
cover to the spot where the girl must pass—the shot fired and
a rapid retreat. But as yet, *mon ami*, we are not even sure
that we have arrived at all the *dramatis personæ* in the
drama. There is the respectable Ellen—and her so far unseen husband. Both inmates of the house and possibly, for
all we know, with a grudge against our little Mademoiselle.
There are even the unknown Australians at the lodge. And
there may be others, friends and intimates of Miss Buckley's
whom she has no reason for suspecting and consequently has
not mentioned. I cannot help feeling, Hastings, that there is
something *behind* this—*something* that has not yet come to
light. I have a little idea that Miss Buckley knows more
than she told us."

" You think she is keeping something back?"

" Yes."

" Possibly with an idea of shielding whoever it is?"

Poirot shook his head with the utmost energy.

" No, no. As far as that goes, she gave me the impression
of being utterly frank. I am convinced that as regards

these attempts on her life, she was telling all she knew. But there is something else—something that she believes has nothing to do with that at all. And I should like to know what that something is. For I—I say it in all modesty—am a great deal more intelligent than *une petite comme ça*. I, Hercule Poirot, might see a connection where she sees none. It might give me the clue I am seeking. For I announce to you, Hastings, quite frankly and humbly, that I am as you express it, all on the sea. Until I can get some glimmering of the *reason* behind all this, I am in the dark. There must be *something*—some factor in the case that I do not grasp. What is it? *Je me demande ça sans cesse. Qu'est-ce que c'est?*"

" You will find out," I said, soothingly.

" So long," he said sombrely, " as I do not find out too late."

CHAPTER FIVE

MR. AND MRS. CROFT

THERE was dancing that evening at the hotel. Nick Buckley dined there with her friends and waved a gay greeting to us. She was dressed that evening in floating scarlet chiffon that dragged on the floor. Out of it rose her white neck and shoulders and her small impudent dark head.

" An engaging young devil," I remarked.

" A contrast to her friend—eh?"

Frederica Rice was in white. She danced with a languorous weary grace that was as far removed from Nick's animation as anything could be.

" She is very beautiful," said Poirot suddenly.

" Who? Our Nick?"

" No—the other. Is she evil? Is she good? Is she merely unhappy? One cannot tell. She is a mystery. She is, per-

haps, nothing at all. But I tell you, my friend, she is an
allumeuse."

"What do you mean?" I asked curiously.

He shook his head, smiling.

"You will feel it sooner or later. Remember my words."

Presently to my surprise, he rose. Nick was dancing with
George Challenger. Frederica and Lazarus had just stopped
and had sat down at their table. Then Lazarus got up and
went away. Mrs. Rice was alone. Poirot went straight to her
table. I followed him.

His methods were direct and to the point.

"You permit?" He laid a hand on the back of a chair
then slid into it. "I am anxious to have a word with you
while your friend is dancing."

"Yes?" Her voice sounded cool, uninterested.

"Madame, I do not know whether your friend has told
you. If not, I will. To-day her life has been attempted."

Her great grey eyes widened in horror and surprise. The
pupils, dilated black pupils, widened too.

"What do you mean?"

"Mademoiselle Buckley was shot at in the garden of
this hotel."

She smiled suddenly—a gentle, pitying, incredulous
smile.

"Did Nick tell you so?"

"No, Madame, I happened to see it with my own eyes.
Here is the bullet."

He held it out to her and she drew back a little.

"But, then—but, then——"

"It is no fantasy of Mademoiselle's imagination, you
understand. I vouch for that. And there is more. Several
very curious accidents have happened in the last few days.
You will have heard—no, perhaps you will not. You only
arrived yesterday, did you not?"

"Yes—yesterday."

"Before that you were staying with friends, I understand.
At Tavistock."

"Yes."

"I wonder, Madame, what were the names of the friends with whom you were staying."

She raised her eyebrows.

"Is there any reason why I should tell you that?" she asked coldly.

Poirot was immediately all innocent surprise.

"A thousand pardons, Madame. I was most *maladroit*. But I myself, having friends at Tavistock, fancied that you might have met them there. . . . Buchanan—that is the name of my friends."

Mrs. Rice shook her head.

"I don't remember them. I don't think I can have met them." Her tone now was quite cordial. "Don't let us talk about boring people. Go on about Nick. Who shot at her? Why?"

"I do not know who—*as yet*," said Poirot. "But I shall find out. Oh! yes, I shall find out. I am, you know, a detective. Hercule Poirot is my name."

"A very famous name."

"Madame is too kind."

She said slowly:

"What do you want me to do?"

I think she surprised us both there. We had not expected just that.

"I will ask you, Madame, to watch over your friend."

"I will."

"That is all."

He got up, made a quick bow, and we returned to our own table.

"Poirot," I said, "aren't you showing your hand very plainly?"

"*Mon ami*, what else can I do? It lacks subtlety, perhaps, but it makes for safety. *I can take no chances*. At any rate one thing emerges plain to see."

"What is that?"

"*Mrs. Rice was not at Tavistock*. Where was she? Ah!

but I will find out. Impossible to keep information from
Hercule Poirot. See—the handsome Lazarus has returned.
She is telling him. He looks over at us. He is clever, that
one. Note the shape of his head. Ah! I wish I knew——"

"What?" I asked, as he came to a stop.

"What I shall know on Monday," he returned, ambig-
uously.

I looked at him but said nothing. He sighed.

"You have no longer the curiosity, my friend. In the old
days——"

"There are some pleasures," I said, coldly, "that it is
good for you to do without."

"You mean——?"

"The pleasure of refusing to answer questions."

"Ah c'est malin."

"Quite so."

"Ah, well, well," murmured Poirot. "The strong silent
man beloved of novelists in the Edwardian age."

His eyes twinkled with their old glint.

Nick passed our table shortly afterwards. She detached
herself from her partner and swooped down on us like a
gaily-coloured bird.

"Dancing on the edge of death," she said lightly.

"It is a new sensation, Mademoiselle?"

"Yes. Rather fun."

She was off again, with a wave of her hand.

"I wish she hadn't said that," I said, slowly. "Dancing
on the edge of death. I don't like it."

"I know. It is too near the truth. She has courage, that
little one. Yes, she has courage. But unfortunately it is not
courage that is needed at this moment. Caution, not courage
—voilà ce qu'il nous faut!"

The following day was Sunday. We were sitting on the
terrace in front of the hotel, and it was about half-past
eleven when Poirot suddenly rose to his feet.

"Come, my friend. We will try a little experiment. I have

ascertained that M. Lazarus and Madame have gone out in the car and Mademoiselle with them. The coast is clear."

"Clear for what?"

"You shall see."

We walked down the steps and across a short stretch of grass to where a gate gave on to the zig-zag path leading down to the sea. A couple of bathers were coming up it. They passed us laughing and talking.

When they had gone, Poirot walked to the point where an inconspicuous small gate, rather rusty on its hinges, bore the words in half obliterated letters, "End House. Private." There was no one in sight. We passed quietly through.

In another minute we came out on the stretch of lawn in front of the house. There was no one about. Poirot strolled to the edge of the cliff and looked over. Then he walked towards the house itself. The French windows on to the verandah were open and we passed straight into the drawing-room. Poirot wasted no time there. He opened the door and went out into the hall. From there he mounted the stairs, I at his heels. He went straight to Nick's bedroom— sat down on the edge of the bed and nodded to me with a twinkle.

"You see, my friend, how easy it is. No one has seen us come. No one will see us go. We could do any little affair we had to do in perfect safety. We could, for instance, fray through a picture wire so that it would be bound to snap before many hours had passed. And supposing that by chance anyone did happen to be in front of the house and see us coming. Then we would have a perfectly natural excuse —providing that we were known as friends of the house."

"You mean that we can rule out a stranger?"

"That is what I mean, Hastings. It is no stray lunatic who is at the bottom of this. We must look nearer home than that."

He turned to leave the room and I followed him. We neither of us spoke. We were both, I think, troubled in mind.

And then, at the bend of the staircase, we both stopped abruptly. A man was coming up.

He too stopped. His face was in shadow but his attitude was of one completely taken aback. He was the first to speak, in a loud, rather bullying voice.

" What the hell are you doing here, I'd like to know?"

" Ah!" said Poirot. " Monsieur—Croft, I think?"

" That's my name, but what——"

" Shall we go into the drawing-room to converse? It would be better, I think."

The other gave way, turned abruptly and descended, we following close on his heels. In the drawing-room, with the door shut, Poirot made a little bow.

" I will introduce myself. Hercule Poirot at your service."

The other's face cleared a little.

" Oh!" he said slowly. " You're the detective chap. I've read about you."

" In the St. Loo *Herald*?"

" Eh? I've read about you way back in Australia. French, aren't you?"

" Belgian. It makes no matter. This is my friend, Captain Hastings."

" Glad to meet you. But look, what's the big idea? What are you doing here? Anything—wrong?"

" It depends what you call—wrong."

The Australian nodded. He was a fine-looking man in spite of his bald head and advancing years. His physique was magnificent. He had a heavy, rather underhung face— a crude face, I called it to myself. The piercing blue of his eyes was the most noticeable thing about him.

" See here," he said. " I came round to bring little Miss Buckley a handful of tomatoes and a cucumber. That man of hers is no good—bone idle—doesn't grow a thing. Lazy hound. Mother and I—why, it makes us mad, and we feel it's only neighbourly to do what we can! We've got a lot more tomatoes than we can eat. Neighbours should be matey, don't you think? I came in, as usual, through the window and dumped the basket down. I was just going off again when I heard footsteps and men's voices overhead. That struck me as odd. We don't deal much in burglars round here—but after all it was possible. I thought I'd just make sure everything was all right. Then I met you two on the stairs coming down. It gave me a bit of a surprise. And now you tell me you're a bonza detective. What's it all about?"

"It is very simple," said Poirot, smiling. "Mademoiselle had a rather alarming experience the other night. A picture fell above her bed. She may have told you of it?"

"She did. A mighty fine escape."

"To make all secure I promised to bring her some special chain—it will not do to repeat the occurrence, eh? She tells me she is going out this morning, but I may come and measure what amount of chain will be needed. *Voilà*—it is simple."

He flung out his hands with a childlike simplicity and his most engaging smile.

Croft drew a deep breath.

"So that's all it is?"

"Yes—you have had the scare for nothing. We are very law-abiding citizens, my friend and I."

"Didn't I see you yesterday?" said Croft, slowly. "Yesterday evening it was. You passed our little place."

"Ah! yes, you were working in the garden and were so polite as to say good-afternoon when we passed."

"That's right. Well—well. And you're the Monsieur Hercule Poirot I've heard so much about. Tell me, are you busy, Mr. Poirot? Because if not, I wish you'd come back with me now—have a cup of morning tea, Australian fashion, and meet my old lady. She's read all about you in the newspapers."

"You are too kind, M. Croft. We have nothing to do and shall be delighted."

" That's fine."

" You have the measurements correctly, Hastings?" asked Poirot, turning to me.

I assured him that I had the measurements correctly and we accompanied our new friend.

Croft was a talker; we soon realised that. He told us of his home near Melbourne, of his early struggles, of his meeting with his wife, of their combined efforts and of his final good fortune and success.

" Right away we made up our minds to travel," he said. " We'd always wanted to come to the old country. Well, we did. We came down to this part of the world—tried to look up some of my wife's people—they came from round about here. But we couldn't trace any of them. Then we took a trip on the Continent—Paris, Rome, the Italian Lakes, Florence—all those places. It was while we were in Italy that we had the train accident. My poor wife was badly smashed up. Cruel, wasn't it? I've taken her to the best doctors and they all say the same—there's nothing for it but time—time and lying up. It's an injury to the spine."

" What a misfortune!"

" Hard luck, isn't it? Well, there it was. And she'd only got one kind of fancy—to come down here. She kind of felt if we had a little place of our own—something small—it would make all the difference. We saw a lot of messy-looking shacks, and then by good luck we found this. Nice and quiet and tucked away—no cars passing, or gramophones next door. I took it right away."

With the last words we had come to the lodge itself. He sent his voice echoing forth in a loud " Cooee," to which came an answering " Cooee."

" Come in," said Mr. Croft. He passed through the open door and up the short flight of stairs to a pleasant bedroom. There, on a sofa, was a stout middle-aged woman with pretty grey hair and a very sweet smile.

" Who do you think this is, mother?" said Mr. Croft. " The extra-special, world-celebrated detective, Mr. Hercule

Poirot. I brought him right along to have a chat with you."

"If that isn't too exciting for words," cried Mrs. Croft, shaking Poirot warmly by the hand. "Read about that Blue Train business, I did, and you just happening to be on it, and a lot about your other cases. Since this trouble with my back, I've read all the detective stories that ever were, I should think. Nothing else seems to pass the time away so quick. Bert, dear, call out to Edith to bring the tea along."

"Right you are, mother."

"She's a kind of nurse attendant, Edith is," Mrs. Croft explained. "She comes along each morning to fix me up. We're not bothering with servants. Bert's as good a cook and a house-parlourman as you'd find anywhere, and it gives him occupation—that and the garden."

"Here we are," cried Mr. Croft, reappearing with a tray. "Here's the tea. This is a great day in our lives, mother."

"I suppose you're staying down here, Mr. Poirot?" Mrs. Croft asked, as she leaned over a little and wielded the tea-pot.

"Why, yes, Madame, I take the holiday."

"But surely I read that you had retired—that you'd taken a holiday for good and all."

"Ah! Madame, you must not believe everything you read in the papers."

"Well, that's true enough. So you still carry on business?"

"When I find a case that interests me."

"Sure you're not down here on work?" inquired Mr. Croft, shrewdly. "Calling it a holiday might be all part of the game."

"You mustn't ask him embarrassing questions, Bert," said Mrs. Croft. "Or he won't come again. We're simple people, Mr. Poirot, and you're giving us a great treat coming here to-day—you and your friend. You really don't know the pleasure you're giving us."

She was so natural and so frank in her gratification that my heart quite warmed to her.

"That was a bad business about that picture," said Mr. Croft.

"That poor little girl might have been killed," said Mrs. Croft, with deep feeling. "She *is* a live wire. Livens the place up when she comes down here. Not much liked in the neighbourhood, so I've heard. But that's the way in these stuck English places. They don't like life and gaiety in a girl. I don't wonder she doesn't spend much time down here, and that long-nosed cousin of hers has no more chance of persuading her to settle down here for good and all than—than—well, I don't know what."

"Don't gossip, Milly," said her husband.

"Aha!" said Poirot. "The wind is in that quarter. Trust the instinct of Madame! So M. Charles Vyse is in love with our little friend?"

"He's silly about her," said Mrs. Croft. "But she won't marry a country lawyer. And I don't blame her. He's a poor stick, anyway. I'd like her to marry that nice sailor—what's his name, Challenger. Many a smart marriage might be worse than that. He's older than she is, but what of that? Steadying—that's what she needs. Flying about all over the place, the Continent even, all alone or with that queer-looking Mrs. Rice. She's a sweet girl, Mr. Poirot—I know that well enough. But I'm worried about her. She's looked none too happy lately. She's had what I call a haunted kind of look. And it worries me! I've got my reasons for being interested in that girl, haven't I, Bert?"

Mr. Croft got up from his chair rather suddenly.

"No need to go into that, Milly," he said. "I wonder, Mr. Poirot, if you'd care to see some snapshots of Australia?"

The rest of our visit passed uneventfully. Ten minutes later we took our leave.

"Nice people," I said. "So simple and unassuming. Typical Australians."

"You liked them?"

"Didn't you?"

"They were very pleasant—very friendly."

"Well, what is it, then? There's something, I can see."

"They were, perhaps, just a shade too 'typical,' " said Poirot, thoughtfully. "That cry of Cooee—that insistence on showing us snapshots—was it not playing a part just a little too thoroughly?"

"What a suspicious old devil you are!"

"You are right, *mon ami*. I am suspicious of everyone —of everything. I am afraid, Hastings—afraid."

CHAPTER SIX

A CALL UPON MR. VYSE

POIROT clung firmly to the Continental breakfast. To see me consuming eggs and bacon upset and distressed him—so he always said. Consequently he breakfasted in bed upon coffee and rolls and I was free to start the day with the traditional Englishman's breakfast of bacon and eggs and marmalade.

I looked into his room on Monday morning as I went downstairs. He was sitting up in bed arrayed in a very marvellous dressing-gown.

"*Bon jour*, Hastings. I was just about to ring. This note that I have written, will you be so good as to get it taken over to End House and delivered to Mademoiselle at once."

I held out my hand for it. Poirot looked at me and sighed.

"If only—if only, Hastings, you would part your hair in the middle instead of at the side! What a difference it would make to the symmetry of your appearance. And your moustache. If you *must* have a moustache, let it be a real moustache—a thing of beauty such as mine."

Repressing a shudder at the thought, I took the note firmly from Poirot's hand and left the room.

I had rejoined him in our sitting-room when word was

sent up to say Miss Buckley had called. Poirot gave the order for her to be shown up.

She came in gaily enough, but I fancied that the circles under her eyes were darker than usual. In her hand she held a telegram which she handed to Poirot.

" There," she said. " I hope that will please you!"

Poirot read it aloud.

" Arrive 5.30 to-day. Maggie."

" My nurse and guardian!" said Nick. " But you're wrong, you know. Maggie's got no kind of brains. Good works is about all she's fit for. That and never seeing the point of jokes. Freddie would be ten times better at spotting hidden assassins. And Jim Lazarus would be better still. I never feel one has got to the bottom of Jim."

" And the Commander Challenger?"

" Oh! George! He'd never see anything till it was under his nose. But he'd let them have it when he did see. Very useful when it came to a show-down, George would be."

She tossed off her hat and went on :

" I gave orders for the man you wrote about to be let in. It sounds mysterious. Is he installing a dictaphone or something like that?"

Poirot shook his head.

" No, no, nothing scientific. A very simple little matter of opinion, Mademoiselle. Something I wanted to know."

" Oh, well," said Nick. " It's all great fun, isn't it?"

" Is it, Mademoiselle?" asked Poirot, gently.

She stood for a minute with her back to us, looking out of the window. Then she turned. All the brave defiance had gone out of her face. It was childishly twisted awry, as she struggled to keep back the tears.

" No," she said. " It—it isn't, really. I'm afraid—I'm afraid. Hideously afraid. And I always thought I was brave."

" So you are, *mon enfant*, so you are. Both Hastings and I, we have both admired your courage."

" Yes, indeed," I put in warmly.

" No," said Nick, shaking her head. " I'm not brave. It's
—it's the *waiting*. Wondering the whole time if anything
more's going to happen. And *how* it'll happen! And
expecting it to happen."

" Yes, yes—it is the strain."

" Last night I pulled my bed out into the middle of the
room. And fastened my window and bolted my door. When
I came here this morning, I came round by the road. I
couldn't—I simply couldn't come through the garden. It's
as though my nerve had gone all of a sudden. It's this thing
coming on top of everything else."

" What do you mean exactly by that, Mademoiselle? On
top of everything else?"

There was a momentary pause before she replied.

" I don't mean anything particular. What the newspapers
call ' the strain of modern life,' I suppose. Too many cocktails, too many cigarettes—all that sort of thing. It's just that
I've got into a ridiculous—sort of—of state."

She had sunk into a chair and was sitting there, her small
fingers curling and uncurling themselves nervously.

" You are not being frank with me, Mademoiselle. There
is something."

" There isn't—there really isn't."

" There is something you have not told me."

" I've told you every single smallest thing."

She spoke sincerely and earnestly.

" About these accidents—about the attacks upon you, yes."

" Well—then?"

" But you have not told me everything that is in your
heart—in your life. . . ."

She said slowly :

" Can anyone do that . . . ?"

" Ah! then," said Poirot, with triumph. " You admit it!"

She shook her head. He watched her keenly.

" Perhaps," he suggested, shrewdly. " It is not *your*
secret?"

I thought I saw a momentary flicker of her eyelids. But almost immediately she jumped up.

"Really and truly, M. Poirot, I've told you every single thing I know about this stupid business. If you think I know something about someone else, or have suspicions, you are wrong. It's having *no* suspicions that's driving me mad! Because I'm not a fool. I can see that if those ' accidents ' weren't accidents, they must have been engineered by somebody very near at hand—somebody who—knows me. And that's what is so awful. Because I haven't the least idea—not the very least—who that somebody might be."

She went over once more to the window and stood looking out. Poirot signed to me not to speak. I think he was hoping for some further revelation, now that the girl's self-control had broken down.

When she spoke, it was in a different tone of voice, a dreamy far-away voice.

"Do you know a queer wish I've always had? I love End House. I've always wanted to produce a play there. It's got an—an atmosphere of drama about it. I've seen all sorts of plays staged there in my mind. And now it's as though a drama were being acted there. Only I'm not producing it . . . I'm *in* it! I'm *right* in it! I am, perhaps, the person who—dies in the first act."

Her voice broke.

"Now, now, Mademoiselle." Poirot's voice was resolutely brisk and cheerful. "This will not do. This is hysteria."

She turned and looked at him sharply.

"Did Freddie tell you I was hysterical?" she asked. "She says I am, sometimes. But you mustn't always believe what Freddie says. There are times, you know, when—when she isn't quite herself."

There was a pause, then Poirot asked a totally irrelevant question :

"Tell me, Mademoiselle," he said. "Have you ever received an offer for End House?"

"To sell it, do you mean?"

" That is what I meant."

" No."

" Would you consider selling it if you got a good offer?"

Nick considered for a moment.

" No, I don't think so. Not, I mean, unless it was such a ridiculously good offer that it would be perfectly foolish not to."

" *Précisément.*"

" I don't want to sell it, you know, because I'm fond of it."

" Quite so. I understand."

Nick moved slowly towards the door.

" By the way, there are fireworks to-night. Will you come? Dinner at eight o'clock. The fireworks begin at nine-thirty. You can see them splendidly from the garden where it overlooks the harbour."

" I shall be enchanted."

" Both of you, of course," said Nick.

" Many thanks," I said.

" Nothing like a party for reviving the drooping spirits," remarked Nick. And with a little laugh she went out.

" *Pauvre enfant,*" said Poirot.

He reached for his hat and carefully flicked an infinitesimal speck of dust from its surface.

" We are going out?" I asked.

" *Mais oui*, we have legal business to transact, *mon ami.*"

" Of course. I understand."

" One of your brilliant mentality could not fail to do so, Hastings."

The offices of Messrs. Vyse, Trevannion & Wynnard were situated in the main street of the town. We mounted the stairs to the first floor and entered a room where three clerks were busily writing. Poirot asked to see Mr. Charles Vyse.

A clerk murmured a few words down a telephone, received, apparently, an affirmative reply, and remarking that Mr. Vyse would see us now, he led us across the passage, tapped on a door and stood aside for us to pass in.

From behind a large desk covered with legal papers, Mr. Vyse rose up to greet us.

He was a tall young man, rather pale, with impassive features. He was going a little bald on either temple and wore glasses. His colouring was fair and indeterminate.

Poirot had come prepared for the encounter. Fortunately he had with him an agreement, as yet unsigned, and on some technical points in connection with this, he wanted Mr. Vyse's advice.

Mr. Vyse, speaking carefully and correctly, was soon able to allay Poirot's alleged doubts, and to clear up some obscure points of the wording.

"I am very much obliged to you," murmured Poirot. "As a foreigner, you comprehend, these legal matters and phrasing are most difficult."

It was then that Mr. Vyse asked who had sent Poirot to him.

"Miss Buckley," said Poirot, promptly. "Your cousin, is she not? A most charming young lady. I happened to mention that I was in perplexity and she told me to come to you. I tried to see you on Saturday morning—about half-past twelve—but you were out."

"Yes, I remember. I left early on Saturday."

"Mademoiselle your cousin must find that large house very lonely? She lives there alone, I understand."

"Quite so."

"Tell me, Mr. Vyse, if I may ask, is there any chance of that property being in the market?"

"Not the least, I should say."

"You understand, I do not ask idly. I have a reason! I am in search, myself, of just such a property. The climate of St. Loo enchants me. It is true that the house appears to be in bad repair, there has not been, I gather, much money to spend upon it. Under those circumstances, is it not possible that Mademoiselle would consider an offer?"

"Not the least likelihood of it." Charles Vyse shook his

head with the utmost decision. "My cousin is absolutely devoted to the place. Nothing would induce her to sell, I know. It is, you understand, a family place."

"I comprehend that, but——"

"It is absolutely out of the question. I know my cousin. She has a fanatical devotion to the house."

A few minutes later we were out in the street again.

"Well, my friend," said Poirot. "And what impression did this M. Charles Vyse make upon you?"

I considered.

"A very negative one," I said at last. "He is a curiously negative person."

"Not a strong personality, you would say?"

"No, indeed. The kind of man you would never remember on meeting him again. A mediocre person."

"His appearance is certainly not striking. Did you notice any discrepancy in the course of our conversation with him?"

"Yes," I said slowly, "I did. With regard to the selling of End House."

"Exactly. Would you have described Mademoiselle Buckley's attitude towards End House as one of 'fanatical devotion'?"

"It is a very strong term."

"Yes—and Mr. Vyse is not given to using strong terms. His normal attitude—a legal attitude—is to under, rather than over, state. Yet he says that Mademoiselle has a fanatical devotion to the home of her ancestors."

"She did not convey that impression this morning," I said. "She spoke about it very sensibly, I thought. She's obviously fond of the place—just as anyone in her position would be—but certainly nothing more."

"So, in fact, one of the two is lying," said Poirot, thoughtfully.

"One would not suspect Vyse of lying."

"Clearly a great asset if one has any lying to do," remarked Poirot. "Yes, he has quite the air of a George Washington, that one. Did you notice another thing, Hastings?"

"What was that?"

"*He was not in his office at half-past twelve on Saturday.*"

CHAPTER SEVEN

TRAGEDY

The first person we saw when we arrived at End House that evening was Nick. She was dancing about the hall wrapped in a marvellous kimono covered with dragons.

"Oh! it's only you!"

"Mademoiselle—I am desolated!"

"I know. It did sound rude. But you see, I'm waiting for my dress to arrive. They promised—the brutes—promised faithfully!"

"Ah! if it is a matter of *la toilette*! There is a dance to-night, is there not?"

"Yes. We are all going on to it after the fireworks. That is, I suppose we are."

There was a sudden drop in her voice. But the next minute she was laughing.

"Never give in! That's my motto. Don't think of trouble and trouble won't come! I've got my nerve back to-night. I'm going to be gay and enjoy myself."

There was a footfall on the stairs. Nick turned.

"Oh! here's Maggie. Maggie, here are the sleuths that are protecting me from the secret assassin. Take them into the drawing-room and let them tell you about it."

In turn we shook hands with Maggie Buckley, and, as requested, she took us into the drawing-room. I formed an immediate favourable opinion of her.

It was, I think, her appearance of calm good sense that so

attracted me. A quiet girl, pretty in the old-fashioned sense
—certainly not smart. Her face was innocent of make-up
and she wore a simple, rather shabby, black evening dress.
She had frank blue eyes, and a pleasant slow voice.

"Nick has been telling me the most amazing things,"
she said. "Surely she must be exaggerating? Who ever
would want to harm Nick? She can't have an enemy in the
world."

Incredulity showed strongly in her voice. She was looking at Poirot in a somewhat unflattering fashion. I realised
that to a girl like Maggie Buckley, foreigners were always
suspicious.

"Nevertheless, Miss Buckley, I assure you that it is the
truth," said Poirot quietly.

She made no reply, but her face remained unbelieving.

"Nick seems quite fey to-night," she remarked. "I don't
know what's the matter with her. She seems in the wildest
spirits."

That word—fey! It sent a shiver through me. Also, something in the intonation of her voice had set me wondering.

"Are you Scotch, Miss Buckley?" I asked, abruptly.

"My mother was Scottish," she explained.

She viewed me, I noticed with more approval than she
viewed Poirot. I felt that my statement of the case would
carry more weight with her than Poirot's would.

"Your cousin is behaving with great bravery," I said.
"She's determined to carry on as usual."

"It's the only way, isn't it?" said Maggie. "I mean—
whatever one's inward feelings are—it is no good making a
fuss about them. That's only uncomfortable for everyone
else." She paused and then added in a soft voice. "I'm
very fond of Nick. She's been very good to me always."

We could say nothing more for at that moment Frederica
Rice drifted into the room. She was wearing a gown of
Madonna blue and looked very fragile and ethereal. Lazarus
soon followed her and then Nick danced in. She was wear-

ing a black frock, and round her was wrapped a marvellous old Chinese shawl of vivid lacquer red.

" Hello, people," she said. " Cocktails?"

We all drank, and Lazarus raised his glass to her.

" That's a marvellous shawl, Nick," he said. " It's an old one, isn't it?"

" Yes—brought back by Great-Great-Great-Uncle Timothy from his travels."

" It's a beauty—a real beauty. You wouldn't find another to match it if you tried."

" It's warm," said Nick. " It'll be nice when we're watching the fireworks. And it's gay. I—I hate black."

" Yes," said Frederica. " I don't believe I've ever seen you in a black dress before, Nick. Why did you get it?"

" Oh! I don't know." The girl flung aside with a petulant gesture, but I had caught a curious curl of her lips as though of pain. " Why does one do anything?"

We went in to dinner. A mysterious manservant had appeared—hired, I presume, for the occasion. The food was indifferent. The champagne, on the other hand, was good.

" George hasn't turned up," said Nick. " A nuisance his having to go back to Plymouth last night. He'll get over this evening sometime or other, I expect. In time for the dance, anyway. I've got a man for Maggie. Presentable, if not passionately interesting."

A faint roaring sound drifted in through the window.

" Oh! curse that speedboat," said Lazarus. " I get so tired of it."

" That's not the speedboat," said Nick. " That's a seaplane."

" I believe you're right."

" Of course I'm right. The sound's quite different."

" When are you going to get your Moth, Nick?"

" When I can raise the money," laughed Nick.

" And then, I suppose, you'll be off to Australia like that girl—what's her name?"

" I'd love to——"

"I admire her enormously," said Mrs. Rice, in her tired voice. "What marvellous nerve! All by herself too."

"I admire all these flying people," said Lazarus. "If Michael Seton had succeeded in his flight round the world he'd have been the hero of the day—and rightly so. A thousand pities he's come to grief. He's the kind of man England can't afford to lose."

"He may still be all right," said Nick.

"Hardly. It's a thousand to one against by now. Poor Mad Seton."

"They always called him Mad Seton, didn't they?" asked Frederica.

Lazarus nodded.

"He comes of rather a mad family," he said. "His uncle, Sir Matthew Seton, who died about a week ago—he was as mad as a hatter."

"He was the mad millionaire who ran bird sanctuaries, wasn't he?" asked Frederica.

"Yes. Used to buy up islands. He was a great woman-hater. Some girl chucked him once, I believe, and he took to Natural History by way of consoling himself."

"Why do you say Michael Seton is dead?" persisted Nick. "I don't see any reason for giving up hope—yet?"

"Of course, you knew him, didn't you?" said Lazarus. "I forgot."

"Freddie and I met him at Le Touquet last year," said Nick. "He was too marvellous, wasn't he, Freddie?"

"Don't ask me, darling. He was your conquest, not mine. He took you up once, didn't he?"

"Yes—at Scarborough. It was simply too wonderful."

"Have you done any flying, Captain Hastings?" Maggie asked of me in polite conversational tones.

I had to confess that a trip to Paris and back was the extent of my acquaintance with air travel.

Suddenly, with an exclamation, Nick sprang up.

"There's the telephone. Don't wait for me. It's getting late. And I've asked lots of people."

c

She left the room. I glanced at my watch. It was just nine o'clock. Dessert was brought, and port. Poirot and Lazarus were talking Art. Pictures, Lazarus was saying, were a great drug in the market just now. They went on to discuss new ideas in furniture and decoration.

I endeavoured to do my duty by talking to Maggie Buckley, but I had to admit that the girl was heavy in hand. She answered pleasantly, but without throwing the ball back. It was uphill work.

Frederica Rice sat dreamily silent, her elbows on the table and the smoke from her cigarette curling round her fair head. She looked like a meditative angel.

It was just twenty past nine when Nick put her head round the door.

" Come out of it, all of you! The animals are coming in two by two."

We rose obediently. Nick was busy greeting arrivals. About a dozen people had been asked. Most of them were rather uninteresting. Nick, I noticed, made a good hostess. She sank her modernisms and made everyone welcome in an old-fashioned way. Among the guests I noticed Charles Vyse.

Presently we all moved out into the garden to a place overlooking the sea and the harbour. A few chairs had been placed there for the elderly people, but most of us stood. The first rocket flamed to Heaven.

At that moment I heard a loud familiar voice, and turned my head to see Nick greeting Mr. Croft.

" It's too bad," she was saying, " that Mrs. Croft can't be here too. We ought to have carried her on a stretcher or something."

" It's bad luck on poor mother altogether. But she never complains—that woman's got the sweetest nature—Ha! that's a good one." This as a shower of golden rain showed up in the sky.

The night was a dark one—there was no moon—the new moon being due in three days' time. It was also, like most summer evenings, cold. Maggie Buckley, who was next me, shivered.

"I'll just run in and get a coat," she murmured.

"Let me."

"No, you wouldn't know where to find it."

She turned towards the house. At that moment Frederica Rice's voice called :

"Oh, Maggie, get mine too. It's in my room."

"She didn't hear," said Nick. "I'll get it, Freddie. I want my fur one—this shawl isn't nearly hot enough. It's this wind."

There was, indeed, a sharp breeze blowing off the sea.

Some set pieces started down on the quay. I fell into conversation with an elderly lady standing next to me who put me through a rigorous catechism as to life, career, tastes and probable length of stay.

Bang! A shower of green stars filled the sky. They changed to blue, then red, then silver.

Another and yet another.

"'Oh!' and then 'Ah!' that is what one says," observed Poirot suddenly close to my ear. "At the end it becomes monotonous, do you not find? Brrr! The grass, it is damp to the feet! I shall suffer for this—a chill. And no possibility of obtaining a proper *tisane*!"

"A chill? On a lovely night like this?"

"A lovely night! A lovely night! You say that, because the rain it does not pour down in sheets! Always when the rain does not fall, it is a lovely night. But I tell you, my friend, if there were a little thermometer to consult you would see."

"Well," I admitted. "I wouldn't mind putting on a coat myself."

"You are very sensible. You have come from a hot climate."

"I'll bring yours."

Poirot lifted first one, then the other foot from the ground with a cat-like motion.

"It is the dampness of the feet I fear. Would it, think you, be possible to lay hands on a pair of goloshes?"

I repressed a smile.

"Not a hope," I said. "You understand, Poirot, that it is no longer done."

"Then I shall sit in the house," he declared. "Just for the Guy Fawkes show, shall I want only *enrhumer* myself? And catch, perhaps, a *fluxion de poitrine?*"

Poirot still murmuring indignantly, we bent our footsteps towards the house. Loud clapping drifted up to us from the quay below where another set piece was being shown—a ship, I believe, with *Welcome to Our Visitors* displayed across it.

"We are all children at heart," said Poirot, thoughtfully. "*Les Feus D'Artifices,* the party, the games with balls—yes, and even the conjurer, the man who deceives the eye, however carefully it watches—*mais qu'est-ce que vous avez?*"

I had caught him by the arm, and was clutching him with one hand, while with the other I pointed.

We were within a hundred yards of the house, and just in front of us, between us and the open French window, *there lay a huddled figure wrapped in a scarlet Chinese shawl. . . .*

"*Mon Dieu!*" whispered Poirot. "*Mon Dieu . . .*"

CHAPTER EIGHT

THE FATAL SHAWL

I suppose it was not more than forty seconds that we stood there, frozen with horror, unable to move, but it seemed like an hour. Then Poirot moved forward, shaking off my hand. He moved stiffly like an automaton.

"It has happened," he murmured, and I can hardly describe the anguished bitterness of his voice. "In spite of everything—in spite of my precautions, it has happened.

Ah! miserable criminal that I am, why did I not guard her better. I should have foreseen. Not for one instant should I have left her side."

" You mustn't blame yourself," I said.

My tongue stuck to the roof of my mouth, and I could hardly articulate.

Poirot only responded with a sorrowful shake of his head. He knelt down by the body.

And at that moment we received a second shock.

For Nick's voice rang out, clear and gay, and a moment later Nick appeared in the square of the window silhouetted against the lighted room behind.

" Sorry I've been so long, Maggie," she said. " But——"

Then she broke off—staring at the scene before her.

With a sharp exclamation, Poirot turned over the body on the lawn and I pressed forward to see.

I looked down into the dead face of Maggie Buckley.

In another minute Nick was beside us. She gave a sharp cry.

" Maggie—oh! Maggie—it—it—can't——"

Poirot was still examining the girl's body. At last very slowly he rose to his feet.

" Is she—is——" Nick's voice broke off.

" Yes, Mademoiselle. She is dead."

" But why? But why? Who could have wanted to kill her?"

Poirot's reply came quickly and firmly.

" It was not her they meant to kill, Mademoiselle! It was you! They were misled by the shawl."

A great cry broke from Nick.

" Why couldn't it have been me?" she wailed. " Oh! why couldn't it have been me? I'd so much rather. I don't want to live—now. I'd be glad—willing—happy—to die."

She flung up her arms wildly and then staggered slightly. I passed an arm round her quickly to support her.

" Take her into the house, Hastings," said Poirot. " Then ring up the police."

" The police?"

" *Mais oui!* Tell them someone has been shot. And afterwards stay with Mademoiselle Nick. *On no account leave her.*"

I nodded comprehension of these instructions, and supporting the half-fainting girl, made my way through the drawing-room window. I laid the girl on the sofa there, with a cushion under her head, and then hurried out into the hall in search of the telephone.

I gave a slight start on almost running into Ellen. She was standing there with a most peculiar expression on her meek, respectable face. Her eyes were glittering and she was passing her tongue repeatedly over her dry lips. Her hands were trembling, as though with excitement. As soon as she saw me, she spoke.

" Has—has anything happened, sir?"

" Yes," I said curtly. " Where's the telephone?"

" Nothing—nothing wrong, sir?"

" There's been an accident," I said evasively. " Somebody hurt. I must telephone."

" Who has been hurt, sir?"

There was a positive eagerness in her face.

" Miss Buckley. Miss Maggie Buckley."

" Miss Maggie? Miss *Maggie*? Are you sure, sir—I mean are you sure that—that it's Miss Maggie?"

" I'm quite sure," I said. " Why?"

" Oh!—nothing. I—I thought it might be one of the other ladies. I thought perhaps it might be—Mrs. Rice."

" Look here," I said. " Where's the telephone?"

" It's in the little room here, sir." She opened the door for me and indicated the instrument.

" Thanks," I said. And, as she seemed disposed to linger, I added : " That's all I want, thank you."

" If you want Dr. Graham——"

" No, no," I said. " That's all. Go, please."

She withdrew reluctantly, as slowly as she dared. In all probability she would listen outside the door, but I could not help that. After all, she would soon know all there was to be known.

I got the police station and made my report. Then, on my own initiative, I rang up the Dr. Graham Ellen had mentioned. I found his number in the book. Nick, at any rate, should have medical attention, I felt—even though a doctor could do nothing for that poor girl lying out there. He promised to come at once and I hung up the receiver and came out into the hall again.

If Ellen had been listening outside the door she had managed to disappear very swiftly. There was no one in sight when I came out. I went back into the drawing-room. Nick was trying to sit up.

"Do you think—could you get me—some brandy?"

"Of course."

I hurried into the dining-room, found what I wanted and came back. A few sips of the spirit revived the girl. The colour began to come back into her cheeks. I rearranged the cushion for her head.

"It's all—so awful." She shivered. "Everything—everywhere."

"I know, my dear, I know."

"No, you don't! You can't. And it's all such a *waste*. If it were only me. It would be all over. . . ."

"You mustn't," I said, "be morbid."

She only shook her head, reiterating : "You don't know! You don't *know!*"

Then, suddenly, she began to cry. A quiet, hopeless sobbing like a child. That, I thought, was probably the best thing for her, so I made no effort to stem her tears.

When their first violence had died down a little, I stole across to the window and looked out. I had heard an outcry of voices a few minutes before. They were all there by now, a semi-circle round the scene of the tragedy, with Poirot like a fantastical sentinel, keeping them back.

As I watched, two uniformed figures came striding across the grass. The police had arrived.

I went quietly back to my place by the sofa. Nick lifted her tear-stained face.

"Oughtn't I to be doing something?"

"No, my dear. Poirot will see to it. Leave it to him." Nick was silent for a minute or two, then she said:

"Poor Maggie. Poor dear old Maggie. Such a good sort who never harmed a soul in her life. That this should happen to *her*. I feel as though I'd killed her—bringing her down in the way that I did."

I shook my head sadly. How little one can foresee the future. When Poirot insisted on Nick's inviting a friend, how little did he think that he was signing an unknown girl's death warrant.

We sat in silence. I longed to know what was going on outside, but I loyally fulfilled Poirot's instructions and stuck to my post.

It seemed hours later when the door opened and Poirot and a police inspector entered the room. With them came a man who was evidently Dr. Graham. He came over at once to Nick.

"And how are you feeling, Miss Buckley? This must have been a terrible shock." His fingers were on her pulse.

"Not too bad."

He turned to me.

"Has she had anything?"

"Some brandy," I said.

"I'm all right," said Nick, bravely.

"Able to answer a few questions, eh?"

"Of course."

The police inspector moved forward with a preliminary cough. Nick greeted him with the ghost of a smile.

"Not impeding the traffic this time," she said.

I gathered they were not strangers to each other.

"This is a terrible business, Miss Buckley," said the inspector. "I'm very sorry about it. Now Mr. Poirot here, whose name I'm very familiar with (and proud we are to have him with us, I'm sure), tells me that to the best of his belief you were shot at in the grounds of the Majestic Hotel the other morning?"

Nick nodded.

"I thought it was just a wasp," she explained. "But it wasn't."

"And you'd had some rather peculiar accidents before that?"

"Yes—at least it was odd their happening so close together."

She gave a brief account of the various circumstances.

"Just so. Now how came it that your cousin was wearing your shawl to-night?"

"We came in to fetch her coat—it was rather cold watching the fireworks. I flung off the shawl on the sofa here. Then I went upstairs and put on the coat I'm wearing now— a light nutria one. I also got a wrap for my friend Mrs. Rice out of her room. There it is on the floor by the window. Then Maggie called out that she couldn't find her coat. I said it must be downstairs. She went down and called up she still couldn't find it. I said it must have been left in the car—it was a tweed coat she was looking for—she hasn't got an evening furry one—and I said I'd bring her down something of mine. But she said it didn't matter—she'd take my shawl if I didn't want it. And I said of course but would that be enough? And she said Oh, yes, because she really didn't feel it particularly cold after Yorkshire. She just wanted *something*. And I said all right, I'd be out in a minute. And when I did—did come out——"

She stopped, her voice breaking. . . .

"Now, don't distress yourself, Miss Buckley. Just tell me this. Did you hear a shot—or two shots?"

Nick shook her head.

"No—only just the fireworks popping and the squibs going off."

"That's just it," said the inspector. "You'd never notice

a shot with all that going on. It's no good asking you, I suppose, if you've any clue to who it is making these attacks upon you?"

" I haven't the least idea," said Nick. " I can't imagine."

" And you wouldn't be likely to," said the inspector. " Some homicidal maniac—that's what it looks like to me. Nasty business. Well, I won't need to ask you any more questions to-night, miss. I'm more sorry about this than I can say."

Dr. Graham stepped forward.

" I'm going to suggest, Miss Buckley, that you don't stay here. I've been talking it over with M. Poirot. I know of an excellent nursing home. You've had a shock, you know. What you need is complete rest——"

Nick was not looking at him. Her eyes had gone to Poirot.

" Is it—because of the shock?" she asked.

He came forward.

" I want you to feel safe, *mon enfant*. And *I* want to feel, too, that you *are* safe. There will be a nurse there—a nice practical unimaginative nurse. She will be near you all night. When you wake up and cry out—she will be there, close at hand. You understand?"

" Yes," said Nick, " I understand. But *you* don't. I'm not afraid any longer. I don't care one way or another. If any one wants to murder me, they can."

" Hush, hush," I said. " You're over-strung."

" You don't know. None of you know!"

" I really think M. Poirot's plan is a very good one," the doctor broke in soothingly. " I will take you in my car. And we will give you a little something to ensure a good night's rest. Now what do you say?"

" I don't mind," said Nick. " Anything you like. It doesn't matter."

Poirot laid his hand on hers.

" I know, Mademoiselle. I know what you must feel. I stand before you ashamed and stricken to the heart. I, who

promised protection, have not been able to protect. I have
failed. I am a miserable. But believe me, Mademoiselle, my
heart is in agony because of that failure. If you knew what
I am suffering you would forgive, I am sure."

" That's all right," said Nick, still in the same dull voice.
" You mustn't blame yourself. I'm sure you did the best you
could. Nobody could have helped it—or done more, I'm
sure. Please don't be unhappy."

" You are very generous, Mademoiselle."

" No, I——"

There was an interruption. The door flew open and
George Challenger rushed into the room.

" What's all this?" he cried. " I've just arrived. To find
a policeman at the gate and a rumour that somebody's dead.
What is it all about? For God's sake, tell me. Is it—is it—
Nick?"

The anguish in his tone was dreadful to hear. I suddenly
realised that Poirot and the doctor between them completely
blotted out Nick from his sight.

Before anyone had time to answer, he repeated his question.

" Tell me—it can't be true—Nick isn't *dead*?"

" No, *mon ami*," said Poirot, gently. " She is alive."

And he drew back so that Challenger could see the little
figure on the sofa.

For a moment or two Challenger stared at her incred-
ulously. Then, staggering a little, like a drunken man, he
muttered :

" Nick—Nick."

And suddenly dropping on his knees beside the sofa and
hiding his head in his hands, he cried in a muffled voice :

" Nick—my darling—I thought that you were dead."

Nick tried to sit up.

" It's all right, George. Don't be an idiot. I'm quite
safe."

He raised his head and looked round wildly.

" But *somebody's* dead? The policeman said so."

" Yes," said Nick. " Maggie. Poor old Maggie. Oh!——"

A spasm twisted her face. The doctor and Poirot came forward. Graham helped her to her feet. He and Poirot, one on each side, helped her from the room.

" The sooner you get to your bed the better," remarked the doctor. " I'll take you along at once in my car. I've asked Mrs. Rice to pack a few things ready for you to take."

They disappeared through the door. Challenger caught my arm.

" I don't understand. Where are they taking her?"

I explained.

" Oh! I see. Now, then, Hastings, for God's sake give me the hang of this thing. What a ghastly tragedy! That poor girl."

" Come and have a drink," I said. " You're all to pieces."

" I don't mind if I do."

We adjourned to the dining-room.

" You see," he explained, as he put away a stiff whisky and soda. " I thought it was Nick."

There was very little doubt as to the feelings of Commander George Challenger. A more transparent lover never lived.

CHAPTER NINE

A. TO J.

I DOUBT if I shall ever forget the night that followed. Poirot was a prey to such an agony of self-reproach that I was really alarmed. Ceaselessly he strode up and down the room heaping anathemas on his own head and deaf to my well-meant remonstrances.

" What it is to have too good an opinion of oneself. I am punished—yes, I am punished. I, Hercule Poirot. I was too sure of myself."

" No, no," I interpolated.

" But who would imagine—who could imagine—such unparalleled audacity? I had taken, as I thought, all possible precautions. I had warned the murderer——"

" Warned the murderer?"

" *Mais oui.* I had drawn attention to myself. I had let him see that I suspected—someone. I had made it, or so I thought, too dangerous for him to dare to repeat his attempts at murder. I had drawn a cordon round Mademoiselle. And he slips through it! Boldly—under our very eyes almost, he slips through it! In spite of us all—of everyone being on the alert, he achieves his object."

" Only he doesn't," I reminded him.

" That is the chance only! From my point of view, it is the same. A human life has been taken, Hastings—whose life is non-essential."

" Of course," I said. " I didn't mean that."

" But on the other hand, what you say is true. And that makes it worse—ten times worse. For the murderer is still as far as ever from achieving his object. Do you understand, my friend? The position is changed—for the worse. It may mean that not one life—but two—will be sacrificed."

" Not while you're about," I said stoutly.

He stopped and wrung my hand.

" *Merci, mon ami! Merci!* You still have confidence in the old one—you still have the faith. You put new courage into me. Hercule Poirot will not fail again. No second life shall be taken. I will rectify my error—for, see you, there must have been an error! Somewhere there has been a lack of order and method in my usually so well arranged ideas. I will start again. Yes, I will start at the beginning. And this time—I will not fail."

" You really think, then," I said, " that Nick Buckley's life is still in danger?"

" My friend, for what other reason did I send her to this nursing home?"

" Then it wasn't the shock——"

"The shock! Pah! One can recover from shock as well in one's own home as in a nursing home—better, for that matter. It is not amusing there, the floors of green linoleum, the conversation of the nurses—the meals on trays, the ceaseless washing. No, no, it is for safety and safety only. I take the doctor into my confidence. He agrees. He will make all arrangements. No one, *mon ami, not even her dearest friend*, will be admitted to see Miss Buckley. You and I are the only ones permitted. *Pour les autres—eh bien!* 'Doctor's orders,' they will be told. A phrase very convenient and one not to be gainsayed."

"Yes," I said. "Only——"

"Only what, Hastings?"

"That can't go on for ever."

"A very true observation. But it gives us a little breathing space. And you realise, do you not, that the character of our operations has changed."

"In what way?"

"Our original task was to ensure the safety of Mademoiselle. Our task now is a much simpler one—a task with which we are well acquainted. It is neither more nor less than the hunting down of a murderer."

"You call that simpler?"

"Certainly it is simpler. The murderer has, as I said the other day, *signed his name to the crime*. He has come out into the open."

"You don't think——" I hesitated, then went on. "You don't think that the police are right? That this is the work of a madman, some wandering lunatic with homicidal mania?"

"I am more than ever convinced that such is not the case."

"You really think that——"

I stopped. Poirot took up my sentence, speaking very gravely.

"That the murderer is someone in Mademoiselle's own circle? Yes, *mon ami*, I do."

"But surely last night must almost rule out that possibility. We were all together and——"

He interrupted.

"Could you swear, Hastings, that any particular person had never left our little company there on the edge of the cliff? Is there any one person there whom you could swear you had seen *all* the time?"

"No," I said slowly, struck by his words. "I don't think I could. It was dark. We all moved about, more or less. On different occasions I noticed Mrs. Rice, Lazarus, you, Croft, Vyse—but all the time—no."

Poirot nodded his head.

"Exactly. It would be a matter of a very few minutes. The two girls go to the house. The murderer slips away unnoticed, hides behind that sycamore tree in the middle of the lawn. Nick Buckley, or so he thinks, comes out of the window, passes within a foot of him, he fires three shots in rapid succession——"

"Three?" I interjected.

"Yes. He was taking no chances this time. We found three bullets in the body."

"That was risky, wasn't it?"

"Less risky in all probability than one shot would have been. A Mauser pistol does not make a great deal of noise. It would resemble more or less the popping of the fireworks and blend in very well with the noise of them."

"Did you find the pistol?" I asked.

"No. And there, Hastings, lies to my mind the indisputable proof that no stranger is responsible for this. We agree, do we not, that Miss Buckley's own pistol was taken in the first place for one reason only—to give her death the appearance of suicide."

"Yes."

"That is the only possible reason, is it not? But now, you observe, there is no pretence of suicide. *The murderer knows that we should not any longer be deceived by it.* He knows, in fact, what we know!"

I reflected, admitting to myself the logic of Poirot's deduction.

" What did he do with the pistol, do you think?"

Poirot shrugged his shoulders.

." For that, it is difficult to say. But the sea was exceedingly handy. A good toss of the arm, and the pistol sinks, never to be recovered. We cannot, of course, be absolutely sure—but that is what *I* should have done."

His matter-of-fact tone made me shiver a little.

" Do you think—do you think he realised that he'd killed the wrong person?"

" I am quite sure he did not," said Poirot, grimly. " Yes, that must have been an unpleasant little surprise for him when he learnt the truth. To keep his face and betray nothing—it cannot have been easy."

At that moment I bethought me of the strange attitude of the maid, Ellen. I gave Poirot an account of her peculiar demeanour. He seemed very interested.

" She betrayed surprise, did she, that it was Maggie who was dead?"

" Great surprise."

" That is curious. And yet, the fact of a tragedy was clearly *not* a surprise to her. Yes, there is something there that must be looked into. Who is she, this Ellen? So quiet, so respectable in the English manner? Could it be she who ——?" He broke off.

" If you're going to include the accidents," I said, " surely it would take a man to have rolled that heavy boulder down the cliff."

" Not necessarily. It is very largely a question of leverage. Oh, yes, it could be done."

He continued his slow pacing up and down of the room.

" Anyone who was at End House last night comes under suspicion. But those guests—no, I do not think it was one of them. For the most part, I should say, they were mere acquaintances. There was no intimacy between them and the young mistress of the house."

"Charles Vyse was there," I remarked.

"Yes, we must not forget him. He is, logically, our strongest suspect." He made a gesture of despair and threw himself into a chair opposite mine. "*Voilà*—it is always that we come back to! Motive! We must find the motive if we are to understand this crime. And it is there, Hastings, that I am continually baffled. Who can possibly have a motive for doing away with Mademoiselle Nick? I have let myself go to the most absurd suppositions. I, Hercule Poirot, have descended to the most ignominious flights of fancy. I have adopted the mentality of the cheap thriller. The grandfather —the 'Old Nick'—he who is supposed to have gambled his money away. Did he really do so, I have asked myself? Did he, on the contrary, hide it away? Is it hidden somewhere in End House? Buried somewhere in the grounds? With that end in view (I am ashamed to say it) I inquired of Mademoiselle Nick whether there had ever been any offers to buy the house."

"Do you know, Poirot," I said. "I call that rather a bright idea. There may be something in it."

Poirot groaned.

"You would say that! It would appeal, I knew, to your romantic but slightly mediocre mind. Buried treasure—yes, you would enjoy that idea."

"Well—I don't see why not——"

"Because, my friend, the more prosaic explanation is nearly always more probable. Then Mademoiselle's father— I have played with even more degrading ideas concerning him. He was a traveller. Supposing, I say to myself, that he has stolen a jewel—the eye of a God. Jealous priests are on his tracks. Yes, I, Hercule Poirot, have descended to depths such as these.

"I have had other ideas concerning this father," he went on. "Ideas at once more dignified and more probable. Did he, in the course of his wanderings, contract a second marriage? Is there a nearer heir than M. Charles Vyse? But again, that leads nowhere, for we are up against the same difficulty—that there is really nothing of value to inherit.

"I have neglected no possibility. Even that chance reference of Mademoiselle Nick's to the offer made her by M. Lazarus. You remember? The offer to purchase her grandfather's portrait. I telegraphed on Saturday for an expert to come down and examine that picture. He was the man about whom I wrote to Mademoiselle this morning. Supposing, for instance, it were worth several thousand pounds?"

"You surely don't think a rich man like young Lazarus——?"

"Is he rich? Appearances are not everything. Even an old-established firm with palatial showrooms and every appearance of prosperity may rest on a rotten basis. And what does one do then? Does one run about crying out that times are hard? No, one buys a new and luxurious car. One spends a little more money than usual. One lives a little more ostentatiously. For credit, see you, is everything! But sometimes a monumental business has crashed—for no more than a few thousand pounds—*of ready money.*

"Oh! I know," he continued, forestalling my protests. "It is far-fetched—but it is not so bad as revengeful priests or buried treasure. It bears, at any rate, some relationship to things as they happen. And we can neglect nothing—nothing that might bring us nearer the truth."

With careful fingers he straightened the objects on the table in front of him. When he spoke, his voice was grave and, for the first time, calm.

"*Motive!*" he said. "Let us come back to that, and regard this problem calmly and methodically. To begin with, how many kinds of motive are there for murder? What are the motives which lead one human being to take another human being's life?

"We exclude for the moment homicidal mania. Because I am absolutely convinced that the solution of our problem does not lie there. We also exclude killing done on the spur of the moment under the impulse of an ungovernable temper. This is cold-blooded deliberate murder. What are the motives that actuate such a murder as that?

"There is, first, *Gain*. Who stood to gain by Mademoiselle Buckley's death? Directly or indirectly? Well, we can put down Charles Vyse. He inherits a property that, from the financial point of view, is probably not worth inheriting. He might, perhaps, pay off the mortgage, build small villas on the land and eventually make a small profit. It is possible. The place might be worth something to him if he had any deeply cherished love of it—if, it were, for instance, a family place. That is, undoubtedly, an instinct very deeply implanted in some human beings, and it has, in cases I have known, actually led to crime. But I cannot see any such motive in M. Vyse's case.

"The only other person who would benefit at all by Mademoiselle Buckley's death is her friend, Madame Rice. But the amount would clearly be a very small one. Nobody else, as far as I can see, *gains* by Mademoiselle Buckley's death.

"What is another motive? Hate—or love that has turned to hate. The *crime passionnel*. Well, there again we have the word of the observant Madame Croft that both Charles Vyse and Commander Challenger are in love with the young lady."

"I think we can say that we have observed the latter phenomenon for ourselves," I remarked, with a smile.

"Yes—he tends to wear his heart on his sleeve, the honest sailor. For the other, we rely on the word of Madame Croft. Now, if Charles Vyse felt that he were supplanted, would he be so powerfully affected that he would kill his cousin rather than let her become the wife of another man?"

"It sounds very melodramatic," I said, doubtfully.

"It sounds, you would say, un-English. I agree. But even the English have emotions. And a type such as Charles Vyse, is the most likely to have them. He is a repressed young man. One who does not show his feelings easily.

Such often have the most violent feelings. I would never suspect the Commander Challenger of murder for emotional reasons. No, no, he is not the type. But with Charles Vyse—yes, it is possible. But it does not entirely satisfy me.

"Another motive for crime—Jealousy. I separate it from the last, because jealousy may not, necessarily, be a sexual emotion. There is envy—envy of possession—of supremacy. Such a jealousy as drove the Iago of your great Shakespeare to one of the cleverest crimes (speaking from the professional point of view) that has ever been committed."

"Why was it so clever?" I asked, momentarily diverted.

"*Parbleu*—because he got others to execute it. Imagine a criminal nowadays on whom one was unable to put the handcuffs because he had never done anything himself. But this is not the subject we were discussing. Can jealousy, of any kind, be responsible for this crime? Who has reason to envy Mademoiselle? Another woman? There is only Madame Rice, and as far as we can see, there was no rivalry between the two women. But again, that is only ' as far as we can see.' There may be something there.

"Lastly—Fear. Does Mademoiselle Nick, by any chance, hold somebody's secret in her power? Does she know something which, if it were known, might ruin another life? If so, I think we can say very definitely, *that she herself is unaware of it*. But that might be, you know. That might be. And if so, it makes it very difficult. Because, whilst she holds the clue in her hands, she holds it unconsciously and will be quite unable to tell us what it is."

"You really think that is possible?"

"It is a hypothesis. I am driven to it by the difficulty of finding a reasonable theory elsewhere. When you have eliminated other possibilities you turn to the one that is left and say—since the other is not—*this must be so....*"

He was silent a long time.

At last, rousing himself from his absorption, he drew a sheet of paper towards him and began to write.

"What are you writing?" I asked, curiously.

"*Mon ami*, I am composing a list. It is a list of people surrounding Mademoiselle Buckley. Within that list, if my theory is correct, there must be the name of the murderer."

He continued to write for perhaps twenty minutes—then shoved the sheets of paper across to me.

"*Voilà, mon ami.* See what you make of it."

The following is a reproduction of the paper :

> A. Ellen.
> B. Her gardener husband.
> C. Their child.
> D. Mr. Croft.
> E. Mrs. Croft.
> F. Mrs. Rice.
> G. Mr. Lazarus.
> H. Commander Challenger.
> I. Mr. Charles Vyse.
> J.

Remarks:

A. *Ellen*—Suspicious circumstances. Her attitude and words on hearing of the crime. Best opportunity of anyone to have staged accidents and to have known of pistol, *but* unlikely to have tampered with car, and general mentality of crime seems above her level.

Motive.—None—unless hate arising out of some incident unknown.

Note.—Further inquiries as to her antecedents and general relations with N. B.

B. *Her Husband.*—Same as above. More likely to have tampered with car.

Note.—Should be interviewed.

C. *Child.*—Can be ruled out.

Note.—Should be interviewed. Might give valuable information.

D. *Mr. Croft.*—Only suspicious circumstance the fact that we met him mounting the stair to bedroom floor. Had ready explanation which may be true. But it may not!

Nothing known of antecedents.

Motive.—None.

E. *Mrs. Croft.*—Suspicious circumstances.—None.

Motive.—None.

F. *Mrs. Rice.*—Suspicious circumstances. Full opportunity. Asked N. B. to fetch wrap. Has deliberately tried to create impression that N. B. is a liar and her account of " accidents " not to be relied on. Was not at Tavistock when accidents occurred. Where was she?

Motive.—*Gain?* Very slight. *Jealousy?* Possible, but nothing known. *Fear?* Also possible, but nothing known.

Note.—Converse with N. B. on subject. See if any light is thrown upon matter. Possibly something to do with F. R.'s marriage.

G. *Mr. Lazarus.*—Suspicious circumstances. General opportunity. Offer to buy picture. Said brakes of car were quite all right (according to F. R.). May have been in neighbourhood prior to Friday.

Motive.—None—unless profit on picture. *Fear?*—unlikely.

Note.—Find out where J. L. was before arriving at St. Loo. Find out financial position of Aaron Lazarus & Son.

H. *Commander Challenger.*—Suspicious circumstances. None. Was in neighbourhood all last week, so opportunity for " accidents " good. Arrived half an hour after murder.

Motive.—None.

I. *Mr. Vyse.*—Suspicious circumstances. Was absent from office at time when shot was fired in garden of hotel. Opportunity good. Statement about selling of End House open to doubt. Of a repressed temperament. Would probably know about pistol.

    Motive.—Gain? (slight) *Love or Hate?* Possible with one of his temperament. *Fear?* Unlikely.

    Note.—Find out who held mortgage. Find out position of Vyse's firm.

J. ?.—There *could* be a J., *e.g.* an outsider. *But* with a link in the form of one of the foregoing. If so, probably connected with A. D. and E. or F. The existence of J. would explain (1) Ellen's lack of surprise at crime and her pleasurable satisfaction. (But that might be due to natural pleasurable excitement of her class over deaths.) (2) The reason for Croft and his wife coming to live in lodge. (3) Might supply motive for F. R.'s *fear* of secret being revealed or for *jealousy*.

Poirot watched me as I read.

" It is very English, is it not?" he remarked, with pride. " I am more English when I write than when I speak."

" It's an excellent piece of work," I said, warmly. " It sets all the possibilities out most clearly."

" Yes," he said, thoughtfully, as he took it back from me. " And one name leaps to the eye, my friend. *Charles Vyse.* He has the best opportunities. We have given him the choice of two motives. *Ma foi*—if that was a list of racehorses, he would start favourite, *n'est-ce pas?*"

" He is certainly the most likely suspect."

"You have a tendency, Hastings, to prefer the least likely. That, no doubt, is from reading too many detective stories.

In real life, nine times out of ten, it is the most likely and the most obvious person who commits the crime."

"But you don't really think that is so this time?"

"There is only one thing that is against it. The boldness of the crime! That has stood out from the first. Because of that, as I say, the motive *cannot be obvious*."

"Yes, that is what you said at first."

"And that is what I say again."

With a sudden brusque gesture he crumpled the sheets of paper and threw them on the floor.

"No," he said, as I uttered an exclamation of protest. "That list has been in vain. Still, it has cleared my mind. *Order and method!* That is the first stage. To arrange the facts with neatness and precision. The next stage——"

"Yes."

"The next stage is that of the psychology. The correct employment of the little grey cells! I advise you, Hastings, to go to bed."

"No," I said. "Not unless you do. I'm not going to leave you."

"Most faithful of dogs! But see you, Hastings, you cannot assist me to think. That is all I am going to do— think."

I still shook my head.

"You might want to discuss some point with me."

"Well—well—you are a loyal friend. Take at least, I beg of you, the easy-chair."

That proposal I did accept. Presently the room began to swim and dip. The last thing I remember was seeing Poirot carefully retrieving the crumpled sheets of paper from the floor and putting them away tidily in the waste-paper basket.

Then I must have fallen asleep.

CHAPTER TEN

NICK'S SECRET

IT was daylight when I awoke.

Poirot was still sitting where he had been the night before. His attitude was the same, but in his face was a difference. His eyes were shining with that queer cat-like green light that I knew so well.

I struggled to an upright position, feeling very stiff and uncomfortable. Sleeping in a chair is a proceeding not to be recommended at my time of life. Yet one thing at least resulted from it—I awoke not in that pleasant state of lazy somnolence but with a mind and brain as active as when I fell asleep.

"Poirot," I cried. "You have thought of something."

He nodded. He leaned forward, tapping the table in front of him.

"Tell me, Hastings, the answer to these three questions. *Why has Mademoiselle Nick been sleeping badly lately? Why did she buy a black evening dress—she never wears black? Why did she say last night, 'I have nothing to live for—now'?*"

I stared. The questions seemed beside the point.

"Answer those questions, Hastings, answer them?"

"Well—as to the first—she said she had been worried lately."

"Precisely. What has she been worried about?"

"And the black dress—well, everybody wants a change sometimes."

"For a married man, you have very little appreciation of feminine psychology. If a woman thinks she does not look well in a colour, she refuses to wear it."

"And the last—well, it was a natural thing to say after that awful shock."

"No, *mon ami*, it was *not* a natural thing to say. To be horror-struck by her cousin's death, to reproach herself for it —yes, all that is natural enough. But the other, no. She spoke of life with weariness—as of a thing no longer dear to her. Never before had she displayed that attitude. She had been defiant—yes—she had snapped the fingers, yes—and then, when that broke down, she was afraid. Afraid, mark you, because life was sweet and she did not wish to die. But weary of life—no! That never! Even before dinner that was not so. We have there, Hastings, a *psychological change*. And that is interesting. What was it caused her point of view to change?"

"The shock of her cousin's death."

"I wonder. It was the shock that loosed her tongue. But suppose the change was before that. Is there anything else could account for it?"

"I don't know of anything."

"Think, Hastings. Use your little grey cells."

"Really——"

"What was the last moment we had the opportunity of observing her?"

"Well, actually, I suppose, at dinner."

"Exactly. After that, we only saw her receiving guests, making them welcome—purely a formal attitude. What happened at the end of dinner, Hastings?"

"She went to telephone," I said, slowly.

"*A la bonheur*. You have got there at last. She went to telephone. And she was absent a long time. Twenty minutes at least. That is a long time for a telephone call. Who spoke to her over the telephone? What did they say? Did she really telephone? We have got to find out, Hastings, what happened in that twenty minutes. For there, or so I fully believe, we shall find the clue we seek."

"You really think so?"

"*Mais oui, mais oui!* All along, Hastings, I have told you that Mademoiselle has been keeping something back.

She doesn't think it has any connection with the murder—but I, Hercule Poirot, know better! It *must* have a connection. For, all along, I have been conscious that there is a factor lacking. If there were not a factor lacking—why then, the whole thing would be plain to me! And as it is not plain to me—*eh bien*—then the missing factor is the keystone of the mystery! I know I am right, Hastings.

" I must know the answer to those three questions. And then—and then—I shall begin *to see*. . . ."

" Well," I said, stretching my stiffened limbs, " I think a bath and a shave are indicated."

By the time I had had a bath and changed into day clothing I felt better. The stiffness and weariness of a night passed in uncomfortable conditions passed off. I arrived at the breakfast table feeling that one drink of hot coffee would restore me to my normal self.

I glanced at the paper, but there was little news in it beyond the fact that Michael Seton's death was now definitely confirmed. The intrepid airman had perished. I wondered whether, to-morrow, new headlines would have sprung into being : " GIRL MURDERED DURING FIREWORK PARTY. MYSTERIOUS TRAGEDY." Something like that.

I had just finished breakfast when Frederica Rice came up to my table. She was wearing a plain little frock of black marocain with a little soft pleated white collar. Her fairness was more evident than ever.

" I want to see M. Poirot, Captain Hastings. Is he up yet, do you know?"

" I will take you up with me now," I said. " We shall find him in the sitting-room."

" Thank you."

" I hope," I said, as we left the dining-room together; " that you didn't sleep too badly?"

" It was a shock," she said, in a meditative voice. " But, of course, I didn't know the poor girl. It's not as though it had been Nick."

"I suppose you'd never met this girl before?"

"Once—at Scarborough. She came over to lunch with Nick."

"It will be a terrible blow to her father and mother," I said.

"Dreadful."

But she said it very impersonally. She was, I fancied, an egoist. Nothing was very real to her that did not concern herself.

Poirot had finished his breakfast and was sitting reading the morning paper. He rose and greeted Frederica with all his customary Gallic politeness.

"Madame," he said. "*Enchanté!*"

He drew forward a chair.

She thanked him with a very faint smile and sat down. Her two hands rested on the arms of the chair. She sat there very upright, looking straight in front of her. She did not rush into speech. There was something a little frightening about her stillness and aloofness.

"M. Poirot," she said at last. "I suppose there is no doubt that this—sad business last night was all part and parcel of the same thing? I mean—that the intended victim was really Nick?"

"I should say, Madame, that there was no doubt at all."

Frederica frowned a little.

"Nick bears a charmed life," she said.

There was some curious undercurrent in her voice that I could not understand.

"Luck, they say, goes in cycles," remarked Poirot.

"Perhaps. It is certainly useless to fight against it."

Now there was only weariness in her tone. After a moment or two, she went on.

"I must beg your pardon, M. Poirot. Nick's pardon, too. Up till last night I did not believe. I never dreamed that the danger was—serious."

"Is that so, Madame?"

"I see now that everything will have to be gone into—

carefully. And I imagine that Nick's immediate circle of friends will not be immune from suspicion. Ridiculous, of course, but there it is. Am I right, M. Poirot?"

"You are very intelligent, Madame."

"You asked me some questions about Tavistock the other day, M. Poirot. As you will find out sooner or later, I might as well tell you the truth now. I was not at Tavistock."

"No, Madame?"

"I motored down to this part of the world with Mr. Lazarus early last week. We did not wish to arouse more comment than necessary. We stayed at a little place called Shellacombe."

"That is, I think, about seven miles from here, Madame?"

"About that—yes."

Still that quiet far-away weariness.

"May I be impertinent, Madame?"

"Is there such a thing—in these days?"

"Perhaps you are right, Madame. How long have you and M. Lazarus been friends?"

"I met him six months ago."

"And you—care for him, Madame?"

Frederica shrugged her shoulders.

"He is—rich."

"Oh! *là là*," cried Poirot. "That is an ugly thing to say."

She seemed faintly amused.

"Isn't it better to say it myself—than to have you say it for me?"

"Well—there is always that, of course. May I repeat, Madame, that you are *very* intelligent."

"You will give me a diploma soon," said Frederica, and rose.

"There is nothing more you wish to tell me, Madame?"

"I do not think so—no. I am going to take some flowers round to Nick and see how she is."

"Ah, that is very *aimable* of you. Thank you, Madame, for your frankness."

She glanced at him sharply, seemed about to speak, then

thought better of it and went out of the room, smiling faintly at me as I held the door open for her.

"She is intelligent," said Poirot. "Yes, but so is Hercule Poirot!"

"What do you mean?"

"That it is all very well and very pretty to force the richness of M. Lazarus down my throat——"

"I must say that rather disgusted me."

"*Mon cher*, always you have the right reaction in the wrong place. It is not, for the moment, a question of good taste or otherwise. If Madame Rice has a devoted friend who is rich and can give her all she needs—why then obviously Madame Rice would not need to murder her dearest friend for a mere pittance."

"Oh!" I said.

"*Précisément!* 'Oh!'"

"Why didn't you stop her going to the nursing home?"

"Why should I show my hand? Is it Hercule Poirot who prevents Mademoiselle Nick from seeing her friends? *Quelle idée!* It is the doctors and the nurses. Those tiresome nurses! So full of rules and regulations and 'doctor's orders.'"

"You're not afraid that they may let her in after all? Nick may insist."

"Nobody will be let in, my dear Hastings, but you and me. And for that matter, the sooner we make our way there, the better."

The sitting-room door flew open and George Challenger barged in. His tanned face was alive with indignation.

"Look here, M. Poirot," he said. "What's the meaning of this? I rang up that damned nursing home where Nick is. Asked how she was and what time I could come round and see her. And they say the doctor won't allow any visitors. I want to know the meaning of that? To put it plainly, is this your work? Or is Nick really ill from shock?"

"I assure you, Monsieur, that I do not lay down rules for

nursing homes. I would not dare. Why not ring up the good doctor—what was his name now?—Ah, yes, Graham."

"I have. He says she's going on as well as could be expected—usual stuff. But I know all the tricks—my uncle's a doctor. Harley Street. Nerve specialist. Psycho-analysis—all the rest of it. Putting relations and friends off with soothing words. I've heard about it all. I don't believe Nick isn't up to seeing any one. I believe you're at the bottom of this, M. Poirot."

Poirot smiled at him in a very kindly fashion. Indeed, I have always observed that Poirot has a kindly feeling for a lover.

"Now listen to me, *mon ami*," he said. "If one guest is admitted, others cannot be kept out. You comprehend? It must be all or none. We want Mademoiselle's safety, you and I, do we not? Exactly. Then, you understand—it must be *none*."

"I get you," said Challenger, slowly. "But then——"

"Chut! We will say no more. We will forget even what we have said. The prudence, the extreme prudence, is what is needed at present."

"I can hold my tongue," said the sailor quietly.

He turned away to the door, pausing as he went out to say :

"No embargo on flowers, is there? So long as they are not white ones."

Poirot smiled.

"And now," he said, as the door shut behind the impetuous Challenger, "whilst M. Challenger and Madame and perhaps M. Lazarus all encounter each other in the flower shop, you and I will drive quietly to our destination."

"And ask for the answer to the three questions?" I said.

"Yes. We will ask. Though, as a matter of fact, I know the answer."

"What?" I exclaimed.

"Yes."

"But when did you find out?"

"Whilst I was eating my breakfast, Hastings. It stared me in the face."

"Tell me."

"No, I will leave you to hear it from Mademoiselle."

Then, as if to distract my mind, he pushed an open letter across to me.

It was a report by the expert Poirot had sent to examine the picture of old Nicholas Buckley. It stated definitely that the picture was worth at most twenty pounds.

"So that is one matter cleared up," said Poirot.

"No mouse in that mousehole," I said, remembering a metaphor of Poirot's on one past occasion.

"Ah! you remember that? No, as you say, no mouse in that mousehole. Twenty pounds and M. Lazarus offered fifty. What an error of judgment for a seemingly astute young man. But there, there, we must start on our errand."

The nursing home was set high on a hill overlooking the bay. A white-coated orderly received us. We were put into a little room downstairs and presently a brisk-looking nurse came to us.

One glance at Poirot seemed to be enough. She had clearly received her instructions from Dr. Graham together with a minute description of the little detective. She even concealed a smile.

"Miss Buckley has passed a very fair night," she said. "Come up, will you?"

In a pleasant room with the sun streaming into it, we found Nick. In the narrow iron bed, she looked like a tired child. Her face was white and her eyes were suspiciously red, and she seemed listless and weary.

"It's good of you to come," she said in a flat voice.

Poirot took her hand in both of his.

"Courage, Mademoiselle. There is always something to live for."

The words startled her. She looked up in his face.

"Oh!" she said. "Oh!"

"Will you not tell me now, Mademoiselle, what it was

that has been worrying you lately? Or shall I guess? And may I offer you, Mademoiselle, my very deepest sympathy."

Her face flushed.

"So you know. Oh, well, it doesn't matter who knows now. Now that it's all over. Now that I shall never see him again."

Her voice broke.

"Courage, Mademoiselle."

"I haven't got any courage left. I've used up every bit in these last weeks. Hoping and hoping and—just lately—hoping against hope."

I stared. I could not understand one word.

"Regard the poor Hastings," said Poirot. "He does not know what we are talking about."

Her unhappy eyes met mine.

"Michael Seton, the airman," she said. "I was engaged to him—and he's dead."

CHAPTER ELEVEN

THE MOTIVE

WAS dumbfounded.

I turned on Poirot.

"Is this what you meant?"

"Yes, *mon ami*. This morning—I knew."

"How did you know? How did you guess? You said it stared you in the face at breakfast."

"So it did, my friend. From the front page of the newspaper. I remembered the conversation at dinner last night—and I saw everything."

He turned to Nick again.

"You heard the news last night?"

"Yes. On the wireless. I made an excuse about the telephone. I wanted to hear the news alone—in case. . . ." She swallowed hard. "And I heard it. . . ."

D

" I know, I know." He took her hand in both of his.

" It was—pretty ghastly. And all the people arriving. I don't know how I got through it. It all felt like a dream. I could see myself from outside—behaving just as usual. It was queer somehow."

" Yes, yes, I understand."

" And then, when I went to fetch Freddie's wrap—I broke down for a minute. I pulled myself together quite quickly. But Maggie kept calling up about her coat. And then at last she took my shawl and went, and I put on some powder and some rouge and followed her out. And there she was— dead. . . ."

" Yes, yes, it must have been a terrible shock."

" You don't understand. I was angry! I wished it had been *me*! I wanted to be dead—and there I was—alive and perhaps to live for years! And Michael dead—drowned far away in the Pacific."

" *Pauvre enfant.*"

" I don't want to be alive. I don't want to live, I tell you!" she cried, rebelliously.

" I know—I know. To all of us, Mademoiselle, there comes a time when death is preferable to life. But it passes —sorrow passes and grief. You cannot believe that now, I know. It is useless for an old man like me to talk. Idle words—that is what you think—idle words."

" You think I'll forget—and marry someone else? Never!"

She looked rather lovely as she sat up in bed, her two hands clenched and her cheeks burning.

Poirot said gently :

" No, no. I am not thinking anything of the kind. You are very lucky, Mademoiselle. You have been loved by a brave man—a hero. How did you come to meet him?"

" It was at Le Touquet—last September. Nearly a year ago."

" And you became engaged—when?"

" Just after Christmas. But it had to be a secret."

" Why was that?"

" Michael's uncle—old Sir Matthew Seton. He loved birds and hated women."

" *Ah! ce n'est pas raisonable!*"

" Well—I don't mean quite that. He was a complete crank. Thought women ruined a man's life. And Michael was absolutely dependent on him. He was frightfully proud of Michael and it was he who financed the building of the *Albatross* and the expenses of the round-the-world flight. It was the dearest dream of his life as well as of Michael's. If Michael had pulled it off—well, then he could have asked his uncle anything. And even if old Sir Matthew had still cut up rough, well, it wouldn't have really mattered. Michael would have been made—a kind of world hero. His uncle would have come round in the end."

" Yes, yes, I see."

" But Michael said it would be fatal if anything leaked out. We must keep it a dead secret. And I did. I never told anyone—not even Freddie."

Poirot groaned.

" If only you had told me, Mademoiselle."

Nick stared at him.

" But what difference would it have made? It couldn't have anything to do with these mysterious attacks on me? No, I'd promised Michael—and I kept my word. But it was awful—the anxiety, wondering and getting in a state the whole time. And everyone saying one was so nervy. And being unable to explain."

" Yes, I comprehend all that."

" He was missing once before, you know. Crossing the desert on the way to India. That was pretty awful, and then after all, it was all right. His machine was damaged, but it was put right, and he went on. And I kept saying to myself that it would be the same this time. Everyone said he must be dead—and I kept telling myself that he must be all right, really. And then—last night. . . ."

Her voice trailed away.

"You had hoped up till then?"

"I don't know. I think it was more that I refused to believe. It was awful never being able to talk to anyone."

"Yes, I can imagine that. Were you never tempted to tell Madame Rice, for instance?"

"Sometimes I wanted to frightfully."

"You do not think she—guessed?"

"I don't think so." Nick considered the idea carefully. "She never said anything. Of course she used to hint things sometimes. About our being great friends and all that."

"You never considered telling her when M. Seton's uncle died? You know that he died about a week ago?"

"I know. He had an operation or something. I suppose I might have told anybody then. But it wouldn't have been a nice way of doing it, would it? I mean, it would have seemed rather boastful—to do it just then—when all the papers were full of Michael. And reporters would have come and interviewed me. It would all have been rather cheap. And Michael would have hated it."

"I agree with you, Mademoiselle. You could not have announced it publicly. I only meant that you could have spoken of it privately to a friend."

"I did sort of hint to one person," said Nick. "I—thought it was only fair. But I don't know how much he—the person took in."

Poirot nodded.

"Are you on good terms with your cousin, M. Vyse?" he asked, with a rather abrupt change of subject.

"Charles? What put him into your head?"

"I was just wondering—that was all."

"Charles means well," said Nick. "He's a frightful stick, of course. Never moves out of this place. He disapproves of me, I think."

"Oh! Mademoiselle, Mademoiselle. And I hear that he has laid all his devotion at your feet!"

"Disapproving of a person doesn't keep you from having a pash for them. Charles thinks my mode of life is repre-

nensible and he disapproves of my cocktails, my complexion,
my friends and my conversation. But he still feels my fatal
fascination. He always hopes to reform me, I think."

She paused and then said, with a ghost of a twinkle :

" Who have you been pumping to get the local information?"

" You must not give me away, Mademoiselle. I had a
little conversation with the Australian lady, Madame Croft."

" She's rather an old dear—when one has time for her.
Terribly sentimental. Love and home and children—you
know the sort of thing."

" I am old-fashioned and sentimental myself, Mademoiselle."

" Are you? I should have said that Captain Hastings was
the sentimental one of you two."

I blushed indignantly.

" He is furious," said Poirot, eyeing my discomfiture with
a good deal of pleasure. " But you are right, Mademoiselle.
Yes, you are right."

" Not at all," I said, angrily.

" Hastings has a singularly beautiful nature. It has been
the greatest hindrance to me at times."

" Don't be absurd, Poirot."

" He is, to begin with, reluctant to see evil anywhere, and
when he does see it his righteous indignation is so great that
he is incapable of dissembling. Altogether a rare and beautiful nature. No, *mon ami*, I will not permit you to contra-
dict me. It is as I say."

" You've both been very kind to me," said Nick, gently.

" *Là, là,* Mademoiselle. That is nothing. We have much
more to do. To begin with, you will remain here. You will
obey orders. You will do what I tell you. At this juncture I
must not be hampered."

Nick sighed wearily.

" I'll do anything you like. I don't care what I do."

" You will see no friends for the present."

" I don't care. I don't want to see anyone."

"For you the passive part—for us the active one. Now Mademoiselle, I am going to leave you. I will not intrude longer upon your sorrow."

He moved towards the door, pausing with his hand on the handle to say over his shoulder :

"By the way, you once mentioned a will you made. Where is it, this will?"

"Oh! it's knocking round somewhere."

"At End House?"

"Yes."

"In a safe? Locked up in your desk?"

"Well, I really don't know. It's somewhere about." She frowned. "I'm frightfully untidy, you know. Papers and things like that would be mostly in the writing-table in the library. That's where most of the bills are. The will is probably with them. Or it might be in my bedroom."

"You permit me to make the search—yes?"

"If you want to—yes. Look at anything you like."

"*Merci,* Mademoiselle. I will avail myself of your permission."

CHAPTER TWELVE

ELLEN

Poirot said no word till we had emerged from the nursing home into the outer air. Then he caught me by the arm.

"You see, Hastings? You see? Ah! *Sacré tonnerre!* I was right! I was right! Always I knew there was something lacking—some piece of the puzzle that was not there. And without that missing piece the whole thing was meaningless."

His almost despairing triumph was double-Dutch to me. I could not see that anything very epoch-making had occurred.

"It was there all the time. And I could not see it. But

how should I? To know there is *something*—that, yes—but to know what that something is. *Ah! Ça c'est bien plus difficile*."

"Do you mean that this has some direct bearing on the crime?"

"*Ma foi*, do you not see?"

"As a matter of fact, I don't."

"Is it possible? Why, it gives us what we have been looking for—the motive—the hidden obscure motive!"

"I may be very dense, but I can't see it. Do you mean jealousy of some kind?"

"Jealousy? No, no, my friend. The usual motive—the inevitable motive. Money, my friend, money!"

I stared. He went on, speaking more calmly.

"Listen, *mon ami*. Just over a week go Sir Matthew Seton dies. And Sir Matthew Seton was a millionaire—one of the richest men in England."

"Yes, but——"

"*Attendez*. One step at a time. He has a nephew whom he idolises and to whom, we may safely assume, he has left his vast fortune."

"But——"

"*Mais oui*—legacies, yes, an endowment to do with his hobby, yes, but the bulk of the money would go to Michael Seton. Last Tuesday, Michael Seton is reported missing—*and on Wednesday the attacks on Mademoiselle's life begin*. Supposing, Hastings, that Michael Seton made a will before he started on this flight, and that in that will he left all he had to his fiancée."

"That's pure supposition."

"It is supposition—yes. *But it must be so.* Because, if it is not so, there is no meaning in anything that has happened. It is no paltry inheritance that is at stake. It is an enormous fortune."

I was silent for some minutes, turning the matter over in my mind. It seemed to me that Poirot was leaping to con-clusions in a most reckless manner, and yet I was secretly convinced that he was right. It was his extraordinary flair for being right that influenced me. Yet it seemed to me that there was a good deal to be proved still.

" But if nobody knew of the engagement," I argued.

"Pah! Somebody *did* know. For the matter of that, somebody always *does* know. If they do not know, they guess. Madame Rice suspected. Mademoiselle Nick admitted as much. She may have had means of turning those suspicions into certainties."

" How?"

" Well, for one thing, there must have been letters from Michael Seton to Mademoiselle Nick. They had been engaged some time. And her best friend could not call that young lady anything but careless. She leaves things here and there, and everywhere. I doubt if she has ever locked up anything in her life. Oh, yes, there would be means of making sure."

" And Frederica Rice would know about the will that her friend had made?"

" Doubtless. Oh, yes, it narrows down now. You remember my list—a list of persons numbered from A. to J. It has narrowed down to only two persons. I dismiss the servants. I dismiss the Commander Challenger—even though he did take one hour and a half to reach here from Plymouth— and the distance is only thirty miles. I dismiss the long-nosed M. Lazarus who offered fifty pounds for a picture that was only worth twenty (it is odd, that, when you come to think of it. Most uncharacteristic of his race). I dismiss the Australians—so hearty and so pleasant. I keep two people on my list still."

" One is Frederica Rice," I said slowly.

I had a vision of her face, the golden hair, the white fragility of the features.

" Yes. She is indicated very clearly. However carelessly worded Mademoiselle's will may have been, she would be plainly indicated as residuary legatee. Apart from End

House, everything was to go to her. If Mademoiselle Nick instead of Mademoiselle Maggie had been shot last night, Madame Rice would be a rich woman to-day."

"I can hardly believe it!"

"You mean that you can hardly believe that a beautiful woman can be a murderess? One often has a little difficulty with members of a jury on that account. But you may be right. There is still another suspect."

"Who?"

"Charles Vyse."

"But he only inherits the house."

"Yes—but he may not know that. Did he make Mademoiselle's will for her? I think not. If so, it would be in his keeping, not 'knocking around somewhere,' or whatever the phrase was that Mademoiselle used. So, you see, Hastings, *it is quite probable that he knows nothing about that will.* He may believe that she has never made a will and that, in that case, he will inherit as next of kin."

"You know," I said, "that really seems to me much more probable."

"That is your romantic mind, Hastings. The wicked solicitor. A familiar figure in fiction. If as well as being a solicitor he has an impassive face, it makes the matter almost certain. It is true that, in some ways, he is more in the picture than Madame. He would be more likely to know about the pistol and more likely to use one."

"And to send the boulder crashing down."

"Perhaps. Though, as I have told you, much can be done by leverage. And the fact that the boulder was dislodged at the wrong minute, and consequently missed Mademoiselle, is more suggestive of feminine agency. The idea of tampering with the interior of a car seems masculine in conception—though many women are as good mechanics as men nowadays. On the other hand, there are one or two gaps in the theory against M. Vyse."

"Such as——?"

"He is less likely to have known of the engagement than Madame. And there is another point. His action was rather precipitate."

"What do you mean?"

"Well, until last night there was no *certitude* that Seton was dead. To act rashly, without due assurance, seems very uncharacteristic of the legal mind."

"Yes," I said. "A woman would jump to conclusions."

"Exactly. *Ce que femme veut, Dieu veut.* That is the attitude."

"It's really amazing the way Nick has escaped. It seems almost incredible."

And suddenly I remembered the tone in Frederica's voice as she had said : "Nick bears a charmed life."

I shivered a little.

"Yes," said Poirot, thoughtfully. "And I can take no credit to myself. Which is humiliating."

"Providence," I murmured.

"Ah! *mon ami*, I would not put on the shoulders of the good God the burden of men's wrongdoing. You say that in your Sunday morning voice of thankfulness—without reflecting that what you are really saying is that *le bon Dieu* has killed Miss Maggie Buckley."

"Really, Poirot!"

"Really, my friend! But I will not sit back and say '*le bon Dieu* has arranged everything, I will not interfere.' Because I am convinced that *le bon Dieu* created Hercule Poirot for the express purpose of interfering. It is my *métier*."

We had been slowly ascending the zig-zag path up the cliff. It was at this juncture that we passed through the little gate into the grounds of End House.

"Pouf!" said Poirot. "That ascent is a steep one. I am hot. My moustaches are limp. Yes, as I was saying just now, I am on the side of the innocent. I am on the side of Mademoiselle Nick because she was attacked. I am on the side of Mademoiselle Maggie because she has been killed."

"And you are against Frederica Rice and Charles Vyse."

"No, no, Hastings. I keep an open mind. I say only that at the moment one of those two is indicated. Chut!"

We had come out on the strip of lawn by the house, and a man was driving a mowing machine. He had a long, stupid face and lack-lustre eyes. Beside him was a small boy of about ten, ugly but intelligent-looking.

It crossed my mind that we had not heard the mowing machine in action, but I presumed that the gardener was not overworking himself. He had probably been resting from his labours, and had sprung into action on hearing our voices approaching.

"Good-morning," said Poirot.

"Good-morning, sir."

"You are the gardener, I suppose. The husband of Madame who works in the house."

"He's my Dad," said the small boy.

"That's right, sir," said the man. "You'll be the foreign gentleman, I take it, that's really a detective. Is there any news of the young mistress, sir?"

"I come from seeing her at the immediate moment. She has passed a satisfactory night."

"We've had policemen here," said the small boy. "That's where the lady was killed. Here by the steps. I seen a pig killed once, haven't I, Dad?"

"Ah!" said his father, unemotionally.

"Dad used to kill pigs when he worked on a farm. Didn't you, Dad? I seen a pig killed. I liked it."

"Young 'uns like to see pigs killed," said the man, as though stating one of the unalterable facts of nature.

"Shot with a pistol, the lady was," continued the boy. "She didn't have her throat cut. No!"

We passed on to the house, and I felt thankful to get away from the ghoulish child.

Poirot entered the drawing-room, the windows of which

were open and rang the bell. Ellen, neatly attired in black, came in answer to the bell. She showed no surprise at seeing us.

Poirot explained that we were here by permission of Miss Buckley to make a search of the house.

"Very good sir."

"The police have finished?"

"They said they had seen everything they wanted, sir. They've been about the garden since very early in the morning. I don't know whether they've found anything."

She was about to leave the room when Poirot stopped her with a question.

"Were you very surprised last night when you heard Miss Buckley had been shot?"

"Yes, sir, very surprised. Miss Maggie was a nice young lady, sir. I can't imagine anyone being so wicked as to want to harm her."

"If it had been anyone else, you would not have been so surprised—eh?"

"I don't know what you mean, sir."

"When I came into the hall last night," I said, "you asked at once whether anyone had been hurt. Were you expecting anything of the kind?"

She was silent. Her fingers pleated a corner of her apron. She shook her head and murmured:

"You gentlemen wouldn't understand."

"Yes, yes," said Poirot, "I would understand. However fantastic what you may say, I would understand."

She looked at him doubtfully, then seemed to make up her mind to trust him.

"You see, sir," she said, "this isn't a good house."

I was surprised and a little contemptuous. Poirot, however, seemed to find the remark not in the least unusual.

"You mean it is an old house."

"Yes, sir, not a good house."

"You have been here long?"

"Six years, sir. But I was here as a girl. In the kitchen

s kitchen-maid. That was in the time of old Sir Nicholas. t was the same then."

Poirot looked at her attentively.

"In an old house," he said, "there is sometimes an atmosphere of evil."

"That's it, sir," said Ellen, eagerly. "Evil. Bad thoughts nd bad deeds too. It's like dry rot in a house, sir, you can't get it out. It's a sort of feeling in the air. I always knew omething bad would happen in this house, some day."

"Well, you have been proved right."

"Yes, sir."

There was a very slight underlying satisfaction in her tone, he satisfaction of one whose gloomy prognostications have een shown to be correct.

"But you didn't think it would be Miss Maggie."

"No, indeed, I didn't, sir. Nobody hated *her*—I'm sure of it."

It seemed to me that in those words was a clue. I expected Poirot to follow it up, but to my surprise he shifted to quite different subject.

"You didn't hear the shots fired?"

"I couldn't have told with the fireworks going on. Very noisy they were."

"You weren't out watching them?"

"No, I hadn't finished clearing up dinner."

"Was the waiter helping you?"

"No, sir, he'd gone out into the garden to have a look at the fireworks."

"But you didn't go."

"No, sir."

"Why was that?"

"I wanted to get finished."

"You don't care for fireworks?"

"Oh, yes, sir, it wasn't that. But you see, there's two nights of them, and William and I get the evening off tomorrow and go down into the town and see them from there."

"I comprehend. And you heard Mademoiselle Maggie asking for her coat and unable to find it?"

"I heard Miss Nick run upstairs, sir, and Miss Buckley call up from the front hall saying she couldn't find something and I heard her say, 'All right—I'll take the shawl——'"

"Pardon," Poirot interrupted. "You did not endeavour to search for the coat for her—or get it from the car where it had been left."

"I had my work to do, sir."

"Quite so—and doubtless neither of the two young ladies asked you because they thought you were out looking at the fireworks?"

"Yes, sir."

"So that, other years, you *have* been out looking at the fireworks?"

A sudden flush came into her pale cheeks.

"I don't know what you mean, sir. We're always allowed to go out into the garden. If I didn't feel like it this year, and would rather get on with my work and go to bed, well, that's my business, I imagine."

"*Mais oui. Mais oui.* I did not intend to offend you. Why should you not do as you prefer. To make a change, it is pleasant."

He paused and then added:

"Now another little matter in which I wonder whether you can help me. This is an old house. Are there, do you know, any secret chambers in it?"

"Well—there's a kind of sliding panel—in this very room. I remember being shown it as a girl. Only I can't remember just now where it is. Or was it in the library? I can't say, I'm sure."

"Big enough for a person to hide in?"

"Oh, no, indeed, sir! A little cupboard place—a kind of niche. About a foot square, sir, not more than that."

"Oh! that is not what I mean at all."

The blush rose to her face again.

"If you think I was hiding anywhere—I wasn't! I heard Miss Nick run down the stairs and out and I heard her cry out—and I came into the hall to see if—if anything was the matter. And that's the gospel truth, sir. That's the gospel truth."

CHAPTER THIRTEEN

LETTERS

HAVING successfully got rid of Ellen, Poirot turned a somewhat thoughtful face towards me.

"I wonder now—did she hear those shots? I think she did. She heard them, she opened the kitchen door. She heard Nick rush down the stairs and out, and she herself came into the hall to find out what had happened. That is natural enough. But why did she not go out and watch the fireworks that evening? That is what I should like to know, Hastings."

"What was your idea in asking about a secret hiding place?"

"A mere fanciful idea that, after all, we might not have disposed of J."

"J?"

"Yes. The last person on my list. The problematical outsider. Supposing for some reason connected with Ellen, that J. had come to the house last night. He (I assume a he) conceals himself in a secret chamber in this room. A girl passes through whom he takes to be Nick. He follows her out—and shoots her. *Non—c'est idiot!* And anyway, we know that there is no hiding place. Ellen's decision to remain in the kitchen last night was a pure hazard. Come, let us search for the will of Mademoiselle Nick."

There were no papers in the drawing-room. We adjourned to the library, a rather dark room looking out on the drive.

Here there was a large old-fashioned walnut bureau-writing-table.

It took us some time to go through it. Everything was in complete confusion. Bills and receipts were mixed up together. Letters of invitation, letters pressing for payment of accounts, letters from friends.

"We will arrange these papers," said Poirot, sternly, "with order and method."

He was as good as his word. Half an hour later, he sat back with a pleased expression on his face. Everything was neatly sorted, docketed and filed.

"*C'est bien, ça.* One thing is at least to the good. We have had to go through everything so thoroughly that there is no possibility of our having missed anything."

"No, indeed. Not that there's been much to find."

"Except possibly this."

He tossed across a letter. It was written in large sprawling handwriting, almost indecipherable.

"DARLING,—Party was too too marvellous. Feel rather a worm to-day. You were wise not to touch that stuff—don't ever start, darling. It's too damned hard to give up. I'm writing the boy friend to hurry up the supply. What Hell life is!

"Yours,
"FREDDIE."

"Dated last February," said Poirot, thoughtfully. "She takes drugs, of course, I knew that as soon as I looked at her."

"Really? I never suspected such a thing."

"It is fairly obvious. You have only to look at her eyes. And then there are her extraordinary variations of mood. Sometimes she is all on edge, strung up—sometimes she is lifeless—inert."

"Drug-taking affects the moral sense, does it not?"

"Inevitably. But I do not think Madame Rice is a real addict. She is at the beginning—not the end."

"And Nick?"

"There are no signs of it. She may have attended a dope party now and then for fun, but she is no taker of drugs."

"I'm glad of that."

I remembered suddenly what Nick had said about Frederica, that she was not always herself. Poirot nodded and tapped the letter he held.

"This is what she was referring to, undoubtedly. Well, we have drawn the blank, as you say, here. Let us go up to Mademoiselle's room."

There was a desk in Nick's room also, but comparatively little was kept in it. Here again, there was no sign of a will. We found the registration book of her car and a perfectly good dividend warrant of a month back. Otherwise there was nothing of importance.

Poirot sighed in an exasperated fashion.

"The young girls—they are not properly trained nowadays. The order, the method, it is left out of their bringing up. She is charming, Mademoiselle Nick, but she is a feather-head. Decidedly she is a feather-head."

He was now going through the contents of a chest of drawers.

"Surely, Poirot," I said, with some embarrassment, "those are underclothes."

He paused in surprise.

"And why not, my friend?"

"Don't you think—I mean—we can hardly——"

He broke into a roar of laughter.

"Decidedly, my poor Hastings, you belong to the Victorian era. Mademoiselle Nick would tell you so if she were here. In all probability she would say that you had the mind like the sink! Young ladies are not ashamed of their underclothes nowadays. The camisole, the cami-knicker, it is no longer a shameful secret. Every day, on the beach, all these garments will be discarded within a few feet of you. And why not?"

"I don't see any need for what you are doing."

"*Ecoutez*, my friend. Clearly, she does not lock up her treasures, Mademoiselle Nick. If she wished to hide anything from sight—where would she hide it? Underneath the stockings and the petticoats. Ah! what have we here?"

He held up a packet of letters tied with a faded pink ribbon.

"The love letters of M. Michael Seton, if I mistake not."

Quite calmly he untied the ribbon and began to open out the letters.

"Poirot," I cried, scandalised. "You really can't do that. It isn't playing the game."

"I am not playing a game, *mon ami*." His voice rang out suddenly harsh and stern. "I am hunting down a murderer."

"Yes, but private letters——"

"May have nothing to tell me—on the other hand, they may. I must take every chance, my friend. Come, you might as well read them with me. Two pairs of eyes are no worse than one pair. Console yourself with the thought that the staunch Ellen probably knows them by heart."

I did not like it. Still I realised that in Poirot's position he could not afford to be squeamish, and I consoled myself by the quibble that Nick's last word had been, "Look at anything you like."

The letters spread over several dates, beginning last winter.

New Year's Day.

"DARLING,—The New Year is in and I'm making good resolutions. It seems too wonderful to be true—that you should actually love me. You've made all the difference to my life. I believe we both knew—from the very first moment we met. Happy New Year, my lovely girl.

　　　　　　　　"Yours for ever, MICHAEL."

February 8th.

"DEAREST LOVE,—How I wish I could see you more often. This is pretty rotten, isn't it? I hate all this beastly concealment, but I explained to you how things are. I know how much you hate lies and concealment. I do too. But honestly, it might upset the whole apple cart. Uncle Matthew has got an absolute bee in his bonnet about early marriages and the way they wreck a man's career. As though you could wreck mine, you dear angel!

"Cheer up, darling. Everything will come right.

"Yours,
"MICHAEL."

March 2nd.

"I oughtn't to write to you two days running, I know. But I must. When I was up yesterday I thought of you. I flew over Scarborough. Blessed, blessed, blessed Scarborough —the most wonderful place in the world. Darling, you don't know how I love you!

"Yours,
"MICHAEL."

April 18th.

"DEAREST,—The whole thing is fixed up. Definitely. If I pull this off (and I shall pull it off) I shall be able to take a firm line with Uncle Matthew—and if he doesn't like it— well, what do I care? It's adorable of you to be so interested in my long technical descriptions of the *Albatross*. How I long to take you up in her. Some day! Don't for goodness' sake, worry about me. The thing isn't half so risky as it sounds. I simply couldn't get killed now that I know you care for me. Everything will be all right, sweetheart. Trust your Michael."

April 20th.

"YOU ANGEL,—Every word you say is true and I shall

treasure that letter always. I'm not half good enough for you. You are so different from everybody else. I adore you.

"Your

"MICHAEL."

The last was undated.

"DEAREST,—Well—I'm off to-morrow. Feeling tremendously keen and excited and absolutely certain of success. The old *Albatross* is all tuned up. She won't let me down.

"Cheer up, sweetheart, and don't worry. There's a risk, of course, but all life's risk really. By the way, somebody said I ought to make a will (tactful fellow—but he meant well), so I have—on a half sheet of notepaper—and sent it to old Whitfield. I'd no time to go round there. Somebody once told me that a man made a will of three words, 'All to Mother,' and it was legal all right. My will was rather like that—I remembered your name was really Magdala, which was clever of me! A couple of the fellows witnessed it.

"Don't take all this solemn talk about wills to heart, will you? (I didn't mean that pun. An accident.) I shall be as right as rain. I'll send you telegrams from India and Australia and so on. And keep up heart. *It's going to be all right.* See?

"Good-night and God bless you,

"MICHAEL."

Poirot folded the letters together again.

"You see, Hastings? I had to read them—to make sure. It is as I told you."

"Surely you could have found out some other way?"

"No, *mon cher*, that is just what I could not do. It had to be this way. We have now some very valuable evidence."

"In what way?"

"We now know that the fact of Michael's having made a will in favour of Mademoiselle Nick is actually recorded in writing. Anyone who had read those letters would know the fact. And with letters carelessly hidden like that, anyone could read them."

"Ellen?"

"Ellen, almost certainly, I should say. We will try a little experiment on her before passing out."

"There is no sign of the will."

"No, that is curious. But in all probability it is thrown on top of a bookcase, or inside a china jar. We must try to awaken Mademoiselle's memory on that point. At any rate, there is nothing more to be found here."

Ellen was dusting the hall as we descended.

Poirot wished her good-morning very pleasantly as we passed. He turned back from the front door to say:

"You knew, I suppose, that Miss Buckley was engaged to the airman, Michael Seton?"

She stared.

"What? The one there's all the fuss in the papers about?"

"Yes."

"Well, I never. To think of that. Engaged to Miss Nick."

"Complete and absolute surprise registered very convincingly," I remarked, as we got outside.

"Yes. It really seemed genuine."

"Perhaps it was," I suggested.

"And that packet of letters reclining for months under the *lingerie*? No, *mon ami*."

"All very well," I thought to myself. "But we are not all Hercule Poirots. We do not all go nosing into what does not concern us."

But I said nothing.

"This Ellen—she is an enigma," said Poirot. "I do not like it. There is something here that I do not understand."

CHAPTER FOURTEEN

THE MYSTERY OF THE MISSING WILL

We went straight back to the nursing home.

Nick looked rather surprised to see us.

"Yes, Mademoiselle," said Poirot, answering her look. "I am like the Jack in the Case. I pop up again. To begin with I will tell you that I have put the order in your affairs. Everything is now neatly arranged."

"Well, I expect it was about time," said Nick, unable to help smiling. "Are you *very* tidy, M. Poirot?"

"Ask my friend Hastings here."

The girl turned an inquiring gaze on me.

I detailed some of Poirot's minor peculiarities—toast that had to be made from a square loaf—eggs matching in size—his objection to golf as a game "shapeless and haphazard," whose only redeeming feature was the tee boxes! I ended by telling her the famous case which Poirot had solved by his habit of straightening ornaments on the mantelpiece.

Poirot sat by smiling.

"He makes the good tale of it, yes," he said, when I had finished. "But on the whole it is true. Figure to yourself, Mademoiselle, that I never cease trying to persuade Hastings to part his hair in the middle instead of on the side. See what an air, lop-sided and unsymmetrical, it gives him."

"Then you must disapprove of me, M. Poirot," said Nick. "I wear a side parting. And you must approve of Freddie who parts her hair in the middle."

"He was certainly admiring her the other evening," I put in maliciously. "Now I know the reason."

"*C'est assez,*" said Poirot. "I am here on serious business. Mademoiselle, this will of yours, I find it not."

"Oh!" She wrinkled her brows. "But does it matter so

118

much? After all, I'm not dead. And wills aren't really important till you are dead, are they?"

"That is correct. All the same, I interest myself in this will of yours. I have various little ideas concerning it. Think, Mademoiselle. Try to remember where you placed it—where you saw it last?"

"I don't suppose I put it anywhere particular," said Nick. "I never do put things in places. I probably shoved it into a drawer."

"You did not put it in the secret panel by any chance?"

"The secret *what*?"

"Your maid, Ellen, says that there is a secret panel in the drawing-room or the library."

"Nonsense," said Nick. "I've never heard of such a thing. *Ellen* said so?"

"*Mais oui.* It seems she was in service at End House as a young girl. The cook showed it to her."

"It's the first I've ever heard of it. I suppose Grandfather must have known about it, but, if so, he didn't tell me. And I'm sure he *would* have told me. M. Poirot, are you sure Ellen isn't making it all up?"

"No, Mademoiselle, I am not at all sure! *Il me semble* that there is something—odd about this Ellen of yours."

"Oh! I wouldn't call her odd. William's a half-wit, and the child is a nasty little brute, but Ellen's all right. The essence of repectability."

"Did you give her leave to go out and see the fireworks last night, Mademoiselle?"

"Of course. They always do. They clear up afterwards."

"Yet she did not go out."

"Oh, yes, she did."

"How do you know, Mademoiselle?"

"Well—well—I suppose I don't know. I told her to go and she thanked me—and so, of course, I assumed that she did go."

"On the contrary—she remained in the house."

"But—how very odd!"

" You think it odd?"

" Yes, I do. I'm sure she's never done such a thing before. Did she say why?"

" She did not tell me the real reason—of that I am sure."

Nick looked at him questioningly.

" Is it—important?"

Poirot flung out his hands.

" That is just what I cannot say, Mademoiselle. *C'est curieux.* I leave it like that."

" This panel business too," said Nick, reflectively. " I can't help thinking that's frightfully queer—and unconvincing. Did she show you where it was?"

" She said she couldn't remember."

" I don't believe there is such a thing."

" It certainly looks like it."

" She must be going batty, poor thing."

" She certainly recounts the histories! She said also that End House was not a good house to live in."

Nick gave a little shiver.

" Perhaps she's right there," she said slowly. " Sometimes I've felt that way myself. There's a queer feeling in that house. . . ."

Her eyes grew large and dark. They had a fated look. Poirot hastened to recall her to other topics.

" We have wandered from our subject, Mademoiselle. The will. The last will and testament of Magdala Buckley."

" I put that," said Nick, with some pride. " I remember putting that, and I said pay all debts and testamentary expenses. I remembered that out of a book I'd read."

" You did not use a will form, then?"

" No, there wasn't time for that. I was just going off to the nursing home, and besides Mr. Croft said will forms were very dangerous. It was better to make a simple will and not try to be too legal."

" M. Croft? He was there?"

" Yes. It was he who asked me if I'd made one. I'd never

have thought of it myself. He said if you died in—in——"

"Intestate," I said.

"Yes, that's it. He said if you died intestate, the Crown pinched a lot and that would be a pity."

"Very helpful, the excellent M. Croft!"

"Oh, he was," said Nick warmly. "He got Ellen in and her husband to witness it. Oh! of course! What an idiot I've been!"

We looked at her inquiringly.

"I've been a perfect idiot. Letting you hunt round End House. Charles has got it, of course! My cousin, Charles Vyse."

"Ah! so that is the explanation."

"Mr. Croft said a lawyer was the proper person to have charge of it."

"*Trés correcte, ce bon M. Croft.*"

"Men are useful sometimes," said Nick. "A lawyer or the Bank—that's what he said. And I said Charles would be best. So we stuck it in an envelope and sent it off to him straight away."

She lay back on her pillows with a sigh.

"I'm sorry I've been so frightfully stupid. But it is all right now. Charles has got it, and if you really want to see it, of course he'll show it to you."

"Not without an authorisation from you," said Poirot, smiling.

"How silly."

"No, Mademoiselle. Merely prudent."

"Well, I think it's silly." She took a piece of paper from a little stack that lay beside her bed. "What shall I say? Let the dog see the rabbit?"

"*Comment?*"

I laughed at his startled face.

He dictated a form of words, and Nick wrote obediently.

"Thank you, Mademoiselle," said Poirot, as he took it.

"I'm sorry to have given you such a lot of trouble. But I

really had forgotten. You know how one forgets things almost at once?"

"With order and method in the mind one does not forget."

"I'll have to have a course of some kind," said Nick. "You're giving me quite an inferiority complex."

"That is impossible. *Au revoir, Mademoiselle.*" He looked round the room. "Your flowers are lovely."

"Aren't they? The carnations are from Freddie and the roses from George and the lilies from Jim Lazarus. And look here——"

She pulled the wrapping from a large basket of hothouse grapes by her side.

Poirot's face changed. He stepped forward sharply.

"You have not eaten any of them?"

"No. Not yet."

"Do not do so. You must eat nothing, Mademoiselle, that comes in from outside. *Nothing.* You comprehend?"

"Oh!"

She stared at him, the colour ebbing slowly from her face.

"I see. You think—you think it isn't over yet. You think that they're still trying?" she whispered.

He took her hand.

"Do not think of it. You are safe here. But remember—nothing that comes in from outside."

I was conscious of that white frightened face on the pillow as we left the room.

Poirot looked at his watch.

"*Bon.* We have just time to catch M. Vyse at his office before he leaves it for lunch."

On arrival we were shown into Charles Vyse's office after the briefest of delays.

The young lawyer rose to greet us. He was as formal and unemotional as ever.

"Good-morning, M. Poirot. What can I do for you?"

Without more ado Poirot presented the letter Nick had

written. He took it and read it, then gazed over the top of it at us in a perplexed manner.

"I beg your pardon. I really am at a loss to understand?"

"Has not Mademoiselle Buckley made her meaning clear?"

"In this letter," he tapped it with his finger-nail, "she asks me to hand over to you a will made by her and entrusted to my keeping in February last."

"Yes, Monsieur."

"But, my dear sir, no will has been entrusted to my keeping!"

"*Comment?*"

"As far as I know my cousin never made a will. I certainly never made one for her."

"She wrote this herself, I understand, on a sheet of notepaper and posted it to you."

The lawyer shook his head.

"In that case all I can say is that I never received it."

"Really, M. Vyse——"

"I never received anything of the kind, M. Poirot."

There was a pause, then Poirot rose to his feet.

"In that case, M. Vyse, there is nothing more to be said. There must be some mistake."

"Certainly there must be some mistake."

He rose also.

"Good-day, M. Vyse."

"Good-day, M. Poirot."

"And that is that," I remarked, when we were out in the street once more.

"*Précisément.*"

"Is he lying, do you think?"

"Impossible to tell. He has the good poker face, M. Vyse, besides looking as though he had swallowed one. One thing is clear, he will not budge from the position he has taken up. *He never received the will.* That is his point."

"Surely Nick will have a written acknowledgment of its receipt."

"*Cette petite,* she would never bother her head about a thing like that. She despatched it. It was off her mind. *Voilà.* Besides, on that very day, she went into a nursing home to have her appendix out. She had her emotions, in all probability."

"Well, what do we do now?"

"*Parbleu,* we go and see M. Croft. Let us see what he can remember about this business. It seems to have been very much his doing."

"He didn't profit by it in any way," I said, thoughtfully.

"No. No, I cannot see anything in it from his point of view. He is probably merely the busybody—the man who likes to arrange his neighbour's affairs."

Such an attitude was indeed typical of Mr. Croft, I felt. He was the kindly knowall who causes so much exasperation in this world of ours.

We found him busy in his shirt sleeves over a steaming pot in the kitchen. A most savoury smell pervaded the little lodge.

He relinquished his cookery with enthusiasm, being clearly eager to talk about the murder.

"Half a jiffy," he said. "Walk upstairs. Mother will want to be in on this. She'd never forgive us for talking down here. Cooee—Milly. Two friends coming up."

Mrs. Croft greeted us warmly and was eager for news of Nick. I liked her much better than her husband.

"That poor dear girl," she said. "In a nursing home, you say? Had a complete breakdown, I shouldn't wonder. A dreadful business, M. Poirot—perfectly dreadful. An innocent girl like that shot dead. It doesn't bear thinking about—it doesn't indeed. And no lawless wild part of the world either. Right here in the heart of the old country. Kept me awake all night, it did."

"It's made me nervous about going out and leaving you, old lady," said her husband, who had put on his coat and joined us. "I don't like to think of your having been left all alone here yesterday evening. It gives me the shivers."

"You're not going to leave me again, I can tell you," said Mrs. Croft. "Not after dark, anyway. And I'm thinking I'd like to leave this part of the world as soon as possible. I shall never feel the same about it. I shouldn't think poor Nicky Buckley could ever bear to sleep in that house again."

It was a little difficult to reach the object of our visit. Both Mr. and Mrs. Croft talked so much and were so anxious to know all about everything. Were the poor dead girl's relations coming down? When was the funeral? Was there to be an inquest? What did the police think? Had they any clue yet? Was it true that a man had been arrested in Plymouth?

Then, having answered all these questions, they were insistent on offering us lunch. Only Poirot's mendacious statement that we were obliged to hurry back to lunch with the Chief Constable saved us.

At last a momentary pause occurred and Poirot got in the question he had been waiting to ask.

"Why, of course," said Mr. Croft. He pulled the blind cord up and down twice, frowning at it abstractedly. "I remember all about it. Must have been when we first came here. I remember. Appendicitis—that's what the doctor said——"

"And probably not appendicitis at all," interrupted Mrs. Croft. "These doctors—they always like cutting you up if they can. It wasn't the kind you *have* to operate on anyhow. She'd had indigestion and one thing and another, and they'd X-rayed her and they said out it had better come. And there she was, poor little soul, just going off to one of those nasty Homes."

"I just asked her," said Mr. Croft, "if she'd made a will. More as a joke than anything else."

"Yes?"

"And she wrote it out then and there. Talked about getting a will form at the post office—but I advised her not to. Lot of trouble they cause sometimes, so a man told me.

Anyway, her cousin is a lawyer. He could draw her out a proper one afterwards if everything was all right—as, of course, I knew it would be. This was just a precautionary matter."

" Who witnessed it?"

" Oh! Ellen, the maid, and her husband."

" And afterwards? What was done with it?"

" Oh! we posted it to Vyse. The lawyer, you know."

" You know that it was posted?"

" My dear M. Poirot, I posted it myself. Right in this box here by the gate."

" So if M. Vyse says he never got it——"

Croft stared.

" Do you mean that it got lost in the post? Oh! but surely that's impossible."

" Anyway, you are certain that you posted it."

" Certain sure," said Mr. Croft, heartily. " I'll take my oath on that any day."

" Ah! well," said Poirot. " Fortunately it does not matter. Mademoiselle is not likely to die just yet awhile."

" *Et voilà!*" said Poirot, when we were out of earshot and walking down to the hotel. " Who is lying? M. Croft? Or M. Charles Vyse? I must confess I see no reason why M. Croft should be lying. To suppress the will would be of no advantage to him—especially when he had been instrumental in getting it made. No, his statement seems clear enough and tallies exactly with what was told us by Mademoiselle Nick. But all the same——"

" Yes?"

" All the same, I am glad that M. Croft was doing the cooking when we arrived. He left an excellent impression of a greasy thumb and first finger on a corner of the newspaper that covered the kitchen table. I managed to tear it off unseen by him. We will send it to our good friend Inspector Japp of Scotland Yard. There is just a chance that he might know something about it."

" Yes?"

"You know, Hastings, I cannot help feeling that our genial M. Croft is a little too good to be genuine."

"And now," he added. "*Le déjeuner*. I faint with hunger."

CHAPTER FIFTEEN

STRANGE BEHAVIOUR OF FREDERICA

Poirot's inventions about the Chief Constable were proved not to have been so mendacious after all. Colonel Weston called upon us soon after lunch.

He was a tall man of military carriage with considerable good-looks. He had a suitable reverence for Poirot's achievements, with which he seemed to be well acquainted.

"Marvellous piece of luck for us having you down here, M. Poirot," he said again and again.

His one fear was that he should be compelled to call in the assistance of Scotland Yard. He was anxious to solve the mystery and catch the criminal without their aid. Hence his delight at Poirot's presence in the neighbourhood.

Poirot, so far as I could judge, took him completely into his confidence.

"Deuced odd business," said the Colonel. "Never heard of anything like it. Well, the girl ought to be safe enough in a nursing home. Still, you can't keep her there for ever!"

"That, M. le Colonel, is just the difficulty. There is only one way of dealing with it."

"And that is?"

"We must lay our hands on the person responsible."

"If what you suspect is true, that isn't going to be so easy."

"*Ah! je le sais bien.*"

"Evidence! Getting evidence is going to be the devil." He frowned abstractedly.

"Always difficult, these cases, where there's no routine work. If we could get hold of the pistol——"

"In all probability it is at the bottom of the sea. That is, if the murderer had any sense."

"Ah!" said Colonel Weston. "But often they haven't. You'd be surprised at the fool things people do. I'm not talking of murders—we don't have many murders down in these parts, I'm glad to say—but in ordinary police court cases. The sheer damn foolishness of these people would surprise you."

"They are of a different mentality, though."

"Yes—perhaps. If Vyse is the chap, well, we'll have our work cut out. He's a cautious man and a sound lawyer. He'll not give himself away. The woman—well, there would be more hope there. Ten to one she'll try again. Women have no patience."

He rose.

"Inquest to-morrow morning. Coroner will work in with us and give away as little as possible. We want to keep things dark at present."

He was turning towards the door when he suddenly came back.

"Upon my soul, I'd forgotten the very thing that will interest you most, and that I want your opinion about."

Sitting down again, he drew from his pocket a torn scrap of paper with writing on it and handed it to Poirot.

"My police found this when they were searching the grounds. Not far from where you were all watching the fireworks. It's the only suggestive thing they did find."

Poirot smoothed it out. The writing was large and straggling.

"... must have money at once. If not you ... what will happen. I'm warning you."

Poirot frowned. He read and re-read it.

"This is interesting," he said. "I may keep it?"

"Certainly. There are no fingerprints on it. I'll be glad if you can make anything of it."

Colonel Weston got to his feet again.

"I really must be off. Inquest to-morrow, as I said. By the way, you are not being called as witness—only Captain Hastings. Don't want the newspaper people to get wise to your being on the job."

"I comprehend. What of the relations of the poor young lady?"

"The father and mother are coming from Yorkshire to-day. They'll arrive about half-past five. Poor souls. I'm heartily sorry for them. They are taking the body back with them the following day."

He shook his head.

"Unpleasant business. I'm not enjoying this, M. Poirot."

"Who could, M. le Colonel? It is, as you say, an unpleasant business."

When he had gone, Poirot examined the scrap of paper once more.

"An important clue?" I asked.

He shrugged his shoulders.

"How can one tell? There is a hint of blackmail about it! Someone of our party that night was being pressed for money in a very unpleasant way. Of course, it is possible that it was one of the strangers."

He looked at the writing through a little magnifying glass.

"Does this writing look at all familiar to you, Hastings?"

"It reminds me a little of something—Ah! I have it—that note of Mrs. Rice's."

"Yes," said Poirot, slowly. "There are resemblances. Decidedly there are resemblances. It is curious. Yet I do not think that this is the writing of Madame Rice. Come in," he said, as a knock came at the door.

It was Commander Challenger.

"Just looked in," he explained. "Wanted to know if you were any further forward."

E

"*Parbleu*," said Poirot. "At this moment I am feeling that I am considerably further back. I seem to progress *en reculant*."

"That's bad. But I don't really believe it, M. Poirot. I've been hearing all about you and what a wonderful chap you are. Never had a failure, they say."

".That is not true," said Poirot. "I had a bad failure in Belgium in 1893. You recollect, Hastings? I recounted it to you. The affair of the box of chocolates."

"I remember," I said.

And I smiled, for at the time that Poirot told me that tale, he had instructed me to say "chocolate box" to him if ever I should fancy he was growing conceited! He was then bitterly offended when I used the magical words only a minute and a quarter later.

"Oh, well," said Challenger, "that is such a long time ago it hardly counts. You are going to get to the bottom of this, aren't you?"

"That I swear. On the word of Hercule Poirot. I am the dog who stays on the scent and does not leave it."

"Good. Got any ideas?"

"I have suspicions of two people."

"I suppose I mustn't ask who they are?"

"I should not tell you! You see, I might possibly be in error."

"*My alibi* is satisfactory, I trust," said Challenger, with a faint twinkle.

Poirot smiled indulgently at the bronzed face in front of him. "You left Devonport at a few minutes past 8.30. You arrived here at five minutes past ten—twenty minutes after the crime had been committed. But the distance from Devonport is only just over thirty miles, and you have often done it in an hour since the road is good. So, you see, your alibi is not good at all!"

"Well, I'm——"

"You comprehend, I inquire into everything. Your *alibi*, as I say, is not good. But there are other things beside alibis. You would like, I think, to marry Mademoiselle Nick?"

The sailor's face flushed.

"I've always wanted to marry her," he said huskily.

"Precisely. *Eh bien*—Mademoiselle Nick was engaged to another man. A reason, perhaps, for killing the other man. But that is unnecessary—he dies the death of a hero."

"So it *is* true—that Nick was engaged to Michael Seton? There's a rumour to that effect all over the town this morning."

"Yes—it is interesting how soon news spreads. You never suspected it before?"

"I knew Nick was engaged to someone—she told me so two days ago. But she didn't give me a clue as to whom it was."

"It was Michael Seton. *Entre nous*, he has left her, I fancy, a very pretty fortune. Ah! assuredly, it is not a moment for killing Mademoiselle Nick—from your point of view. She weeps for her lover now, but the heart consoles itself. She is young. And I think, Monsieur, that she is very fond of you. . . ."

Challenger was silent for a moment or two.

"If it should be. . . ." he murmured.

There was a tap on the door.

It was Frederica Rice.

"I've been looking for you," she said to Challenger. "They told me you were here. I wanted to know if you'd got my wrist-watch back yet."

"Oh, yes, I called for it this morning."

He took it from his pocket and handed it to her. It was a watch of rather an unusual shape—round, like a globe, set on a strap of plain black moirê. I remembered that I had seen one much the same shape on Nick Buckley's wrist.

"I hope it will keep better time now."

"It's rather a bore. Something is always going wrong with it."

"It is for beauty, Madame, and not for utility," said
Poirot.

"Can't one have both?" She looked from one to the other
of us. "Am I interrupting a conference?"

"No, indeed, Madame. We were talking gossip—not
the crime. We were saying how quickly news spreads—how
that everyone now knows that Mademoiselle Nick was engaged to that brave airman who perished."

"So Nick *was* engaged to Michael Seton!" exclaimed
Frederica.

"It surprises you, Madame?"

"It does a little. I don't know why. Certainly I did think
he was very taken with her last autumn. They went about a
lot together. And then, after Christmas, they both seemed to
cool off. As far as I know, they hardly met."

"The secret, they kept it very well."

"That was because of old Sir Matthew, I suppose. He was
really a little off his head, I think."

"You had no suspicion, Madame? And yet Mademoiselle
was such an intimate friend."

"Nick's a close little devil when she likes," murmured
Frederica. "But I understand now why she's been so nervy
lately. Oh! and I ought to have guessed from something
she said only the other day."

"Your little friend is very attractive, Madame."

"Old Jim Lazarus used to think so at one time," said
Challenger, with his loud, rather tactless laugh.

"Oh! Jim——" She shrugged her shoulders, but I
thought she was annoyed.

She turned to Poirot.

"Tell me, M. Poirot, did you——"

She stopped. Her tall figure swayed and her face turned
whiter still. Her eyes were fixed on the centre of the table.

"You are not well, Madame."

I pushed forward a chair, helped her to sink into it. She
shook her head, murmured, "I'm all right," and leaned

forward, her face between her hands. We watched her awkwardly.

She sat up in a minute.

"How absurd! George, darling, don't look so worried. Let's talk about murders. Something exciting. I want to know if M. Poirot is on the track."

"It is early to say, Madame," said Poirot, non-committally.

"But you have ideas—yes?"

"Perhaps. But I need a great deal more evidence."

"Oh!" She sounded uncertain.

Suddenly she rose.

"I've got a head. I think I'll go and lie down. Perhaps to-morrow they'll let me see Nick."

She left the room abruptly. Challenger frowned.

"You never know what that woman's up to. Nick may have been fond of her, but I don't believe she was fond of Nick. But there, you can't tell with women. It's darling—darling—darling—all the time—and 'damn you' would probably express it much better. Are you going out, M. Poirot?" For Poirot had risen and was carefully brushing a speck off his hat.

"Yes, I am going into the town."

"I've got nothing to do. May I come with you."

"Assuredly. It will be a pleasure."

We left the room. Poirot, with an apology, went back.

"My stick," he explained, as he rejoined us.

Challenger winced slightly. And indeed the stick, with its embossed gold band, was somewhat ornate.

Poirot's first visit was to a florist.

"I must send some flowers to Mademoiselle Nick," he explained.

He proved difficult to suit.

In the end he chose an ornate gold basket to be filled with orange carnations. The whole to be tied up with a large blue bow.

The shopwoman gave him a card and he wrote on it with a flourish : " With the Compliments of Hercule Poirot."

" I sent her some flowers this morning," said Challenger. " I might send her some fruit."

" *Inutile!*" said Poirot.

" What?"

" I said it was useless. The eatable—it is not permitted."

" Who says so?"

" I say so. I have made the rule. It has already been impressed on Mademoiselle Nick. She understands."

" Good Lord!" said Challenger.

He looked thoroughly startled. He stared at Poirot curiously.

" So that's it, is it?" he said. " You're still—afraid."

CHAPTER SIXTEEN

INTERVIEW WITH MR. WHITFIELD

THE inquest was a dry proceeding—mere bare bones. There was evidence of identification, then I gave evidence of the finding of the body. Medical evidence followed.

The inquest was adjourned for a week.

The St. Loo murder had jumped into prominence in the daily press. It had, in fact, succeeded " Seton Still Missing. Unknown Fate of Missing Airman."

Now that Seton was dead and due tribute had been paid to his memory, a new sensation was due. The St. Loo Mystery was a godsend to papers at their wits' end for news in the month of August.

After the inquest, having successfully dodged reporters, I met Poirot, and we had an interview with the Rev. Giles Buckley and his wife.

Maggie's father and mother were a charming pair, completely unworldly and unsophisticated.

Mrs. Buckley was a woman of character, tall and fair and showing very plainly her northern ancestry. Her husband was a small man, grey-headed, with a diffident appealing manner.

Poor souls, they were completely dazed by the misfortune that had overtaken them and robbed them of a well-beloved daughter. "Our Maggie," as they called her.

"I can scarcely realise it even now," said Mr. Buckley. "Such a dear child, M. Poirot. So quiet and unselfish—always thinking of others. Who could wish to harm her?"

"I could hardly understand the telegram," said Mrs. Buckley. "Why it was only the morning before that we had seen her off."

"In the midst of life we are in death," murmured her husband.

"Colonel Weston has been very kind," said Mrs. Buckley. "He assures us that everything is being done to find the man who did this thing. He must be a madman. No other explanation is possible."

"Madame, I cannot tell you how I sympathise with you in your loss—and how I admire your bravery!"

"Breaking down would not bring Maggie back to us," said Mrs. Buckley, sadly.

"My wife is wonderful," said the clergyman. "Her faith and courage are greater than mine. It is all so—so bewildering, M. Poirot."

"I know—I know, Monsieur."

"You are a great detective, M. Poirot?" said Mrs. Buckley.

"It has been said, Madame."

"Oh! I know. Even in our remote country village we have heard of you. You are going to find out the truth, M. Poirot?"

"I shall not rest until I do, Madame."

"It will be revealed to you, M. Poirot," quavered the clergyman. "Evil cannot go unpunished."

"Evil never goes unpunished, Monsieur. But the punishment is sometimes secret."

"What do you mean by that, M. Poirot?"

Poirot only shook his head.

"Poor little Nick," said Mrs. Buckley. "I am really sorriest of all for her. I had a most pathetic letter. She says she feels she asked Maggie down here to her death."

"That is morbid," said Mr. Buckley.

"Yes, but I know how she feels. I wish they would let me see her. It seems so extraordinary not to let her own family visit her."

"Doctors and nurses are very strict," said Poirot, evasively. "They make the rules—so—and nothing will change them. And doubtless they fear for her the emotion —the natural emotion—she would experience on seeing you."

"Perhaps," said Mrs. Buckley, doubtfully. "But I don't hold with nursing homes. Nick would do much better if they let her come back with me—right away from this place."

"It is possible—but I fear they will not agree. It is long since you have seen Mademoiselle Buckley?"

"I haven't seen her since last autumn. She was at Scarborough. Maggie went over and spent the day with her and then she came back and spent a night with us. She's a pretty creature—though I can't say I like her friends. And the life she leads—well, it's hardly her fault, poor child. She's had no upbringing of any kind."

"It is a strange house—End House," said Poirot thoughtfully.

"I don't like it," said Mrs. Buckley. "I never have. There's something all wrong about that house. I disliked old Sir Nicholas intensely. He made me shiver."

"Not a good man, I'm afraid," said her husband. "But he had a curious charm."

"I never felt it," said Mrs. Buckley. "There's an evil

feeling about that house. I wish we'd never let our Maggie go there."

"Ah! wishing," said Mr. Buckley, and shook his head.

"Well," said Poirot. "I must not intrude upon you any longer. I only wished to proffer to you my deep sympathy."

"You have been very kind, M. Poirot. And we are indeed grateful for all you are doing."

"You return to Yorkshire—when?"

"To-morrow. A sad journey. Good-bye, M. Poirot, and thank you again."

"Very simple delightful people," I said, after we had left. Poirot nodded.

"It makes the heart ache, does it not, *mon ami*? A tragedy so useless—so purposeless. *Cette jeune fille*—Ah! but I reproach myself bitterly. I, Hercule Poirot, was on the spot and I did not prevent the crime!"

"Nobody could have prevented it."

"You speak without reflection, Hastings. No ordinary person could have prevented it—but of what good is it to be Hercule Poirot with grey cells of a finer quality than other people's, if you do not manage to do what ordinary people cannot?"

"Well, of course," I said. "If you are going to put it like that——"

"Yes, indeed. I am abashed, downhearted—completely abased."

I reflected that Poirot's abasement was strangely like other people's conceit, but I prudently forebore from making any remark.

"And now," he said, "*en avant. To London.*"

"London?"

"*Mais oui.* We shall catch the two o'clock train very comfortably. All is peaceful here. Mademoiselle is safe in the nursing home. No one can harm her. The watchdogs, therefore, can take leave of absence. There are one or two little pieces of information that I require."

Our first proceeding on arriving in London was to call upon the late Captain Seton's solicitors, Messrs. Whitfield Pargiter & Whitfield.

Poirot had arranged for an appointment beforehand, and although it was past six o'clock, we were soon closeted with Mr. Whitfield, the head of the firm.

He was a very urbane and impressive person. He had in front of him a letter from the Chief Constable and another from some high official at Scotland Yard.

" This is all very irregular and unusual, M.—ah—Poirot," he said, as he polished his eyeglasses.

" Quite so, M. Whitfield. But then murder is also irregular—and, I am glad to say, sufficiently unusual."

" True. True. But rather far-fetched—to make a connection between this murder and my late client's bequest—eh?"

" I think not."

" Ah! you think not. Well—under the circumstances—and I must admit that Sir Henry puts it very strongly in his letter—I shall be—er—happy to do anything that is in my power."

" You acted as legal adviser to the late Captain Seton?"

" To all the Seton family, my dear sir. We have done so—our firm have done so, I mean—for the last hundred years."

" Parfaitement. The late Sir Matthew Seton made a will?"

" We made it for him."

" And he left his fortune—how?"

" There were several bequests—one to the Natural History Museum—but the bulk of his large—his, I may say, very large fortune—he left to Captain Michael Seton absolutely. He had no other near relations."

" A very large fortune, you say?"

" The late Sir Matthew was the second richest man in England," replied Mr. Whitfield, composedly.

" He had somewhat peculiar views, had he not?" Mr. Whitfield looked at him severely.

" A millionaire, M. Poirot, is allowed to be eccentric. It is almost expected of him."

Poirot received this correction meekly and asked another question.

" His death was unexpected, I understand?"

" *Most* unexpected. Sir Matthew enjoyed remarkably good health. He had an internal growth, however, which no one had suspected. It reached a vital tissue and an immediate operation was necessary. The operation was, as always on these occasions, completely successful. But Sir Matthew died."

" And his fortune passed to Captain Seton."

" That is so."

" Captain Seton had, I understand, made a will before leaving England?"

" If you can call it a will—yes," said Mr. Whitfield, with strong distaste.

" It is legal?"

" It is perfectly legal. The intention of the testator is plain and it is properly witnessed. Oh, yes, it is legal."

" But you do not approve of it?"

" My dear sir, what are *we* for?"

I had often wondered. Having once had occasion to make a perfectly simple will myself. I had been appalled at the length and verbiage that resulted from my solicitor's office.

" The truth of the matter was," continued Mr. Whitfield, " that at the time Captain Seton had little or nothing to leave. He was dependent on the allowance he received from his uncle. He felt, I suppose, that anything would do."

And had thought correctly, I whispered to myself.

" And the terms of this will?" asked Poirot.

" He leaves everything of which he dies possessed to his affianced wife, Miss Magdala Buckley absolutely. He names me as his executor."

" Then Miss Buckley inherits?"

" Certainly Miss Buckley inherits."

" And if Miss Buckley had happened to die last Monday?"

"Captain Seton having predeceased her, the money would go to whoever she had named in her will as residuary legatee—or failing a will to her next of kin."

"I may say," added Mr. Whitfield, with an air of enjoyment, "that the death duties would have been enormous. Enormous! Three deaths, remember, in rapid succession." He shook his head. "Enormous!"

"But there would have been something left?" murmured Poirot, meekly.

"My dear sir, as I told you, Sir Matthew was the second richest man in England."

Poirot rose.

"Thank you, Mr. Whitfield, very much for the information that you have given me."

"Not at all. Not at all. I may say that I shall be in communication with Miss Buckley—indeed, I believe the letter has already gone. I shall be happy to be of any service I can to her."

"She is a young lady," said Poirot, "who could do with some sound legal advice."

"There will be fortune hunters, I am afraid," said Mr. Whitfield, shaking his head.

"It seems indicated," agreed Poirot. "Good-day, Monsieur."

"Good-bye, M. Poirot. Glad to have been of service to you. Your name is—ah!—familiar to me."

He said this kindly—with an air of one making a valuable admission.

"It is all exactly as you thought, Poirot," I said, when we were outside.

"*Mon ami*, it was bound to be. *It could not be any other way*. We will go now to the Cheshire Cheese where Japp meets us for an early dinner."

We found Inspector Japp of Scotland Yard awaiting us at the chosen rendezvous. He greeted Poirot with every sign of warmth.

"Years since I've seen you, Moosior Poirot? Thought you were growing vegetable marrows in the country."

"I tried, Japp, I tried. But even when you grow vegetable marrows you cannot get away from murder."

He sighed. I knew of what he was thinking—that strange affair at Fernley Park. How I regretted that I had been far away at that time.

"And Captain Hastings too," said Japp. "How are you, sir?"

"Very fit, thanks," I said.

"And now there are more murders?" continued Japp, facetiously.

"As you say—more murders."

"Well, you mustn't be depressed, old cock," said Japp. "Even if you can't see your way clear—well—you can't go about at your time of life and expect to have the success you used to do. We all of us get stale as the years go by. Got to give the young 'uns a chance, you know."

"And yet the old dog is the one who knows the tricks," murmured Poirot. "He is cunning. He does not leave the scent."

"Oh! well—we're talking about human beings, not dogs."

"Is there so much difference?"

"Well, it depends how you look at things. But you're a caution, isn't he, Captain Hastings? Always was. Looks much the same—hair a bit thinner on top but the face fungus fuller than ever."

"Eh?" said Poirot. "What is that?"

"He's congratulating you on your moustaches," I said, soothingly.

"They are luxuriant, yes," said Poirot, complacently caressing them.

Japp went off into a roar of laughter.

"Well," he said, after a minute or two, "I've done your bit of business. Those fingerprints you sent me——"

"Yes?" said Poirot, eagerly.

"Nothing doing. Whoever the gentleman may be—he hasn't passed through *our* hands. On the other hand, I wired to Melbourne and nobody of that description or name is known there."

"Ah!"

"So there may be something fishy after all. But he's not one of the lads."

"As to the other business," went on Japp.

"Yes?"

"Lazarus and Son have a good reputation. Quite straight and honourable in their dealings. Sharp, of course—but that's another matter. You've got to be sharp in business. But they're all right. They're in a bad way, though—financially, I mean."

"Oh!—is that so?"

"Yes—the slump in pictures has hit them badly. And antique furniture too. All this modern continental stuff coming into fashion. They built new premises last year and —well—as I say, they're not far from Queer Street."

"I am much obliged to you."

"Not at all. That sort of thing isn't my line, as you know. But I made a point of finding out as you wanted to know. We can always get information."

"My good Japp, what should I do without you?"

"Oh! that's all right. Always glad to oblige an old friend. I let you in on some pretty good cases in the old days, didn't I?"

This, I realised, was Japp's way of acknowledging indebtedness to Poirot, who had solved many a case which had baffled the Inspector.

"They were the good days—yes."

"I wouldn't mind having a chat with you now and again even in these days. Your methods may be old-fashioned but you've got your head screwed on the right way, M. Poirot."

"What about my other question. The Dr. MacAllister?"

"Oh, him! He's a woman's doctor. I don't mean a gynæcologist. I mean one of these nerve doctors—tell you to sleep in purple walls and an orange ceiling—talk to you about your libido, whatever that is—tell you to let it rip. He's a bit of a quack, if you ask me—but he gets the women all right. They flock to him. Goes abroad a good deal—does some kind of medical work in Paris, I believe."

"Why Dr. MacAllister?" I asked, bewildered. I had never heard of the name. "Where does he come in?"

"Dr. MacAllister is the uncle of Commander Challenger," explained Poirot. "You remember he referred to an uncle who was a doctor?"

"How thorough you are," I said. "Did you think he had operated on Sir Matthew?"

"He's not a surgeon," said Japp.

"*Mon ami*," said Poirot, "I like to inquire into everything. Hercule Poirot is a good dog. The good dog follows the scent, and if, regrettably, there is no scent to follow, he noses around—seeking always something that is not very nice. So also, does Hercule Poirot. And often—oh! so often—does he find it!"

"It's not a nice profession, ours," said Japp. "Stilton, did you say? I don't mind if I do. No, it's not a nice profession. And yours is worse than mine—not official, you see, and therefore a lot more worming yourself into places in underhand ways."

"I do not disguise myself, Japp. Never have I disguised myself."

"You couldn't," said Japp. "You're unique. Once seen, never forgotten."

Poirot looked at him rather doubtfully.

"Only my fun," said Japp. "Don't mind me. Glass of port? Well, if you say so."

The evening became thoroughly harmonious. We were soon in the middle of reminiscences. This case, that case, and the other. I must say that I, too, enjoyed talking over the past. Those had been good days. How old and experienced I felt now!

Poor old Poirot. He was perplexed by this case—I could

see that. His powers were not what they were. I had the feeling that he was going to fail—that the murderer of Maggie Buckley would never be brought to book.

"Courage, my friend," said Poirot, slapping me on the shoulder. "All is not lost. Do not pull the long face, I beg of you."

"That's all right. I'm all right."

"And so am I. And so is Japp."

"We're all all right," declared Japp, hilariously.

And on this pleasant note we parted.

The following morning we journeyed back to St. Loo. On arrival at the hotel Poirot rang up the nursing home and asked to speak to Nick.

Suddenly I saw his face change—he almost dropped the instrument.

"*Comment?* What is that? Say it again, I beg."

He waited for a minute or two listening. Then he said:

"Yes, yes, I will come at once."

He turned a pale face to me.

"Why did I go away, Hastings? *Mon Dieu!* Why did I go away?"

"What has happened?"

"Mademoiselle Nick is dangerously ill. Cocaine poisoning. They have got at her after all. *Mon Dieu! Mon Dieu! why did I go away?*"

CHAPTER SEVENTEEN

A BOX OF CHOCOLATES

ALL the way to the nursing home Poirot murmured and muttered to himself. He was full of self-reproach.

"I should have known," he groaned. "I should have known! And yet, what could I do? I took every precaution. It is impossible—impossible. *No one* could get to her! Who has disobeyed my orders?"

At the nursing home we were shown into a little room downstairs, and after a few minutes Dr. Graham came to us. He looked exhausted and white.

" She'll do," he said. " It's going to be all right. The trouble was knowing how much she'd taken of the damned stuff."

" What was it?"

" Cocaine."

" She will live?"

" Yes, yes, she'll live."

" But how did it happen? How did they get at her? Who has been allowed in?" Poirot fairly danced with impotent excitement.

" Nobody has been allowed in."

" Impossible."

" It's true."

" But then——"

" It was a box of chocolates."

" Ah! *sacré*. And I told her to eat *nothing—nothing—* that came from outside."

" I don't know about that. It's hard work keeping a girl from a box of chocolates. She only ate one, thank goodness."

" Was the cocaine in all the chocolates?"

" No. The girl ate one. There were two others in the top layer. The rest were all right."

" How was it done?"

" Quite clumsily. Chocolate cut in half—the cocaine mixed with the filling and the chocolate stuck together again. Amateurishly. What you might call a home-made job."

Poirot groaned.

" Ah! if I knew—if I knew. Can I see Mademoiselle?"

" If you come back in an hour I think you can see her," said the doctor. " Pull yourself together, man. She isn't going to die."

For another hour we walked the streets of St. Loo. I did my best to distract Poirot's mind—pointing out to him that all was well, that, after all, no mischief had been done.

But he only shook his head, and repeated at intervals:

"*I am afraid, Hastings, I am afraid. . . .*"

And the strange way he said it made me, too, feel afraid.

Once he caught me by the arm.

"Listen, my friend. *I am all wrong.* I have been all wrong from the beginning."

"You mean it isn't the money——"

"No, no, I am right about that. Oh, yes. But those two —it is too simple—too easy, that. There is another twist still. Yes, there is something!"

And then in an outburst of indignation:

"*Ah! cette petite!* Did I not *forbid* her? Did I not say, ' Do not touch anything from outside?' And she disobeys me—me, Hercule Poirot. Are not four escapes from death enough for her? Must she take a fifth chance? *Ah, c'est inouï!*"

At last we made our way back. After a brief wait we were conducted upstairs.

Nick was sitting up in bed. The pupils of her eyes were widely dilated. She looked feverish and her hands kept twitching violently.

"At it again," she murmured.

Poirot experienced real emotion at the sight of her. He cleared his throat and took her hand in his.

"Ah! Mademoiselle—Mademoiselle."

"I shouldn't care," she said, defiantly, " If they *had* got me this time. I'm sick of it all—sick of it!"

"*Pauvre petite!*"

"Something in me doesn't like to give them best!"

"That is the spirit—*le sport*—you must be the good sport, Mademoiselle."

"Your old nursing home hasn't been so safe after all," said Nick.

"If you had obeyed orders, Mademoiselle——"

She looked faintly astonished.

"But I have."

"Did I not impress upon you that you were to eat nothing
that came from outside?"

"No more I did."

"But these chocolates——"

"Well, they were all right. *You* sent them."

"What is that you say, Mademoiselle?"

"*You* sent them!"

"Me? Never. Never anything of the kind."

"But you *did*. Your card was in the box."

"What?"

Nick made a spasmodic gesture towards the table by the
bed. The nurse came forward.

"You want the card that was in the box?"

"Yes, please, nurse."

There was a moment's pause. The nurse returned to the
room with it in her hand.

"Here it is."

I gasped. So did Poirot. For on the card, in flourishing
handwriting, was written the same words that I had seen
Poirot inscribe on the card that accompanied the basket of
flowers.

"With the Compliments of Hercule Poirot."

"*Sacré tonnerre!*"

"You see," said Nick, accusingly.

"I did not write this!" cried Poirot.

"What?"

"And yet," murmured Poirot, "and yet it is my handwriting."

"I know. It's exactly the same as the card that came with
the orange carnations. I never doubted that the chocolates
came from you."

Poirot shook his head.

"How should you doubt? Oh! the devil! The clever,
cruel devil! To think of *that*! Ah! but he has genius, this
man genius! '*With the Compliments of Hercule Poirot.*'
So simple. Yes, but one had to think of it. And I—I did
not *think*. I omitted to foresee this move."

Nick moved restlessly.

"Do not agitate yourself, Mademoiselle. You are blame-less—blameless. It is I that am to blame, miserable imbecile that I am! I should have foreseen this move. Yes, I should have foreseen it."

His chin dropped on his breast. He looked the picture of misery.

"I really think——" said the nurse.

She had been hovering nearby, a disapproving expression on her face.

"Eh? Yes, yes, I will go. Courage, Mademoiselle. This is the last mistake I will make. I am ashamed, desolated—I have been tricked, outwitted—as though I were a little schoolboy. *But it shall not happen again.* No. I promise you. Come, Hastings."

Poirot's first proceeding was to interview the matron. She was, naturally, terribly upset over the whole business.

"It seems incredible to me, M. Poirot, absolutely incred-ible. That a thing like that should happen in my nursing home."

Poirot was sympathetic and tactful. Having soothed her sufficiently, he began to inquire into the circumstance of the arrival of the fatal packet. Here, the matron declared, he would do best to interview the orderly who had been on duty at the time of its arrival.

The man in question, whose name was Hood, was a stupid but honest-looking young fellow of about twenty-two. He looked nervous and frightened. Poirot put him at his ease, however.

"No blame can be attached to you," he said kindly. "But I want you to tell me exactly when and how this parcel arrived."

The orderly looked puzzled.

"It's difficult to say, sir," he said, slowly. "Lots of people come and inquire and leave things for the different patients."

"The nurse says this came last night," I said. "About six o'clock."

The lad's face brightened.

"I do remember, now, sir. A gentleman brought it."

"A thin-faced gentleman—fair-haired?"

"He was fair-haired—but I don't know about thin-faced."

"Would Charles Vyse bring it himself?" I murmured to Poirot.

I had forgotten that the lad would know a local name.

"It wasn't Mr. Vyse," he said. "I know him. It was a bigger gentleman—handsome-looking—came in a big car."

"Lazarus," I exclaimed.

Poirot shot me a warning glance and I regretted my precipitance.

"He came in a large car and he left this parcel. It was addressed to Miss Buckley?"

"Yes, sir."

"And what did you do with it?"

"I didn't touch it, sir. Nurse took it up."

"Quite so, but you touched it when you took it from the gentleman, *n'est ce pas?*"

"Oh! that, yes, of course, sir. I took it from him and put it on the table."

"Which table? Show me, if you please."

The orderly led us into the hall. The front door was open. Close to it, in the hall, was a long marble-topped table on which lay letters and parcels.

"Everything that comes is put on here, sir. Then the nurses take things up to the patients."

"Do you remember what time this parcel was left?"

"Must have been about five-thirty, or a little after. I know the post had just been, and that's usually at about half-past five. It was a pretty busy afternoon, a lot of people leaving flowers and coming to see patients."

"Thank you. Now, I think, we will see the nurse who took up the parcel."

This proved to be one of the probationers, a fluffy little person all agog with excitement. She remembered taking the parcel up at six o'clock when she came on duty.

" Six o'clock," murmured Poirot. " Then it must have been twenty minutes or so that the parcel was lying on the table downstairs."

" Pardon?"

" Nothing, Mademoiselle. Continue. You took the parcel to Miss Buckley?"

" Yes, there were several things for her. There was this box and some flowers also—sweet peas—from a Mr. and Mrs. Croft, I think. I took them up at the same time. And there was a parcel that had come by post—and curiously enough *that* was a box of Fuller's chocolates also."

" *Comment?* A second box?"

" Yes, rather a coincidence. Miss Buckley opened them both. She said : ' Oh! what a shame. I'm not allowed to eat them.' Then she opened the lids to look inside and see if they were both just the same, and your card was in one and she said, ' Take the other impure box away, nurse. I might get them mixed up.' Oh! dear, whoever would have thought of such a thing? Seems like an Edgar Wallace, doesn't it?"

Poirot cut short this flood of speech.

" Two boxes, you say? From whom was the other box?"

" There was no name inside."

" And which was the one that came—that had the appearance of coming—from me? The one by post or the other?"

" I declare now—I can't remember. Shall I go up and ask Miss Buckley?"

" If you would be so amiable."

She ran up the stairs.

" Two boxes," murmured Poirot. " There is confusion for you."

The nurse returned breathless.

" Miss Buckley isn't sure. She unwrapped them both before she looked inside. But she thinks it wasn't the box that came by post."

" Eh?" said Poirot, a little confused.

" The box from you was the one that didn't come by post. At least she thinks so, but she isn't quite sure."

" *Diable!*" said Poirot, as we walked away. " Is no one ever quite sure? In detective books—yes. But life—real life —is always full of muddle. Am I sure, myself, about anything at all? No, no—a thousand times, no."

" Lazarus," I said.

" Yes, that is a surprise, is it not?"

" Shall you say anything to him about it?"

" Assuredly. I shall be interested to see how he takes it. By the way, we might as well exaggerate the serious condition of Mademoiselle. It will do no harm to let it be assumed that she is at death's door. You comprehend? The solemn face—yes, admirable. You resemble closely an undertaker. *C'est tout à fait bien.*"

We were lucky in finding Lazarus. He was bending over the bonnet of his car outside the hotel.

Poirot went straight up to him.

" Yesterday evening, Monsieur Lazarus, you left a box of chocolates for Mademoiselle," he began without preamble.

Lazarus looked rather surprised.

" Yes?"

" That was very amiable of you."

" As a matter of fact they were from Freddie, from Mrs. Rice. She asked me to get them."

" Oh! I see."

" I took them round there in the car."

" I comprehend."

He was silent for a minute or two and then said :

" Madame Rice, where is she?"

" I think she's in the lounge."

We found Frederica having tea. She looked up at us with an anxious face.

" What is this I hear about Nick being taken ill?"

" It is a most mysterious affair, Madame. Tell me, did you send her a box of chocolates yesterday?"

" Yes. At least she asked me to get them for her."

" *She* asked you to get them for her?"

" Yes."

" But she was not allowed to see anyone. How did you see her?"

" I didn't. She telephoned."

" Ah! And she said—what?"

" Would I get her a two-pound box of Fuller's chocolates."

" How did her voice sound—weak?"

" No—not at all. Quite strong. But different somehow. I didn't realise it was she speaking at first."

" Until she told you who she was?"

" Yes."

" Are you sure, Madame, that it *was* your friend?"

Frederica looked startled.

" I—I—why, of course it was. Who else could it have been?"

" That is an interesting question, Madame."

" You don't mean——"

" *Could you swear,* Madame, that it was your friend's voice—apart from what she said?"

" No." said Frederica, slowly, " I couldn't. Her voice was certainly different. I thought it was the phone—or perhaps being ill. . . ."

" If she had not told you who she was, you would not have recognised it?"

" No, no, I don't think I should. Who was it, M. Poirot? Who was it?"

" That is what I mean to know, Madame."

The graveness of his face seemed to awaken her suspicions.

" Is Nick—has anything happened?" she asked, breathlessly.

Poirot nodded.

" She is ill—dangerously ill. Those chocolates, Madame—were poisoned."

" The chocolates *I* sent her? But that's impossible—impossible!"

"Not impossible, Madame, since Mademoiselle is at death's door."

"Oh, my God." She hid her face in her hands, then raised it white and quivering. "I don't understand—I don't understand. The other, yes, but not this. They couldn't be poisoned. Nobody ever touched them but me and Jim. You're making some dreadful mistake, M. Poirot."

"It is not I that make a mistake—even though my name was in the box."

She stared at him blankly.

"If Mademoiselle Nick dies——" he said, and made a threatening gesture with his hand.

She gave a low cry.

He turned away, and taking me by the arm, went up to the sitting-room.

He flung his hat on the table.

"I understand nothing—but nothing! I am in the dark. I am a little child. Who stands to gain by Mademoiselle's death? Madame Rice. Who buys the chocolates and admits it and tells a story of being rung up on the telephone that cannot hold water for a minute? Madame Rice. It is too simple—too stupid. And she is not stupid—no."

"Well, then——"

"But she takes cocaine, Hastings. I am certain she takes cocaine. There is no mistaking it. And there was cocaine in those chocolates. And what does she mean when she said, '*The other, yes, but not this.*' It needs explaining, that! And the sleek M. Lazarus—what is *he* doing in all this? What does she know, Madame Rice? She knows something. But I cannot make her speak. She is not of those you can frighten into speech. But she knows something, Hastings. Is her tale of the telephone true, or did she invent it? If it is true, whose voice was it?

"I tell you, Hastings. This is all very black—very black."

"Always darkest before dawn," I said reassuringly.

He shook his head.

"Then the other box—that came by post. Can we rule

that out? No, we cannot, because Mademoiselle is not sure.
It is an annoyance, that!"

He groaned.

I was about to speak when he stopped me.

"No, no. Not another proverb. I cannot bear it. If you
would be the good friend—the good helpful friend——"

"Yes," I said, eagerly.

"Go out, I beg of you, and buy me some playing cards."

I stared.

"Very well," I said coldly.

I could not but suspect that he was making a deliberate
excuse to get rid of me.

Here, however, I misjudged him. That night, when I
came into the sitting-room about ten o'clock, I found Poirot
carefully building card houses—and I remembered!

It was an old trick of his—soothing his nerves. He smiled
at me.

"Yes—you remember. One needs the precision. One
card on another—so—in exactly the right place and that sup-
ports the weight of the card on top and so on, up and up.
Go to bed, Hastings. Leave me here, with my house of
cards. I clear the mind."

It was about five in the morning when I was shaken
awake.

Poirot was standing by my bedside. He looked pleased
and happy.

"It was very just what you said, *mon ami*. Oh! it was
very just. More, it was *spirituel*!"

I blinked at him, being imperfectly awake.

"Always darkest before dawn—that is what you said. It
has been very dark—and now it is dawn."

I looked at the window. He was perfectly right.

"No, no, Hastings. In the head! The mind! The little
grey cells!"

He paused and then said quietly :

"You see, Hastings, Mademoiselle is dead."

"What?" I cried, suddenly wide awake.

"Hush—hush. It is as I say. Not really—*bien entendu*—but it can be arranged. Yes, for twenty-four hours it can be arranged. I arrange it with the doctor, with the nurses.

"You comprehend, Hastings? *The murderer has been successful.* Four times he has tried and failed. The fifth time he has succeeded.

"*And now, we shall see what happens next. . . .*

"It will be very interesting."

CHAPTER TWENTY-EIGHT

THE FACE AT THE WINDOW

THE events of the next day are completely hazy in my memory. I was unfortunate enough to awake with fever on me. I have been liable to these bouts of fever at inconvenient times ever since I once contracted malaria.

In consequence, the events of that day take on in my memory the semblance of a nightmare—with Poirot coming and going as a kind of fantastic clown, making a periodic appearance in a circus.

He was, I fancy, enjoying himself to the full. His pose of baffled despair was admirable. How he achieved the end he had in view and which he had disclosed to me in the early hours of the morning, I cannot say. But achieve it he did.

It cannot have been easy. The amount of deception and subterfuge involved must have been colossal. The English character is averse to lying on a wholesale scale and that, no less, was what Poirot's plan required. He had, first, to get Dr. Graham converted to the scheme. With Dr. Graham on his side, he had to persuade the Matron and some members of the staff of the nursing home to conform to the plan. There again, the difficulties must have been immense. It was probably Dr. Graham's influence that turned the scale.

Then there was the Chief Constable and the police. Here,

Poirot would be up against officialdom. Nevertheless he wrung at last an unwilling consent out of Colonel Weston. The Colonel made it clear that it was in no way his responsibility. Poirot and Poirot alone was responsible for the spreading abroad of these lying reports. Poirot agreed. He would have agreed to anything so long as he was permitted to carry out his plan.

I spent most of the day dozing in a large armchair with a rug over my knees. Every two or three hours or so, Poirot would burst in and report progress.

"*Comment ça va, mon ami?* How I commiserate you. But it is as well, perhaps. The farce, you do not play it as well as I do. I come this moment from ordering a wreath—a wreath immense—stupendous. Lilies, my friend—large quantities of lilies. '*With heartfelt regret. From Hercule Poirot.*' Ah! what a comedy."

He departed again.

"I come from a most poignant conversation with Madame Rice," was his next piece of information. "Very well dressed in black, that one. Her poor friend—what a tragedy! I groan sympathetically. Nick, she says, was so joyous, so full of life. Impossible to think of her as dead. I agree. 'It is, I say, the irony of death that it takes one like that. The old and useless are left.' Oh! *là là!* I groan again."

"How you are enjoying this," I murmured feebly.

"*Du tout.* It is part of my plan, that is all. To play the comedy successfully, you must put the heart into it. Well, then, the conventional expressions of regret over, Madame comes to matters nearer home. All night she has lain awake wondering about those sweets. It is impossible—impossible. 'Madame,' I say, 'it is not impossible. You can see the analyst's report.' Then she says, and her voice is far from steady, 'It was—*cocaine*, you say?' I assent. And she says, 'Oh, my God. I don't understand.'"

"Perhaps that's true."

"She understands well enough that she is in danger. She

is intelligent. I told you that before. Yes, she is in danger, and she knows it."

"And yet it seems to me that for the first time you don't believe her guilty."

Poirot frowned. The excitement of his manner abated.

"It is profound what you say there, Hastings. No—it seems to me that—somehow—the facts no longer fit. These crimes—so far what has marked them most—the subtlety, is it not? And here is no subtlety at all—only the crudity, pure and simple. No, it does not fit."

He sat down at the table.

"*Voilà*—let us examine the facts. There are three possibilities. There are the sweets bought by Madame and delivered by M. Lazarus. And in that case the guilt rests with one or the other or *both*. And the telephone call, supposedly from Mademoiselle Nick, that is an invention pure and simple. That is the straightforward—the obvious solution.

"Solution 2 : The *other* box of sweets—that which came by post. Anyone may have sent those. Any of the suspects on our list from A. to J. (You remember? A very wide field.) But, if that were the guilty box, *what is the point of the telephone call?* Why complicate matters with a second box?"

I shook my head feebly. With a temperature of 102, any complication seemed to me quite unnecessary and absurd.

"Solution 3 : A poisoned box was substituted for the innocent box bought by Madame. In that case the telephone call is ingenious and understandable. Madame is to be what you call the kitten's paw. She is to pull the roasting chestnuts out of the fire. So Solution 3 is the most logical—but, alas, it is also the most difficult. How be sure of substituting a box at the right moment? The orderly might take the box straight upstairs—a hundred and one possibilities might prevent the substitution being effected. No, it does not seem sense."

"Unless it were Lazarus," I said.

Poirot looked at me.

" You have the fever, my friend. It mounts, does it not?"
I nodded.

" Curious how a few degrees of heat should stimulate the
intellect. You have uttered there an observation of profound simplicity. So simple, was it, that I had failed to consider it. But it would suppose a very curious state of affairs.
M. Lazarus, the dear friend of Madame, doing his best to
get her hanged. It opens up possibilities of a very curious
nature. But complex—very complex."

I closed my eyes. I was glad I had been brilliant, but I did
not want to think of anything complex. I wanted to go to
sleep.

Poirot, I think, went on talking, but I did not listen. His
voice was vaguely soothing. . . .

It was late afternoon when I saw him next.

" My little plan, it has made the fortune of the flower
shops," he announced. " Everybody orders wreaths. M.
Croft, M. Vyse, Commander Challenger——"

The last name awoke a chord of compunction in my mind.

" Look here, Poirot," I said. " You must let him in on
this. Poor fellow, he will be distracted with grief. It isn't
fair."

" You have always the tenderness for him, Hastings."

" I like him. He's a thoroughly decent chap. You've got
to take him into the secret."

Poirot shook his head.

" No, mon ami. I do not make the exceptions."

" But you don't suspect him of having anything to do with
it?"

" I do not make the exceptions."

" Think how he must be suffering."

" On the contrary, I prefer to think of what a joyful surprise I prepare for him. To think the loved one dead—and
find her alive! It is a sensation unique—stupendous."

" What a pig-headed old devil you are. He'd keep the
secret all right."

" I am not so sure."

" He's the soul of honour. I'm certain of it."

" That makes it all the more difficult to keep a secret. Keeping a secret is an art that requires many lies magnificently told, and a great aptitude for playing the comedy and enjoying it. Could he dissemble, the Commander Challenger? If he is what you say he is, he certainly could *not*."

" Then you won't tell him?"

" I certainly refuse to imperil my little idea for the sake of the sentiment. It is life and death we play with, *mon cher*. Anyway, the suffering, it is good for the character. Many of your famous clergymen have said so—even a Bishop if I am not mistaken."

I made no further attempt to shake his decision. His mind, I could see, was made up.

" I shall not dress for dinner," he murmured. " I am too much the broken old man. That is my part, you understand. All my self-confidence has crashed—I am broken. I have failed. I shall eat hardly any dinner—the food untasted on the plate. That is the attitude, I think. In my own apartment I will consume some brioches and some chocolate *éclairs* (so called) which I had the foresight to buy at a confectioners. *Et vous?*"

" Some more quinine, I think," I said, sadly.

" Alas, my poor Hastings. But courage, all will be well to-morrow."

" Very likely. These attacks often last only twenty-four hours."

I did not hear him return to the room. I must have been asleep.

When I awoke, he was sitting at the table writing. In front of him was a crumpled sheet of paper smoothed out. I recognised it for the paper on which he had written that list of people—A. to J.—which he had afterwards crumpled up and thrown away.

He nodded in answer to my unspoken thought.

" Yes, my friend. I have resurrected it. I am at work

upon it from a different angle. I compile a list of questions concerning each person. The questions may have no bearing on the crime—they are just things that I do not know— things that remain unexplained, and for which I seek to supply the answer from my own brain."

" How far have you got?"

" I have finished. You would like to hear? You are strong enough?"

" Yes, as a matter of fact, I am feeling a great deal better."

" *A la bonheur!* Very well, I will read them to you. Some of them, no doubt, you will consider puerile."

He cleared his throat.

" A. *Ellen*.—Why did she remain in the house and not go out to see fireworks? (Unusual, as Mademoiselle's evidence and surprise make clear.) What did she think or suspect might happen? Did she admit anyone (J. for instance) to the house? Is she speaking the truth about the secret panel? If there is such a thing why is she unable to remember where it is? (Mademoiselle seems very certain there is no such thing—and she would surely know.) If she invented it, why did she invent it? Had she read Michael Seton's love letters or was her surprise at Mademoiselle Nick's engagement genuine?

" B. *Her Husband*.—Is he as stupid as he seems? Does he share Ellen's knowledge whatever it is, or does he not? Is he, in any respect, a mental case?

" C. *The Child*.—Is his delight in blood a natural instinct common to his age and development, or is it morbid, and is that morbidity inherited from either parent? Has he ever shot with a toy pistol?

" D. *Who is Mr. Croft?*—Where does he really come from? Did he post the will as he swears he did? What motive could he have in *not* posting it?

" E. *Same as above*.—Who *are* Mr. and Mrs. Croft? Are they in hiding for some reason—and if so, what reason? Have they any connection with the Buckley family?

"F. *Mrs. Rice*.—Was she really aware of the engagement between Nick and Michael Seton? Did she merely guess it, or had she actually read the letters which passed between them? (In that case she would know Mademoiselle was Seton's heir.) Did she know that she herself was Mademoiselle's residuary legatee? (This, I think, is likely. Mademoiselle would probably tell her so, adding perhaps that she would not get much out of it.) Is there any truth in Commander Challenger's suggestion that Lazarus was attracted by Mademoiselle Nick? (This might explain a certain lack of cordiality between the two friends which seems to have shown itself in the last few months.) Who is the 'boy friend' mentioned in her note as supplying the drug? *Could this possibly be J.?* Why did she turn faint one day in this room? Was it something that had been said—or was it something she *saw*? Is her account of the telephone message asking her to buy chocolates correct—or is it a deliberate lie? What did she mean by 'I can understand the other —but not this?' If she is not herself guilty, what knowledge has she got that she is keeping to herself?"

"You perceive," said Poirot, suddenly breaking off, "that the questions concerning Madame Rice are almost innumerable. From beginning to end, she is an enigma. And that forces me to a conclusion. Either Madame Rice is guilty—or she knows—or shall we say, thinks she knows—who *is* guilty. But is she right? Does she know or does she merely suspect? And how is it possible to make her speak?"

He sighed.

"Well, I will go on with my list of questions.

F

"G. *Mr. Lazarus.*—Curious—there are practically no questions to ask concerning him—except the crude one, 'Did he substitute the poisoned sweets?' Otherwise I find only one totally irrelevant question. But I have put it down. 'Why did M. Lazarus offer fifty pounds for a picture that was only worth twenty?'"

"He wanted to do Nick a good turn," I suggested.

"He would not do it that way. He is a dealer. He does not buy to sell at a loss. If he wished to be amiable he would lend her money as a private individual."

"It can't have any bearing on the crime, anyway."

"No, that is true—but all the same, I should like to know. I am a student of the psychology, you understand.

"Now we come to H.

"H. *Commander Challenger.*—Why did Mademoiselle Nick tell him she was engaged to someone else? What necessitated her having to tell him that? She told no one else. Had he proposed to her? What are his relations with his uncle?"

"His uncle, Poirot?"

"Yes, the doctor. That rather questionable character. Did any private news of Michael Seton's death come through to the Admiralty before it was announced publicly?"

"I don't quite see what you're driving at, Poirot. Even if Challenger knew beforehand about Seton's death, it does not seem to get us anywhere. It provides no earthly motive for killing the girl he loved."

"I quite agree. What you say is perfectly reasonable. But these are just things I should like to know. I am still the dog, you see, nosing about for the things that are not very nice!

"I. *M. Vyse.*—Why did he say what he did about his

cousin's fanatical devotion to End House? What possible motive could he have in saying that? Did he, or did he not, receive the will? Is he, in fact, an honest man—or is he not an honest man?

"*And now J.*—*Eh bien*, J. is what I put down before—a giant question mark. Is there such a person, or is there not——

"*Mon Dieu!* my friend, what have you?"

I had started from my chair with a sudden shriek. With a shaking hand I pointed at the window.

"A face, Poirot!" I cried. "A face pressed against the glass. A dreadful face! It's gone now—but I saw it."

Poirot strode to the window and pushed it open. He leant out.

"There is no one there now," he said, thoughtfully. "You are sure you did not imagine it, Hastings?"

"Quite sure. It was a horrible face."

"There is a balcony, of course. Anyone could reach there quite easily if they wanted to hear what we were saying. When you say a dreadful face, Hastings, just what do you mean?"

"A white, staring face, hardly human."

"*Mon ami,* that is the fever. A face, yes. An unpleasant face, yes. But a face hardly human—*no*. What you saw was the effect of a face pressed closely against the glass—that allied to the shock of seeing it there at all."

"It was a dreadful face," I said, obstinately.

"It was not the face of—anyone you know?"

"No, indeed."

"H'm—it might have been, though! I doubt if you would recognise it under these circumstances. I wonder now—yes, I very much wonder. . . ."

He gathered up his papers thoughtfully.

"One thing at least is to the good. If the owner of that face overheard our conversation we did not mention that

Mademoiselle Nick was alive and well. Whatever else our visitor may have heard, that at least escaped him."

"But surely," I said, "the results of this—er—brilliant manœuvre of yours have been slightly disappointing up to date. Nick is dead and no startling developments have occurred!"

"I did not expect them yet awhile. Twenty-four hours, I said. *Mon ami*, to-morrow, if I am not mistaken, certain things will arise. Otherwise—otherwise I am wrong from start to finish. There is the post, you see. I have hopes of to-morrow's post."

I awoke in the morning feeling weak but with the fever abated. I also felt hungry. Poirot and I had breakfast served in our sitting-room.

"Well?" I said, maliciously, as he sorted his letters. "Has the post done what you expected of it?"

Poirot, who had just opened two envelopes which patently contained bills, did not reply. I thought he looked rather cast down and not his usual cock-a-hoop self.

I opened my own mail. The first was a notice of a spiritualist meeting.

"If all else fails, we must go to the spiritualists," I remarked. "I often wonder that more tests of this kind aren't made. The spirit of the victim comes back and names the murderer. That would be a proof."

"It would hardly help us," said Poirot, absently. "I doubt if Maggie Buckley knew whose hand it was shot her down. Even if she could speak she would have nothing of value to tell us. *Tiens!* that is odd."

"What is?"

"You talk of the dead speaking, and at that moment I open this letter."

He tossed it across to me. It was from Mrs. Buckley and ran as follows :

"Langley Rectory.

"DEAR MONSIEUR POIROT,—On my return here I found a

letter written by my poor child on her arrival at St. Loo.
There is nothing in it of interest to you, I'm afraid, but I
thought perhaps you would care to see it.

"Thanking you for your kindness,
"Yours sincerely,
"JEAN BUCKLEY."

The enclosure brought a lump to my throat. It was so
terribly commonplace and so completely untouched by any
apprehension of tragedy :

"DEAR MOTHER,—I arrived safely. Quite a comfortable
journey. Only two people in the carriage all the way to
Exeter.

"It is lovely weather here. Nick seems very well and gay
—a little restless, perhaps, but I cannot see why she should
have telegraphed for me in the way she did. Tuesday would
have done just as well.

"No more now. We are going to have tea with some
neighbours. They are Australians and have rented the lodge.
Nick says they are kind but rather awful. Mrs. Rice and Mr.
Lazarus are coming to stay. He is the art dealer. I will post
this in the box by the gate, then it will catch the post. Will
write to-morrow.

"Your loving daughter,
"MAGGIE."

P.S.—Nick says there *is* a reason for her wire. She will tell
me after tea. She is very queer and jumpy."

"The voice of the dead," said Poirot, quietly. "And it
tells us—nothing."

"The box by the gate," I remarked idly. "That's where
Croft said he posted the will."

"Said so—yes. I wonder. How I wonder!"

"There is nothing else of interest among your letters?"

"Nothing. Hastings, I am very unhappy. I am in the
dark. Still in the dark. I comprehend nothing."

At that moment the telephone rang. Poirot went to it.

Immediately I saw a change come over his face. His manner was very restrained, nevertheless he could not disguise from my eyes his intense excitement.

His own contributions to the conversation were entirely non-committal so that I could not gather what it was all about.

Presently, however, with a " *Très bien. Je vous remercie,*" he put back the receiver and came back to where I was sitting. His eyes were sparkling with excitement.

" *Mon ami,*" he said. " *What did I tell you?* Things have begun to happen."

" What was it?"

" That was M. Charles Vyse on the telephone. He informs me that this morning, through the post, he has received a will signed by his cousin, Miss Buckley, and dated the 25th of February last."

" What? *The* will?"

" *Evidemment.*"

" It has turned up?"

" Just at the right moment, *n'est-ce pas?*"

" Do you think he is speaking the truth?"

" Or do I think he has had the will all along? Is that what you would say? Well, it is all a little curious. But one thing is certain; I told you that, if Mademoiselle Nick were supposed to be dead, we should have developments—and sure enough here they are!"

" Extraordinary," I said. " You were right. I suppose this is the will making Frederica Rice residuary legatee?"

" M. Vyse said nothing about the contents of the will. He was far too correct. But there seems very little reason to doubt that this is the same will. It is witnessed, he tells me, by Ellen Wilson and her husband."

" So we are back at the old problem," I said. " Frederica Rice."

" The enigma!"

"Frederica Rice," I murmured, inconsequently. "It's a pretty name."

"Prettier than what her friends call her. Freddie"—he made a face—"*ce n'est pas jolie*—for a young lady."

"There aren't many abbreviations of Frederica," I said. "It's not like Margaret where you can have half a dozen—Maggie, Margot, Madge, Peggie——"

"True. Well, Hastings, are you happier now? That things have begun to happen?"

"Yes, of course. Tell me—did you expect *this* to happen?"

"No—not exactly. I had formulated nothing very precise to myself. All I had said was that given a certain result, the causes of that result must make themselves evident."

"Yes," I said, respectfully.

"What was it that I was going to say just as that telephone rang?" mused Poirot. "Oh, yes, that letter from Mademoiselle Maggie. I wanted to look at it once again. I have an idea in the back of my mind that something in it struck me as rather curious."

I picked it up from where I had tossed it, and handed it to him.

He read it over to himself. I moved about the room, looking out of the window and observing the yachts racing on the bay.

Suddenly an exclamation startled me. I turned round. Poirot was holding his head in his hands and rocking himself to and fro, apparently in an agony of woe.

"Oh!" he groaned. "But I have been blind—blind."

"What's the matter?"

"Complex, I have said? Complicated? *Mais non.* Of a simplicity extreme—extreme. And miserable one that I am, I saw nothing—nothing."

"Good gracious, Poirot, what is this light that has suddenly burst upon you?"

"Wait—wait—do not speak? I must arrange my ideas. Rearrange them in the light of this discovery so stupendous."

Seizing his list of questions, he ran over them silently, his lips moving busily. Once or twice he nodded his head emphatically.

Then he laid them down and leaning back in his chair he shut his eyes. I thought at last that he had gone to sleep.

Suddenly he sighed and opened his eyes.

"But yes!" he said. "It all fits in! All the things that have puzzled me. All the things that have seemed to me a little unnatural. They all have their place."

"You mean—you know everything?"

"Nearly everything. All that matters. In some respects I have been right in my deductions. In other ways ludicrously far from the truth. But now it is all clear. I shall send to-day a telegram asking two questions—but the answers to them I know already—I know *here*!" He tapped his forehead.

"And when you receive the answers?" I asked, curiously.

He sprang to his feet.

"My friend, do you remember that Mademoiselle Nick said she wanted to stage a play at End House? To-night, we stage such a play in End House. But it will be a play produced by Hercule Poirot. Mademoiselle Nick will have a part to play in it." He grinned suddenly. "You comprehend, Hastings, *there will be a ghost in this play*. Yes, a ghost. End House has never seen a ghost. It will have one to-night. No"—as I tried to ask a question—"I will say no more. To-night, Hastings, we will produce our comedy—and reveal the truth. But now, there is much to do—much to do."

He hurried from the room.

CHAPTER NINETEEN

'T was a curious gathering that met that night at End House.

I had hardly seen Poirot all day. He had been out for dinner but had left me a message that I was to be at End House at nine o'clock. Evening dress, he had added, was not necessary.

The whole thing was like a rather ridiculous dream.

On arrival I was ushered into the dining-room and when I looked round I realised that every person on Poirot's list from A. to I. (J. was necessarily excluded, being in the Mrs. Harris-like position of " there ain't no sich person ") was present.

Even Mrs. Croft was there in a kind of invalid chair. She smiled and nodded at me.

" This is a surprise, isn't it?" she said, cheerfully. " It makes a change for me, I must say. I think I shall try and get out now and again. All M. Poirot's idea. Come and sit by me, Captain Hastings. Somehow I feel this is rather a gruesome business—but Mr. Vyse made a point of it."

" Mr. Vyse?" I said, rather surprised.

Charles Vyse was standing by the mantelpiece. Poirot was beside him talking earnestly to him in an undertone.

I looked round the room. Yes, they were all there. After showing me in (I had been a minute or two late) Ellen had taken her place on a chair just beside the door. On another chair, sitting painfully straight and breathing hard, was her husband. The child, Alfred, squirmed uneasily between his father and mother.

The rest sat round the dining-table. Frederica in her black dress, Lazarus beside her, George Challenger and Croft on the other side of the table. I sat a little away from it near Mrs. Croft. And now Charles Vyse, with a final nod of

the head, took his place at the head of the table, and Poirot
slipped unobtrusively into a seat next to Lazarus.

Clearly the producer, as Poirot had styled himself, did not
propose to take a prominent part in the play. Charles Vyse
was apparently in charge of the proceedings. I wondered
what surprises Poirot had in store for him.

The young lawyer cleared his throat and stood up. He
looked just the same as ever, impassive, formal and unemotional.

" This is rather an unconventional gathering we have here
to-night," he said. " But the circumstances are very peculiar.
I refer, of course, to the circumstances surrounding the death
of my cousin, Miss Buckley. There will have, of course, to
be an autopsy—there seems to be no doubt that she met her
death by poison, and that that poison was administered with
the intent to kill. This is police business and I need not go
into it. The police would doubtless prefer me not to do so.

" In an ordinary case, the will of a deceased person is read
after the funeral, but in deference to M. Poirot's especial
wish, I am proposing to read it before the funeral takes
place. In fact, I am proposing to read it here and now.
That is why everyone has been asked to come here. As I
said just now, the circumstances are unusual and justify a
departure from precedent.

" The will itself came into my possession in a somewhat
unusual manner. Although dated last February, it only
reached me by post this morning. However, it is undoubtedly in the handwriting of my cousin—I have no doubt
on that point, and though a most informal document, it is
properly attested."

He paused and cleared his throat once more.

Every eye was upon his face.

From a long envelope in his hand, he drew out an enclosure. It was, as we could see, an ordinary piece of End
House notepaper with writing on it.

" It is quite short," said Vyse. He made a suitable pause,
then began to read :

"*This is the last Will and Testament of Magdala Buckley. I direct that all my funeral expenses should be paid and I appoint my cousin Charles Vyse as my executor. I leave everything of which I die possessed to Mildred Croft in grateful recognition of the services rendered by her to my father, Philip Buckley, which services nothing can ever repay.*

> "*Signed*—MAGDALA BUCKLEY,
> "*Witnesses*—ELLEN WILSON.
>   "WILLIAM WILSON."

I was dumbfounded! So I think was everyone else. Only Mrs. Croft nodded her head in quiet understanding.

"It's true," she said, quietly. "Not that I ever meant to let on about it. Philip Buckley was out in Australia, and if it hadn't been for me—well, I'm not going into that. A secret it's been and a secret it had better remain. She knew about it, though. Nick did, I mean. Her father must have told her. We came down here because we wanted to have a look at the place. I'd always been curious about this End House Philip Buckley talked of. And that dear girl knew all about it, and couldn't do enough for us. Wanted us to come and live with her, she did. But we wouldn't do that. And so she insisted on our having the lodge—and not a penny of rent would she take. We pretended to pay it, of course, so as not to cause talk, but she handed it back to us. And now—this! Well, if anyone says there is no gratitude in the world, I'll tell them they're wrong! This proves it."

There was still an amazed silence. Poirot looked at Vyse.

"Had you any idea of this?"

Vyse shook his head.

"I knew Philip Buckley had been in Australia. But I never heard any rumours of a scandal there."

He looked inquiringly at Mrs. Croft.

She shook her head.

"No, you won't get a word out of me. I never have said

a word and I never shall. The secret goes to the grave with me."

Vyse said nothing. He sat quietly tapping the table with a pencil.

"I presume, M. Vyse"—Poirot leaned forward—" that as next of kin you could contest that will? There is, I understand, a vast fortune at stake which was not the case when the will was made."

Vyse looked at him coldly.

"The will is perfectly valid. I should not dream of contesting my cousin's disposal of her property."

"You're an honest fellow," said Mrs. Croft, approvingly. "And I'll see you don't lose by it."

Charles shrank a little from this well-meant but slightly embarrassing remark.

"Well, Mother," said Mr. Croft, with an elation he could not quite keep out of his voice. "This *is* a surprise! Nick didn't tell *me* what she was doing."

"The dear sweet girl," murmured Mrs. Croft, putting her handkerchief to her eyes. "I wish she could look down and see us now. Perhaps she does—who knows?"

"Perhaps," agreed Poirot.

Suddenly an idea seemed to strike him. He looked round.

"An idea! We are all here seated round a table. Let us hold a *séance*."

"A *séance*?" said Mrs. Croft, somewhat shocked. "But surely——"

"Yes, yes, it will be most interesting. Hastings, here, has pronounced mediumistic powers." (Why fix on *me*, I thought.) "To get through a message from the other world —the opportunity is unique! I feel the conditions are propitious. You feel the same, Hastings."

"Yes," I said resolutely, playing up.

"Good. I knew it. Quick, the lights."

In another minute he had risen and switched them off. The whole thing had been rushed on the company before they had had the energy to protest had they wanted to do so.

As a matter of fact they were, I think, still dazed with astonishment over the will.

The room was not quite dark. The curtains were drawn back and the window was open for it was a hot night, and through those windows came a faint light. After a minute or two, as we sat in silence, I began to be able to make out the faint outlines of the furniture. I wondered very much what I was supposed to do and cursed Poirot heartily for not having given me my instructions beforehand.

However, I closed my eyes and breathed in a rather sterorous manner.

Presently Poirot rose and tiptoed to my chair. Then returning to his own, he murmured.

" Yes, he is already in a trance. Soon—things will begin to happen."

There is something about sitting in the dark, waiting, that fills one with unbearable apprehension. I know that I myself was a prey to nerves and so, I was sure, was everyone else. And yet I had at least an idea of what was about to happen. I knew the one vital fact that no one else knew.

And yet, in spite of all that, my heart leapt into my mouth as I saw the dining-room door slowly opening.

It did so quite soundlessly (it must have been oiled) and the effect was horribly grisly. It swung slowly open and for a minute or two that was all. With its opening a cold blast of air seemed to enter the room. It was, I suppose, a common or garden draught owing to the open window, but it *felt* like the icy chill mentioned in all the ghost stories I have ever read.

And then we all saw it! Framed in the doorway was a white shadowy figure. Nick Buckley . . .

She advanced slowly and noiselessly—with a kind of floating ethereal motion that certainly conveyed the impression of nothing human. . . .

I realised then what an actress the world had missed. Nick had wanted to play a part at End House. Now she was playing it, and I felt convinced that she was enjoying herself to the core. She did it perfectly.

She floated forward into the room—and the silence was broken.

There was a gasping cry from the invalid chair beside me. A kind of gurgle from Mr. Croft. A startled oath from Challenger. Charles Vyse drew back his chair, I think. Lazarus leaned forward. Frederica alone made no sound or movement.

And then a scream rent the room. Ellen sprang up from her chair.

" It's her!" she shrieked. " She's come back. She's walking! Them that's murdered always walks. It's her! It's her!"

And then, with a click the lights went on.

I saw Poirot standing by them, the smile of the ringmaster on his face. Nick stood in the middle of the room in her white draperies.

It was Frederica who spoke first. She stretched out an unbelieving hand—touched her friend.

" Nick," she said. " You're—you're *real*!"

It was almost a whisper.

Nick laughed. She advanced.

" Yes," she said. " I'm real enough. Thank you so much for what you did for my father, Mrs. Croft. But I'm afraid you won't be able to enjoy the benefit of that will just yet."

" Oh, my God," gasped Mrs. Croft. " Oh, my God." She twisted to and fro in her chair. " Take me away, Bert. Take me away. It was all a joke, my dear—all a joke, that's all it was. Honest."

" A queer sort of joke," said Nick.

The door had opened again and a man had entered so quietly that I had not heard him. To my surprise I saw that it was Japp. He exchanged a quick nod with Poirot as though satisfying him of something. Then his face suddenly lit up and he took a step forward towards the squirming figure in the invalid chair.

"Hello-ello-ello," he said. "What's this? An old friend! Milly Merton, I declare! And at your old tricks again, my dear."

He turned round in an explanatory way to the company, disregarding Mrs. Croft's shrill protests.

"Cleverest forger we've ever had, Milly Merton. We knew there had been an accident to the car they made their last getaway in. But there! Even an injury to the spine wouldn't keep Milly from her tricks. She's an artist, she is!"

"Was that will a forgery?" said Vyse.

He spoke in tones of amazement.

"Of course it was a forgery," said Nick scornfully. "You don't think I'd make a silly will like that, do you? I left you End House, Charles, and everything else to Frederica."

She crossed as she spoke and stood by her friend, and just at that moment *it happened!*

A spurt of flame from the window and the hiss of a bullet. Then another and the sound of a groan and a fall outside. . . .

And Frederica on her feet with a thin trickle of blood running down her arm. . . .

CHAPTER TWENTY

J.

IT was all so sudden that for a moment no one knew what had happened.

Then, with a violent exclamation, Poirot ran to the window. Challenger was with him.

A moment later they reappeared, carrying with them the limp body of a man. As they lowered him carefully into a big leather armchair and his face came into view, I uttered a cry.

"*The face—the face at the window. . . .*"

It was the man I had seen looking in on us the previous

evening. I recognised him at once. I realised that when I
had said he was hardly human I had exaggerated as Poirot
had accused me of doing.

Yet there was something about this face that justified my
impression. It was a lost face—the face of one removed from
ordinary humanity.

White, weak, depraved—it seemed a mere mask—as
though the spirit within had fled long ago.

Down the side of it there trickled a stream of blood.

Frederica came slowly forward till she stood by the chair.
Poirot intercepted her.

" You are hurt, Madame?"

She shook her head.

"The bullet grazed my shoulder—that is all."

She put him aside with a gentle hand and bent down.

The man's eyes opened and he saw her looking down at
him.

" I've done for you this time, I hope," he said in a low
vicious snarl, and then, his voice changing suddenly till it
sounded like a child's, " Oh! Freddie, I didn't mean it. I
didn't mean it. You've always been so decent to me. . . ."

" It's all right——"

She knelt down beside him.

" I didn't mean——"

His head dropped. The sentence was never finished.

Frederica looked up at Poirot.

" Yes, Madame, he is dead," he said, gently.

She rose slowly from her knees and stood looking down at
him. With one hand she touched his forehead—pitifully, it
seemed. Then she sighed and turned to the rest of us.

" He was my husband," she said, quietly.

" J.," I murmured.

Poirot caught my remark, and nodded a quick assent.

" Yes," he said softly. " Always I felt that there was a J.
I said so from the beginning, did I not?"

" He was my husband," said Frederica again. Her voice
was terribly tired. She sank into a chair that Lazarus

brought for her. "I might as well tell you everything—now."

"He was—completely debased. He was a drug fiend. He taught me to take drugs. I have been fighting the habit ever since I left him. I think—at last—I am nearly cured. But it has been—difficult. Oh! so horribly difficult. Nobody knows how difficult!

"I could never escape from him. He used to turn up and demand money—with threats. A kind of blackmail. If I did not give him money he would shoot himself. That was always his threat. Then he took to threatening to shoot *me*. He was not responsible. He was mad—crazy. . . .

"I suppose it was he who shot Maggie Buckley. He didn't mean to shoot her, of course. He must have thought it was me.

"I ought to have said, I suppose. But, after all, I wasn't *sure*. And those queer accidents Nick had—that made me feel that perhaps it wasn't him after all. It might have been someone quite different.

"And then—one day—I saw a bit of his handwriting on a torn piece of paper on M. Poirot's table. It was a part of a letter he had sent me. I knew then that M. Poirot was on the track.

"Since then I have felt that it was only a matter of time. . . .

"But I don't understand about the sweets. He wouldn't have wanted to poison *Nick*. And anyway, I don't see how he *could* have had anything to do with that. I've puzzled and puzzled."

She put both hands to her face, then took them away and said with a queer pathetic finality :

"That's all. . . ."

CHAPTER TWENTY-ONE

THE PERSON—K.

Lazarus came quickly to her side.

"My dear," he said. "My dear."

Poirot went to the sideboard, poured out a glass of wine and brought it to her, standing over her while she drank it.

She handed the glass back to him and smiled.

"I'm all right now," she said. "What—what had we better do next?"

She looked at Japp, but the Inspector shook his head. "I'm on a holiday, Mrs. Rice. Just obliging an old friend—that's all I'm doing. The St. Loo police are in charge of the case."

She looked at Poirot.

"And M. Poirot is in charge of the St. Loo police?"

"Oh! *quelle idée, Madame*! I am a mere humble adviser."

"M. Poirot," said Nick. "Can't we hush it up?"

"You wish that, Mademoiselle?"

"Yes. After all—I'm the person most concerned. And there will be no more attacks on me—now."

"No, that is true. There will be no more attacks on you now."

"You're thinking of Maggie. But, M. Poirot, nothing will bring Maggie back to life again! If you make all this public, you'll only bring a terrible lot of suffering and publicity on Frederica—and she hasn't deserved it."

"You say she has not deserved it?"

"Of course she hasn't! I told you right at the beginning that she had a brute of a husband. You've seen to-night—what he was. Well, he's dead. Let that be the end of things. Let the police go on looking for the man who shot Maggie. They just won't find him, that's all."

" So that is what you say, Mademoiselle? *Hush it all up.*"

" Yes. Please. Oh! *please.* Please, *dear* M. Poirot."

Poirot looked slowly round.

" What do you all say?"

Each spoke in turn.

" I agree," I said, as Poirot looked at me.

" I, too," said Lazarus.

" Best thing to do," from Challenger.

" Let's forget everything that's passed in this room to-night." This very determinedly from Croft.

" You *would* say that!" interpolated Japp.

" Don't be hard on me, dearie," his wife sniffed to Nick, who looked at her scornfully but made no reply.

" Ellen?"

" Me and William won't say a word, sir. Least said, soonest mended."

" And you, M. Vyse?"

" A thing like this can't be hushed up," said Charles Vyse. " The facts must be made known in the proper quarter."

" Charles!" cried Nick.

" I'm sorry, dear. I look at it from the legal aspect."

Poirot gave a sudden laugh.

" So you are seven to one. The good Japp is neutral."

" I'm on holiday," said Japp, with a grin. " I don't count."

" Seven to one. Only M. Vyse holds out—on the side of law and order! You know, M. Vyse, you are a man of character!"

Vyse shrugged his shoulders.

" The position is quite clear. There is only one thing to do."

" Yes—you are an honest man. *Eh bien*—I, too, range myself on the side of the minority. *I, too, am for the truth.*"

" M. Poirot!" cried Nick.

" Mademoiselle—you dragged me into the case. I came into it at your wish. You cannot silence me now."

He raised a threatening forefinger in a gesture that I knew well.

"Sit down—all of you, and I will tell you—the truth."

Silenced by his imperious attitude, we sat down meekly and turned attentive faces towards him.

"*Ecoutez!* I have a list here—a list of persons connected with the crime. I numbered them with the letters of the alphabet including the letter J. J. stood for a person unknown—linked to the crime by one of the others. I did not know who J. was until to-night, *but I knew that there was such a person.* The events of to-night have proved that I was right.

"But yesterday, I suddenly realised that I had made a grave error. I had made an omission. I added another letter to my list. The letter K."

"Another person unknown?" asked Vyse, with a slight sneer.

"Not exactly. I adopted J. as the symbol for a person unknown. Another person unknown would be merely another J. K. has a different significance. *It stands for a person who should have been included in the original list, but who was overlooked.*"

He bent over Frederica.

"Reassure yourself, Madame. *Your husband was not guilty of murder.* It was the person K. who shot Mademoiselle Maggie."

She stared.

"But who is K.?"

Poirot nodded to Japp. He stepped forward and spoke in tones reminiscent of the days when he had given evidence in police courts.

"Acting on information received, I took up a position here early in the evening, having been introduced secretly into the house by M. Poirot. I was concealed behind the curtains in the drawing-room. When everyone was assembled in this room, a young lady entered the drawing-room and switched on the light. She made her way to the

fireplace and opened a small recess in the panelling that
appeared to be operated with a spring. She took from the
recess a pistol. With this in her hand she left the room. I
followed her and opening the door a crack I was able to
observe her further movements. Coats and wraps had been
left in the hall by the visitors on arrival. The young lady
carefully wiped the pistol with a handkerchief and then
placed it in the pocket of a grey wrap, the property of Mrs.
Rice——"

A cry burst from Nick.

" This is untrue—every word of it!"

Poirot pointed a hand at her.

" *Voilà!*" he said. " *The person K.! It was Mademoiselle
Nick who shot her cousin, Maggie Buckley.*"

" Are you mad?" cried Nick. " Why should I kill
Maggie?"

" In order to inherit the money left to her by Michael
Seton! Her name too was Magdala Buckley—and it was to
her he was engaged—not you."

" You—you——"

She stood there trembling—unable to speak. Poirot turned
to Japp.

" You telephoned to the police?"

" Yes, they are waiting in the hall now. They've got the
warrant."

" You're all mad!" cried Nick, contemptuously. She
moved swiftly to Frederica's side. " Freddie, give me your
wrist-watch as—as a souvenir, will you?"

Slowly Frederica unclasped the jewelled watch from her
wrist and handed it to Nick.

" Thanks. And now—I suppose we must go through with
this perfectly ridiculous comedy."

" The comedy you planned and produced in End House.
Yes—but you should not have given the star part to Hercule
Poirot. That, Mademoiselle, was your mistake—your very
grave mistake."

CHAPTER TWENTY-TWO

"You want me to explain?"

Poirot looked round with a gratified smile and the air of mock humility I knew so well.

We had moved into the drawing-room and our numbers had lessened. The domestics had withdrawn tactfully, and the Crofts had been asked to accompany the police. Frederica, Lazarus, Challenger, Vyse and I remained.

"*Eh bien*—I confess it—I was fooled—fooled completely and absolutely. The little Nick, she had me where she wanted me, as your idiom so well expresses it. Ah! Madame, when you said that your friend was a clever little liar—how right you were! How right!"

"Nick always told lies," said Frederica, composedly. "That's why I didn't really believe in these marvellous escapes of hers."

"And I—imbecile that I was—did!"

"Didn't they really happen?" I asked. I was, I admit, still hopelessly confused.

"They were invented—very cleverly—to give just the impression they did."

"What was that?"

"They gave the impression that Mademoiselle Nick's life was in danger. But I will begin earlier than that. I will tell you the story as I have pieced it out—not as it came to me imperfectly and in flashes.

"At the beginning of the business then, we have this girl, this Nick Buckley, young and beautiful, unscrupulous, and passionately and fanatically devoted to her home."

Charles Vyse nodded.

"I told you that."

"And you were right. Mademoiselle Nick loved End

182

House. But she had no money. The house was mortgaged. She wanted money—she wanted it feverishly—and she could not get it. She met this young Seton at Le Touquet, he is attracted by her. She knows that in all probability he is his uncle's heir and that that uncle is worth millions. Good, her star is in the ascendant, she thinks. But he is not really seriously attracted. He thinks her good fun, that is all. They meet at Scarborough, he takes her up in his machine and then—the catastrophe occurs. He meets Maggie and falls in love with her at first sight.

"Mademoiselle Nick is dumfounded. Her cousin Maggie whom she has never considered pretty! But to young Seton she is ' different.' The one girl in the world for him. They become secretly engaged. Only one person knows—has to know. That person is Mademoiselle Nick. The poor Maggie—she is glad that there is one person she can talk to. Doubtless she reads to her cousin parts of her fiancé's letters. So it is that Mademoiselle gets to hear of the will. She pays no attention to it at the time. But it remains in her mind.

"Then comes the sudden and unexpected death of Sir Matthew Seton, and hard upon that the rumours of Michael Seton's being missing. And straight away an outrageous plan comes into our young lady's head. Seton does not know that her name is Magdala also. He only knows her as Nick. His will is clearly quite informal—a mere mention of a name. But in the eyes of the world Seton is her friend! It is with *her* that his name has been coupled. If she were to claim to be engaged to him, no one would be surprised. *But to do that successfully Maggie must be out of the way.*

"Time is short. She arranges for Maggie to come and stay in a few days' time. Then she has her escapes from death. The picture whose cord she cuts through. The brake of the car that she tampers with. The boulder—that perhaps was natural and she merely invented the story of being underneath on the path.

"And then—she sees *my* name in the paper. (I told you,

Hastings, everyone knew Hercule Poirot!) and she has the audacity to make *me* an accomplice! The bullet through the hat that falls at my feet. Oh! the pretty comedy. And I am taken in! I believe in the peril that menaces her! *Bon!* She has got a valuable witness on her side. I play into her hands by asking her to send for a friend.

"She seizes the chance and sends for Maggie to come a day earlier.

"How easy the crime is actually! She leaves us at the dinner table and after hearing on the wireless that Seton's death is a fact, she starts to put her plan into action. She has plenty of time, then, to take Seton's letters to Maggie—look through them and select the few that will answer her purpose. These she places in her own room. Then, later, she and Maggie leave the fireworks and go back to the house. She tells her cousin to put on her shawl. Then stealing out after her, she shoots her. Quick, into the house, the pistol concealed in the secret panel (of whose existence she thinks nobody knows). Then upstairs. There she waits till voices are heard. The body is discovered. It is her cue.

"Down she rushes and out through the window.

"How well she played her part! Magnificently! Oh, yes, she staged a fine drama here. The maid, Ellen, said this was an evil house. I am inclined to agree with her. It was from the house that Mademoiselle Nick took her inspiration."

"But those poisoned sweets," said Frederica. "I still don't understand about that."

"It was all part of the same scheme. Do you not see that if Nick's life was attempted *after* Maggie was dead that absolutely settled the question that Maggie's death had been a mistake.

"When she thought the time was ripe she rang up Madame Rice and asked her to get her a box of chocolates."

"Then it *was* her voice?"

"But, yes! How often the simple explanation is the true one! *N'est ce pas?* She made her voice sound a little different—that was all. So that you might be in doubt when questioned. Then, when the box arrived—again how simple. She fills three of the chocolates with cocaine (she had cocaine with her, cleverly concealed), eats one of them and is ill—but not *too* ill. She knows very well how much cocaine to take and just what symptoms to exaggerate.

" And the card—*my* card! *Ah! Sapristi*—she has a nerve! It *was* my card—the one I sent with the flowers. Simple, was it not? Yes, but it had to be thought of. . . ."

There was a pause and then Frederica asked :

" Why did she put the pistol in my coat?"

" I thought you would ask that, Madame. It was bound to occur to you in time. Tell me—had it ever entered your head that Mademoiselle Nick no longer liked you? Did you ever feel that she might—hate you?"

" It's difficult to say," said Frederica, slowly. " We lived an insincere life. She *used* to be fond of me."

" Tell me, M. Lazarus—it is not a time for false modesty, you understand—was there ever anything between you and her?"

" No." Lazarus shook his head. " I was attracted to her at one time. And then—I don't know why—I went off her."

" Ah!" said Poirot, nodding his head sagely. " That was her tragedy. She attracted people—and then they 'went off her.' Instead of liking her better and better you fell in love with her friend. She began to hate Madame—Madame who had a rich friend behind her. Last winter when she made a will, she was fond of Madame. Later it was different.

" She remembered that will. She did not know that Croft had suppressed it—that it had never reached its destination. Madame (or so the world would say) had got a motive for desiring her death. So it was to Madame she telephoned asking her to get the chocolates. To-night, the will would have been read, naming Madame her residuary legatee— and then the pistol would be found in her coat—*the pistol with which Maggie Buckley was shot.* If Madame found it, she might incriminate herself by trying to get rid of it."

" She must have hated me," murmured Frederica.

" Yes, Madame. You had what she had not—the knack of winning love, and *keeping* it."

" I'm rather dense," said Challenger, " but I haven't quite fathomed the will business yet?"

" No? That's a different business altogether—a very simple one. The Crofts are lying low down here. Mademoiselle Nick has to have an operation. She has made no will. The Crofts see a chance. They persuade her to make one and take charge of it for the post. Then, if anything happens to her—if she dies—they produce a cleverly forged will—leaving the money to Mrs. Croft with a reference to Australia and Philip Buckley whom they know once visited the country.

" But Mademoiselle Nick has her appendix removed quite satisfactorily so the forged will is no good. For the moment, that is. Then the attempts on her life begin. The Crofts are hopeful once more. Finally, I announce her death. The chance is too good to be missed. The forged will is immediately posted to M. Vyse. Of course, to begin with, they naturally thought her much richer than she is. They knew nothing about the mortgage."

" What I really want to know, M. Poirot," said Lazarus, " is how you actually got wise to all this. When did you begin to suspect?"

" Ah! there I am ashamed. I was so long—so long. There were things that worried me—yes. Things that seemed not quite right. Discrepancies between what Mademoiselle Nick told me and what other people told me. Unfortunately, I always believed Mademoiselle Nick.

" And then, suddenly, I got a revelation. Mademoiselle Nick made one mistake. She was too clever. When I urged her to send for a friend she promised to do so—and suppressed the fact that she had already sent for Mademoiselle

Maggie. It seemed to her less suspicious—*but it was a mistake.*

"For Maggie Buckley wrote a letter home immediately on arrival, and in it she used one innocent phrase that puzzled me: '*I don't see why Nick should have telegraphed for me the way she did. Tuesday would have done just as well.*' What did that mention of Tuesday mean? *It could only mean one thing.* Maggie had been coming to stay on Tuesday anyway. But in that case Mademoiselle Nick had lied—or had at any rate suppressed the truth.

"And for the first time I looked at her in a different light. I criticised her statements. Instead of believing them, I said, 'Suppose this were not true.' I remembered the discrepancies. 'How would it be if every time it was Mademoiselle Nick who was lying and not the other person?'

"I said to myself. Let us be simple. What has *really* happened?

"And I saw that what had really happened was that *Maggie Buckley* had been killed. Just that! But who could want Maggie Buckley dead?

"And then I thought of something else—a few foolish remarks that Hastings had made not five minutes before. He had said that there were plenty of abbreviations for Margaret—Maggie, Margot, etc. And it suddenly occurred to me to wonder what was Mademoiselle Maggie's real name?

"Then, *tout d'un coup*, it came to me! Supposing her name was *Magdala*! It was a Buckley name, Mademoiselle Nick had told me so. Two Magdala Buckleys. Supposing . . .

"In my mind I ran over the letters of Michael Seton's that I had read. Yes—there was nothing impossible. There was a mention of Scarborough—but Maggie had been in Scarborough with Nick—her mother had told me so.

"And it explained one thing which had worried me. Why were there so *few* letters? If a girl keeps her love-letters at all, she keeps *all* of them. Why these select few? Was there any peculiarity about them?

" And I remembered that there was no *name* mentioned in them. They all began differently—but they began with a term of endearment. Nowhere in them was there the name —*Nick*.

" And there was something else, something that I ought to have seen at once—that cried the truth aloud."

" What was that?"

" Why—this. Mademoiselle Nick underwent an operation for appendicitis on February 27th last. There is a letter of Michael Seton's dated March 2nd, and no mention of anxiety, of illness or anything unusual. That ought to have shown me that the letters were written to a *different person altogether*.

" Then I went through a list of questions that I had made. And I answered them in the light of my new idea.

" In all but a few isolated questions the result was simple and convincing. And I answered, too, another question which I had asked myself earlier. *Why did Mademoiselle Nick buy a black dress?* The answer was that she and her cousin had to be dressed alike, with the scarlet shawl as an additional touch. That was the true and convincing answer, *not* the other. A girl would not buy mourning before she knew her lover was dead. She would be unreal—unnatural.

" And so I, in turn, staged my little drama. And the thing I hoped for happened! Nick Buckley had been very vehement about the question of a secret panel. She had declared there was no such thing. But if there were—and I did not see why Ellen should have invented it—*Nick must know of it*. Why was she so vehement? Was it possible that she had hidden the pistol there? With the secret intention of using it to throw suspicion on somebody later?

" I let her see that appearances were very black against Madame. That was as she had planned. As I foresaw, she was unable to resist the crowning proof. Besides it was safer for herself. That secret panel might be found by Ellen and the pistol in it!

" We are all safely in here. She is waiting outside for her

cue. It is absolutely safe, she thinks, to take the pistol from
its hiding place and put it in Madame's coat. . . .

"And so—at the last—she failed. . . ."

Frederica shivered.

"All the same," she said. "I'm glad I gave her my
watch."

"Yes, Madame."

She looked up at him quickly.

"You know about that too?"

"What about Ellen?" I asked, breaking in. "Did she
know or suspect anything?"

"No. I asked her. She told me that she decided to stay
in the house that night because in her own phrase she
thought something was up.' Apparently Nick urged her
to see the fireworks rather too decisively. She had fathomed
Nick's dislike of Madame. She told me that ' she felt in her
bones something was going to happen,' but she thought it
was going to happen to Madame. She knew Miss Nick's
temper, she said, and she was always a queer little girl."

"Yes," murmured Frederica. "Yes, let us think of her
like that. A queer little girl. A queer little girl who couldn't
help herself. . . . I shall—anyway."

Poirot took her hand and raised it gently to his lips.

Charles Vyse stirred uneasily.

"It's going to be a very unpleasant business," he said,
quietly. "I must see about some kind of defence for her, I
suppose."

"There will be no need, I think," said Poirot, gently.
"Not if I am correct in my assumptions."

He turned suddenly on Challenger.

"That's where you put the stuff, isn't it?" he said. "In
those wrist-watches."

"I—I——" The sailor stammered—at a loss.

"Do not try and deceive me—with your hearty good-
fellow manner. It has deceived Hastings—but it does not
deceive me. You make a good thing out of it, do you not—
the traffic in drugs—you and your uncle in Harley Street."

" M. Poirot."

Challenger rose to his feet.

My little friend blinked up at him placidly.

" You are the useful 'boy friend.' Deny it, if you like. But I advise you, if you do not want the facts put in the hands of the police—to go."

And to my utter amazement, Challenger did go. He went from the room like a flash. I stared after him open-mouthed.

Poirot laughed.

" I told you so, *mon ami*. Your instincts are always wrong. *C'est épatant!*"

" Cocaine was in the wrist-watch——" I began.

" Yes, yes. That is how Mademoiselle Nick had it with her so conveniently at the nursing home. And having finished her supply in the chocolate box she asked Madame just now for hers *which was full*."

" You mean she can't do without it?"

" *Non, non*. Mademoiselle Nick is not an addict. Sometimes—for fun—that is all. But to-night she needed it for a different purpose. It will be a full dose this time."

" You mean——?" I gasped.

" It is the best way. Better than the hangman's rope. But pst! we must not say so before M. Vyse who is all for law and order. Officially I know nothing. The contents of the wrist-watch—it is the merest guess on my part."

" Your guesses are always right, M. Poirot," said Frederica.

" I must be going," said Charles Vyse, cold disapproval in his attitude as he left the room.

Poirot looked from Frederica to Lazarus.

" You are going to get married—eh?"

" As soon as we can."

" And indeed, M. Poirot," said Frederica. " I am not the drug-taker you think. I have cut myself down to a tiny dose. I think now—with happiness in front of me—I shall not need a wrist-watch any more."

" I hope you will have happiness, Madame," said Poirot,

gently. "You have suffered a great deal. And in spite of everything you have suffered, you have still the quality of mercy in your heart. . . ."

"I will look after her," said Lazarus. "My business is in a bad way, but I believe I shall pull through. And if I don't —well, Frederica does not mind being poor—with me."

She shook her head, smiling.

"It is late," said Poirot, looking at the clock.

We all rose.

"We have spent a strange night in this strange house," Poirot went on. "It is, I think, as Ellen says, an evil house. . . ."

He looked up at the picture of old Sir Nicholas.

Then, with a sudden gesture, he drew Lazarus aside.

"I ask your pardon, but, of all my questions, there is one still unanswered. Tell me, why did you offer fifty pounds for that picture? It would give me much pleasure to know —so as, you comprehend, to leave nothing unanswered."

Lazarus looked at him with an impassive face for a minute or two. Then he smiled.

"You see, M. Poirot," he said. "I am a dealer."

"Exactly."

"That picture is not worth a penny more than twenty pounds. I knew that if I offered Nick fifty, she would immediately suspect it was worth more and would get it valued elsewhere. Then she would find that I had offered her far more than it was worth. The next time I offered to buy a picture she would not have got it valued."

"Yes, and then?"

"The picture on the far wall is worth at least five thousand pounds," said Lazarus drily.

"Ah!" Poirot drew a long breath.

"Now I know everything," he said happily.

THE END

FONTANA FOR EXCITEMENT

APPOINTMENT WITH DEATH
Agatha Christie

. . . "You do see, don't you, that she's got to be killed?"
Hercule Poirot thought to himself 'I should know that voice
again . . .' He was to have good reason to remember it. Within
days, a murder did take place. Why didn't Poirot prevent the
murder?

DEAD MAN'S FOLLY
Agatha Christie

Nasse House, and a Fête in progress. In place of a Treasure
Hunt, the well-known novelist Mrs. Ariadne Oliver has organ-
ised a Murder Hunt. The prizes are to be given away by the
celebrated detective M. Hercule Poirot. The 'body' is found—
but it is a real corpse . . .

UNREASONABLE DOUBT
Elizabeth Ferrars

Unwittingly involved in a murder whilst on holiday in the South
of France, Alistair Dirke and his wife had been released by the
French police. Returning home they tried to dismiss the affair
until they received an anonymous scrap of paper. Then Alistair
found himself entertaining doubts, about the pleasant couple
they had met on holiday, about their friends at home, even
about his own wife! But were they unreasonable . . .?

THE WIDOW'S CRUISE
Nicholas Blake

He'd gone to her cabin at the time *she* had arranged. He had
met with violent resistance without a word of explanation.
What was the intriguing link between this episode and the death
of two passengers on board the cruise vessel *Menelaos*?
Nigel Strangeways had just fourteen hours to find the answer.

An

unknown

agent

was

methodically

planning

her

death

—the heavy picture that fell across her bed

—the rock that landed at her feet

—the car brakes that failed

NOW — a bullet that missed her head by inches

 fontana books

KT-094-234

INTRODUCTION

This little book is more than a collection of useful phrases. It also answers many of the questions which a traveller in the Spanish-speaking countries will wish to ask about food, travel, customs and so on.

Of course, it is not possible to give precise details about all these things, because timetables, rates of exchange, passport and customs regulations change. Up-to-date information may be obtained from travel agencies. Labour exchanges also supply information about passports, and banks about currency rates and regulations. A table is provided on page 140 in which the current rate of exchange should be entered.

Trains

There are four types of train in Spain: the *Talgo* (Irun–Madrid) and the *Taf* (from principal coast towns, e.g. Santander, Seville–Madrid) are fast luxury trains; the *expreso* is first and second class only; the *rápido* and *correo* have all three classes and are slow, though recommended for local colour and the "common touch." Other trains have long halts for meals although Spaniards usually take food with them, e.g. cold chops, omelettes, etc. Sleeping-car travel, when available, is good and about the same price as in England. Second class travel is comfortable; some third class compartments have wooden seats. Travellers are advised to book well in advance through an Agency or R.E.N.F.E., since, in the summer especially, there is a great shortage of seats in coast-bound trains. The booking office in the station is open for about one hour before the train leaves, and closes five minutes before the departure of the train.

Local Information

This may be obtained in any city from the *Oficinas de Información de la Dirección General del Turismo.*

Meals

In Spain breakfast consists of coffee and rolls. Lunch and dinner are the main meals and these meals are usually served at about 2 p.m. and 9 p.m. respectively. Afternoon tea is not provided in hotels unless specially ordered.

All milk is boiled, hence tea without milk is preferable where available. *Merienda* is either a picnic tea or an early meal for children, where specially requested. Except at breakfast, *coffee* means black coffee.

The café is very popular in Spain, and provides a constant meeting place for friends or for discussion. Spaniards are very hospitable, talkative and helpful to foreigners.

Tipping
Where a percentage service charge is made, as in restaurants and hotels, an extra tip is optional. One tips porters about 8 pesetas per item of luggage, a nightwatchman (*sereno*) about 4 pesetas and taxi drivers and waiters anything from 10% to 15%.

Amusements
Good cinemas are to be found in all Spanish towns; usually one theatre specialises in programmes of folk music and dancing. Light musical entertainment is known as *revista*, but the *zarzuela*, a lively musical comedy of Madrid life, is unique. Other musical shows may have *flamenco* singing and dancing.

Bull-fighting is mainly a summer entertainment, and although a bull-fight usually takes place once a week in most large towns, the good fights are generally only to be seen during *fiesta* times. The small bull-fights provide all that is unpleasant in the spectacle without affording the visitor any display of skill or artistry.

Motoring (*see also section* MOTORING)
Full information regarding motoring abroad may be obtained from the Automobile Association or the Royal Automobile Club, who also issue the requisite documents. The A.A. or R.A.C. are able to supply current information about the amount of petrol and oil available and the approximate prices.

General Advice (*see section* POLICE, PASSPORTS AND FORMS about the compulsory registration of foreigners)
Visitors are advised to observe as far as possible the general customs of the country in matters relating to dress. Shorts, either for men or women, are not acceptable, except as beach apparel, and all bathing costumes must conform to certain standards. Failure to observe the regulations may result in a fine being imposed by a beach guard, though restrictions are becoming less severe. Women should see that their heads, arms and legs are covered on entering a church and men should not enter in shorts.

Note on Using a Dictionary
The symbols *ch* and *ll* are placed separately in the Spanish alphabet after c and l respectively, hence *chico* will not be found under c, nor *llave* under l.

SCHEME OF PRONUNCIATION

The following scheme is similar to that of *Collins Spanish Gem Dictionary*. It sacrifices complete accuracy to simplicity, but being based on English pronunciation it should be easily understood and used by those whose native speech is English even when they have no knowledge of phonetics. A more energetic delivery is normal in Spanish than is often the case in English. The vowels are represented by only one letter and, unlike those of English, maintain the same sound throughout their length, (cf. Spanish *cosa*, and English h*o*me). Every letter is pronounced except *h*, and *u* in *que* and *qui*.

Vowels

	Comment	English spelling used	Example
a	as in p*a*ssport, never as in p*a*rent	a	p*a*dre
e	as in Scottish English s*ay*,	ay	c*e*na
	also as in p*e*n	e	*e*l
i	always as in mach*i*ne, never as in s*i*de	ee	n*i*ño
o	as in *oh*! also as in *o*n (the difference is made naturally)	o	p*o*ngo
u	as in m*oo*n	oo	l*u*mbre
u+e	silent		Mig*ue*l
u+i	silent		g*uí*a
u+a	as in *wa*n	w	g*ua*rdia
y	as in gentr*y*	ee	m*uy*

Consonants

	Comments	English spelling used	Example
b	almost as in English initially,	b	*b*anco
	but generally more like v	„	ha*b*a
c+a	as in *c*at	k	*c*alle
c+o	as in *c*omb	„	*c*ola
c+u	as in *c*ool, but also as	„	*c*ura
	in *qua*ck	kw	*cua*ndo
c+e	as in *th*ane	th	*c*ena
c+i	as in *th*ree	„	*c*ita
c+h	as in *ch*in, never as in ma*ch*ine	ch	*ch*ica

d	initially and after n, as in dog	d	donde
	between vowels and finally, as in then	dh	tostada*
f	as in English	f	feo
g+a	as in gasp	g	gato
g+o	as in go	,,	gordo
g+u	as in gun (see also u)	,,	gula
g+e	as in Scottish loch	h	gente
g+i	as in Scottish loch	,,	gitano
h	always silent		hombre
j	as in Scottish loch	h	caja
k	as in English	k	kilómetro
l	as in English	l	listo
ll	as in million	ly	calle
m	as in English	m	madre
n	as in English	n	niño
ñ	as in onion	ny	niño
p	as in English	p	padre
q+u	as in king, (never as in question)	k	quisiera
r	always pronounced	r	pero
rr	strongly trilled	rr	perro
s	always hissed, (never as in these)	s	casa
t	as in English	t	toalla
v	as in English with lips almost together	v	vino
w	like English v	v	wagon
x	mostly as in English	x	exacto
y	as in you	y	yo
z	as in thin	th	cerveza

* does not apply to the second-last d of a word ending in —dad, e.g. ciudad, which is hard.

The above remarks apply to Castilian or Standard Spanish (el castellano). The following differences are to be found in Latin America and Southern Spain.

ll	as in you, and also	calle
	as in invasion	,,
c+e	as in centre	cena
c+i	as in city	ciudad
z	as in say	cerveza
d	silent when final and between vowels	tostada
		ciudad
s	sometimes like h	tostada

Stress or Accentuation It is possible to pronounce each letter correctly and still not be understood if the wrong syllable is stressed.

The rules are:—
1) Words ending in a VOWEL, N or S stress the *second-last* syllable: m*a*no, h*o*mbre, par*a*guas, ex*a*men.
2) Words ending in a CONSONANT (other than N or S) stress the *last* syllable: am*o*r, far*o*l, ciud*a*d.

A departure from these rules calls for a written accent: pap*á*, *ú*til, raz*ó*n, ej*é*rcito.

Diphthongs:—*a, o, e* are strong vowels and *u, i,* are weak. Strong + weak (or weak + strong): stress the strong: b*o*ina, su*e*lo. Strong + strong counts as two syllables, stress the second: ma*e*stro. Weak + weak, stress the second: ru*i*do.

A departure from these rules again calls for a written accent: ba*ú*l, he o*í*do.

GRAMMATICAL NOTES

These do not aim at completeness but are a framework into which the traveller (whom we visualise as wanting to speak the language rather than read novels in it) may fit the words and phrases of this book. Accordingly two narrative tenses (the Past Historic and the Imperfect) have been omitted, and also the 2nd person singular. One or two elementary notions of gender, particularly, are worth acquiring as "el mujer" or "yo hablar", for instance, sound ludicrous to Spanish ears.

Nouns
Gender: Male and female beings fall into the appropriate gender, but things are also masculine (words ending in -o) or feminine (words ending in -a).

Words ending in *e* or a consonant may fall into one or the other:
el hombre, el dinero, el papel   are masc.
exceptions: la mano, la radio
la chica, la carta, la llave   are fem.
exceptions: el d*í*a, el tranv*í*a, el idioma, el mapa, el programa, el problema, el telegrama, el sistema, etc.
Plural: The plural is formed by adding -s or -es:
puerta → puertas; hombre → hombres

Definite Article (the)

	Singular	*Plural*
Masc.	el libro	los libros
Fem.	la carta	las cartas

El instead of *las* is used with nouns beginning with stressed *a* or *ha* (without changing the gender):
la acción, las aguas, but el agua
la hacienda, las hachas, but el hacha.

Indefinite Article (a, an)

	Singular	*Plural*
Masc.	un libro	(unos) libros
Fem.	una carta	(unas) cartas

The plural may be used to indicate *some*.

The indefinite article is omitted before a few adjectives including: otra vez=another time; tal cosa=such a thing; cien libras=a hundred pounds.

Demonstratives (this, etc.)

	Singular		*Plural*	
Masc.	este libro=this book		estos libros=these books	
	ese aquel } „,=that book		esos aquellos } „=those books	
	Singular		*Plural*	
Fem.	esta carta = this letter		estas cartas = these letters	
	esa aquella } „ = that letter		esas aquellas } „ = those letters	

The demonstrative pronoun is no different to the ear: este libro y aquél=this book and that one.

Adjectives

Agreement: adjectives ending in -o, agree as follows:

	Singular	*Plural*
Masc.	un pueblo bonito=a pretty town	pueblos bonitos
Fem.	una carta larga=a long letter	cartas largas

Adjectives ending in -e or a consonant merely add -s or -es for the plural. But those of nationality in -és, have four forms:

	Singular	*Plural*
Masc.	inglés (English)	ingleses
Fem.	inglesa	inglesas

Position: it will be noticed that adjectives generally follow their noun. They may precede it, and some in this case shorten in the masculine singular: un buen hotel=a good hotel; el primer día=on the first day; el mal hombre=the bad man; ningún dinero=no money; algún amigo=some friend.

Comparison:
bonito =pretty   más bonito =prettier   el más bonito=prettiest
bueno   =good   mejor   =better   el mejor   =best

malo = bad   peor   = worse   el peor   = worst
malísimo = very bad.
tanto dinero como usted = as much money as you.

Interrogatives
¿ Qué hombre ? = What man ?   cf. ¡ Qué hombre ! = What a man !
¿ Cuál sombrero ? = Which hat ?   ¿ Cuántos   How many
                                       artículos ?   =   articles ?

Numbers: do not agree up to one hundred:
cuatro mujeres = four women. But: doscientas pesetas = 200 pesetas
                     note: cien pesetas   = 100 pesetas

Possessives: agree with the thing possessed and not with the possessor.
The most useful to know are:
mi = my; nuestro = our; su = his, her, their, your.
They are used as follows:

Singular		Plural	
Masc.	*Fem.*	*Masc.*	*Fem.*
mi libro	mi carta	mis libros	mis cartas
nuestro libro	nuestra carta	nuestros libros	nuestras cartas
su libro	su carta	sus libros	sus cartas

Pronouns

	Subject		*Object*
Singular	yo = I	*Singular*	me = me
	*usted = you		le (masc.) la (fem.) = you
	él = he, it		lo = him, it
	ella = she, it		la = her, it
Plural	nosotros = we	*Plural*	nos = us
	*ustedes = you		les (masc.) las (fem.) = you
	ellos } = they		los } them
	ellas }		las }

*Of the subject pronouns, only these (often written Vd. and Vds.)
are used if emphasis or clarity is desired.

Position: object pronouns are normally placed before the verb:
Ustedes *nos* conocen = You know *us*. But not:
1) in the positive imperative: ¡Démelo!   = Give me it!
2) with an infinitive: Voy a verle   = I am going to see him.
3) with a present participle: Estoy lavándome   = I am washing.

Possessive pronouns: mine = el mío, etc. with four forms agreeing with
the nouns referred to.

ours=el nuestro, etc. with four forms agreeing with the nouns referred to.

his, hers, theirs, yours=el suyo, etc. with four forms agreeing with the nouns referred to.

e.g.: nuestro pais y el suyo=our country and yours.

Interrogative Pronouns
¿Quién?=Who?   ¿Qué?=What?   ¿Cómo?=How?
¿Cuándo?=When?   ¿Cuánto?=How much? ¿Dónde?=Where?

Relative pronoun: que will generally suit:
el hombre que veo=the man whom I see.

Questions, Negatives and Indefinites

1) One may ask a question by reversing normal word-order and placing Subject after Verb: ¿Nada Vd.?=Do you swim?
   One may do so by raising the voice: ¿Vd. nada?
2) No entiendo   =I do not understand
   No he entendido =I did not understand
3) ¿Desea Vd. algo? =Do you want something?
   No deseo nada   =I do not want anything.

Verbs

A knowledge of only four forms in each tense will normally suffice. The present, perfect (called here the past) and future are listed as being the most useful to the traveller. The Imperative is given separately and many examples of its use occur in the body of the book. Notice that usted and ustedes are really third person.

Verbs like HABLAR=TO SPEAK

Present Tense	*Past Tense*	*Future Tense*
hablo I speak	he hablado	hablaré
habla you, he, she speak(s)	ha hablado	hablará
hablamos we speak	hemos hablado	hablaremos
hablan they, you speak	han hablado	hablarán

Verbs like APRENDER=TO LEARN

aprendo	he aprendido	aprenderé
aprende	ha aprendido	aprenderá
aprendemos	hemos aprendido	aprenderemos
aprenden	han aprendido	aprenderán

Verbs like VIVIR=TO LIVE

vivo	he vivido	viviré
vive	ha vivido	vivirá
vivimos	hemos vivido	viviremos
viven	han vivido	vivirán

Verbs like ENTENDER (i →ie)=TO UNDERSTAND

entiendo	he entendido	entenderé
entiende	ha entendido	entenderá
entendemos	hemos entendido	entenderemos
entienden	han entendido	entenderán

Verbs like CONTAR (u →ue)=TO COUNT, EXPECT

cuento	he contado	contaré
cuenta	ha contado	contará
contamos	hemos contado	contaremos
cuentan	han contado	contarán

Verbs like PEDIR (e →i)=TO ASK FOR, ORDER

pido	he pedido	pediré
pide	ha pedido	pedirá
pedimos	hemos pedido	pediremos
piden	han pedido	pedirán

Reflexive verbs, like LEVANTARSE=TO GET UP

me levanto	me he levantado	me levantaré
se levanta	se ha levantado	se levantará
nos levantamos	nos hemos levantado	nos levantaremos
se levantan	se han levantado	se levantarán

Irregular verbs   SER=TO BE

soy	he sido	seré
es	ha sido	será
somos	hemos sido	seremos
son	han sido	serán

used 1) with nouns: es estudiante=he is a student
2) with so-called permanent adjectives like: bueno=good;
malo=bad; hermoso=beautiful; feo=ugly; pequeño=small; grande
=big; rico=rich; pobre=poor; joven=young; viejo=old.

ESTAR=TO BE

estoy	he estado	estaré
está	ha estado	estará
estamos	hemos estado	estaremos
están	han estado	estarán

used 1) to indicate position: está aquí=he is here
2) with so-called temporary adjectives such as: bien (or bueno)
=well; malo (or enfermo)=ill; cansado=tired; ocupado=busy;
contento=pleased; muerto=dead.

TENER=TO HAVE, POSSESS

tengo	he tenido	tendré
tiene	ha tenido	tendrá
tenemos	hemos tenido	tendremos
tienen	han tenido	tendrán

IR=TO GO

voy	he ido	iré
va	ha ido	irá
vamos	hemos ido	iremos
van	han ido	irán

VENIR=TO COME

vengo	he venido	vendré
viene	ha venido	vendrá
venimos	hemos venido	vendremos
vienen	han venido	vendrán

DECIR=TO SAY, TELL

digo	he dicho	diré
dice	ha dicho	dirá
decimos	hemos dicho	diremos
dicen	han dicho	dirán

HACER=TO DO, MAKE

hago	he hecho	haré
hace	ha hecho	hará
hacemos	hemos hecho	haremos
hacen	han hecho	harán

DAR=TO GIVE

doy	he dado	daré
da	ha dado	dará
damos	hemos dado	daremos
dan	han dado	darán

VER=TO SEE

veo	he visto	veré
ve	ha visto	verá
vemos	hemos visto	veremos
ven	han visto	verán

The Imperative: is formed
1) regularly, by using the non-characteristic vowel: ¡com*a*!=Eat!
¡Levántese vd!=Get up!
2) irregularly, rather like the first person singular present tense:
¡Salga!=leave! ¡Dígame!=Tell me!

Adverbs
These are regularly formed by adding -mente to the adjective:
distinta-mente=distinctly; general-mente=generally.
Note: bien=well; mal=badly; rápido=quickly.

COMMON WORDS AND PHRASES

VOCABULARY

how?, ¿ cómo ? (kó-mo)
how much?, ¿ cuánto(a) ? (kwán-to/a)
how many?, ¿ cuántos(as) ? (kwán-tos/as)
when?, ¿ cuándo ? (kwán-do)
where?, ¿ dónde ? (dón-day)
why?, ¿ por qué ? (por káy)

above, por encima de (por en-thēē-ma day)
according to, según (say-gōōn)
after, después de* (des-poo-áys day)
against, contra (kón-tra)
almost, casi (ká-see)
also, también (tam-bee-én)
always, siempre (see-ém-pray)
among, entre (én-tray)
and, y (ee)
around, alrededor de* (al-ray-dháy-dhór day)
at, a (a), en (en)
at once, en seguida (en say-gēē-dha)
backwards, atrás (a-trás)
because, porque (pór-kay)
before, antes de* (án-tays day)
behind, detrás de* (day-trás day)
below, debajo de* (day-bá-ho day)
beside, al lado de* (al lá-dho day)
besides, además (a-dhay-más)
between, entre (én-tray)
during, durante (doo-rán-tay)
early, temprano (tem-prá-no)
elsewhere, en otra parte (en ó-tra pár-tay)
everywhere, en todas partes (en tó-dhas pár-tays)
except, excepto (es-thép-to)
far, lejos (láy-hos)
for, para (pára), por (por)
forwards, adelante (a-dhay-lán-tay)
here, aquí (a-kēē)
in: into, en (en)
in order to, para (pá-ra)
inside, dentro de* (dén-tro day)
less, menos (máy-nos)
little, a, un poco (oon pó-ko)
many, muchos(as) (mōō-chos/as)

23

more, más (mas)
much, mucho(a) (mōō-cho/a)
near, cerca de* (tháyr-ka day)
on, en (en), sobre (só-bray)
only, sólo (só-lo), solamente (so-la-mén-tay)
opposite, en frente (en frén-tay)
outside, fuera de* (foo-áy-ra day)
over, por encima de* (por en-thēē-ma day)
over there, por allí (por al-yēē)
quickly, rápido (rá-pee-dho)
scarcely, a penas (a páy-nas)
since (time), desde (dés-day)
since (because), puesto que (poo-áys-to kay)
slowly, despacio (days-pá-thee-o)
so (+adj.), tan (tan)
so (manner), así (a-sēē)
so much/many, tanto(a) (os) (as) (tán-to)
sometimes, algunas veces (al-gōō-nas váy-thays)
soon, pronto (prón-to)
then, entonces (en-tón-thays)
there, allí (al-yēē)
through, por (por)
too (too much), demasiado (day-mas-ee-á-dho)
towards, hacia (á-thee-a)
under, debajo de* (day-bá-ho day)
until, hasta (ás-ta)
upstairs, arriba (a-rēē-ba)
very, muy (mwee)
well, bien (bee-én)
without, sin (seen)
yet, todavía (to-dha-vēē-a)

de is dropped in adverbial use

POLITE EXPRESSIONS

When addressing strangers to ask the way, etc., one should begin *Perdóneme* (per-dó-ne-me); a gentleman is addressed politely as *Señor* (sen-yór); a lady as *Señora,* (sen-yó-ra) and if unmarried as *Señorita* (sen-yo-rēē-ta). *Don* and *Doña* (dón-ya) are forms of address, used only with christian names and for rather more elderly people. Telephone operators are addressed as *Señorita;* waitresses as *Camarera* (ka-ma-ré-ra) and waiters as *Camerero* (ka-ma-ré-ro) or *Mozo* (mó-tho).

Note.—In addressing children, Spaniards use the familiar *tu* form of the verb. Small children use this form when speaking to most adults; older children learn to distinguish, hence will address the visitor as *usted.*

Good morning sir.	Buenos días señor.
	bwáy-nos dēē-as sayn-yór
Good afternoon (evening) madam.	Buenas tardes señora.
	bwáy-nas tár-days sayn-yó-ra
Goodnight miss.	Buenas noches señorita.
	bwáy-nas nó-chays sayn-yo-rēē-ta
Hello. Good-bye.	¡Ola! Adiós.
	ó-la a-dhee-ós
Good-bye (in the meantime)	Hasta luego.
	á-sta loo-áy-go
Till we meet again.	Hasta la vista.
	á-sta la vēēs-ta
Yes. No.	Sí. No.
	see no
Please.	Por favor; haga el favor.
	por fa-vór; á-ga el fa-vór
Thank you.	Gracias.
	grá-thee-as
Thank you very much.	Muchas gracias.
	mōō-chas grá-thee-as
This is Mr. . . .	Le presento al Señor. . . .
	lay pray-sén-to al sen-yór . . .
Glad to meet you. How do you do.	Mucho gusto señor.
	mōō-cho gōōs-to sen-yór
How are you?	¿Cómo está usted?
	kó-mo es-tá oos-táydh
Very well—and you?	Muy bien—¿y usted?
	mwee bee-én ee oos-táydh
With pleasure.	Con mucho gusto.
	kon mōō-cho gōōs-to
I'm sorry. Excuse me.	Perdone.
	per-dó-nay
Pardon?	¿Perdone?
	per-dó-nay

I'm very sorry.	Lo siento mucho.
	lo see-én-to mōō-cho
May I?	¿ Con su permiso ?
	kon su per-mēē-so
Please sit down.	Siéntese por favor.
	see-én-tay-say por favór
You are very kind.	Usted es muy amable.
	oos-táydh es mwee a-má-blay
Don't mention it.	No hay de qué. De nada.
	no á-ee day kay. day ná-dha
May I help you?	¿ Puedo ayudarle ?
	poo-áy-dho a-yoo-dhár-lay
Did you want something?	¿ Deseaba usted algo ?
	day-say-á-ba oos-táydh ál-go
Help yourself.	Sírvase usted mismo.
	sēēr-va-say oos-táydh mēē-smo
Don't bother.	No se moleste.
	no say mo-lés-tay
I'm sorry to disturb you.	Siento molestarle.
	see-én-to mo-les-tár-lay
It's no trouble.	No es ninguna molestia.
	no es neen-gōō-na mo-lés-tee-a
Your good health!	¡Salud!
	sa-lōōdh
Congratulations!	¡Felicitaciones!
	fay-lee-thee-ta-thee-ó-nays
I am glad to see you.	Me alegro de verle.
	may a-láy-gro day vér-lay
I am much obliged to you.	Le estoy muy agradecido.
	lay es-tóy mwee a-gra-dhay-thēē-dho
Thank you for your hospitality.	Le agradecemos su hospitalidad.
	lay a-gra-dhay-tháy-mos su os-pee-tah-lee-dádh
We enjoyed ourselves very much.	Nos divertimos mucho.
	nos dee-ver-tēē-mos mōō-cho

As you please.   Como quiera usted.
                                    kó-mo kee-áy-ra oos-táydh

I'd like to.   Yo quisiera.
                                    yo kee-see-áy-ra

MISCELLANEOUS EXPRESSIONS

What is your name?   ¿Cómo se llama usted?
                                    kó-mo say lyá-ma oos-táydh

My name is ...   Me llamo ...
                                    may lyá-mo ...

I am British (American).   Soy inglés (inglesa) (norte-
                                            americano/a).
                  soy een-gláys (een-glá y-sa) (nor-tay-a-may-ree-ká-no/a)

Do you understand (speak)   ¿Entiende (habla) usted
  Spanish?   español?
                  en-tee-én-day (á-bla) oos-táydh es-pan-yól

I speak it a little.   Lo hablo un poco.
                                    lo á-blo oon pó-ko

Look out!   ¡Cuidado!
                                    kwee-dá-dho

I don't know.   No sé.
                                    no say

On the contrary.   Al contrario.
                                    al kon-trá-ree-o

That's right.   ¡Eso es!
                                    áy-so es

Listen. Look.   Escuche. Mire.
                                    es-kōō-chay. mē̄-ray

Very well.   Muy bien.
                                    mwee bee-én

That's all.   Es todo.
                                    es tó-dho

Whose turn is it?	¿ A quién toca ?
	a kee-én tó-ka
Go. Come.	Vaya. Venga.
	vá-ya. vén-ga
I must go.	Tengo que marcharme.
	tén-go kay mar-chár-may
It is getting late.	Se hace tarde.
	say á-thay tár-day
Are you ready?	¿ Está usted listo(a) ?
	es-tá oos-táydh lées-to(a)
As soon as possible.	Cuanto antes.
	kwán-to án-tays
At the latest.	A más tardar.
	a mas tar-dár
Don't forget.	No olvide.
	no ol-vēē-dhay
Don't be late.	No llegue tarde.
	no lyáy-gay tár-day
I'm glad.	Me alegro.
	may a-láy-gro
I believe so.	Creo que si.
	kráy-o kay see
I'm not surprised.	No me extraña.
	no may es-trán-ya
Isn't that so?	¿ No es verdad ?
	no es ver-dádh
Isn't it? Aren't you?	¿ Verdad ?
(cf. French *n'est-ce pas?*)	
	ver-dádh

I'm hungry (thirsty, sleepy, right, hot, cold, frightened).   Tengo hambre (sed, sueño, razón, calor, frío, miedo).
tén-go ám-bray (sed, swáyn-yo, ra-thón, ka-lór, frēē-o, mee-áy-dho)

Note: Other adjectives are used with *ser* or *estar*;   *see* GRAMMATICAL NOTES pp. 19-20.

| You are mistaken. | Se equivoca. |
| | say ay-kee-vó-ka |

| On the left. On the right. | A la izquierda. A la derecha. |
| | a la eeth-kee-áyr-da. a la day-ráy-cha |

| Straight on. | Todo derecho. |
| | tó-dho day-ráy-cho |

| Turn back. | Vuelva atrás. |
| | voo-áyl-va a-trás |

| Have you a light? | ¿Tiene usted lumbre? |
| | tee-áy-nay oos-táydh lōōm-bray |

| Let's go for a walk. | Vamos a dar un paseo. |
| | vá-mos a dar oon pa-sáy-o |

DIFFICULTIES

| I don't understand you. | No entiendo. |
| | no en-tee-én-do |

| I don't understand Spanish. | No entiendo el español. |
| | no en-tee-én-do el es-pan-yól |

| Do you understand English? | ¿Entiende usted el inglés? |
| | en-tee-én-day oos-táydh el een-gláys |

| Is there anyone who speaks (understands) English? | ¿Hay alguien que hable (entienda) inglés? |
| | á-ee ál-gee-en kay á-blay (en-tee-én-da) een-gláys |

| Please repeat it. | Repítalo por favor. |
| | ray-pḗē-ta-lo por fa-vór |

| Please speak more slowly. | Haga el favor de hablar más despacio. |
| | á-ga el fa-vór day a-blár mas days-pá-thee-o |

| Please write it down. | Escríbalo por favor. |
| | es-crḗē-ba-lo por fa-vór |

| What is the matter? | ¿Qué hay? |
| | kay á-ee |

What do you want?
¿ Qué quiere usted ?
kay kee-áy-ray oos-táydh

Wait, I am looking for the word (phrase) in this book.
Espere, busco la palabra (frase) en este libro.
es-páy-ray, bōōs-ko la pa-lá-bra (frá-say) en és-tay lēē-bro

Will you read this?
¿ Sírvase leer esto ?
sēēr-va-say lay-ér és-to

Where are you going?
¿ A dónde va usted ?
a dón-day va oos-táydh

Come quickly!
¡ Venga rápido !
vén-ga rá-pee-dho

My . . . has been stolen.
Me han robado . . .
may an ro-bá-dho . . .

That man is following me everywhere.
Ese hombre me sigue por todas partes.
áy-say óm-bray may sēē-gay por tó-dhas pár-tays

I shall call a policeman.
Llamaré un policía.
lya-ma-ráy oon po-lee-thēē-a

Fetch a policeman.
Mande buscar un guardia.
mán-day boos-kár oon gwár-dee-a

I shall stay here.
Me quedáre aquí.
may kay-dhá-ray a-kēē

Will you help me?
¿ Quiere usted ayudarme ?
kee-áy-ray oos-táydh a-yoo-dhár-may

Help!
¡ Socorro !
so-kó-ro

Fire!
¡ Hay fuego !
á-ee foo-áy-go

Thief!
¡ Ladrón !
la-drón

Who are you?
¿ Quién es usted ?
kee-én es oos-táydh

What are you doing here?
¿ Que hace usted aquí ?
kay á-thay oos-táydh a-kēē

I don't know you.
No le conozco.
no lay ko-nóth-ko

I don't wish to speak to you.	No quiero hablar con usted.
	no kee-áy-ro a-blár kon oos-táydh
Leave me alone!	¡Déjeme!
	dáy-hay-may
That will do!	¡Basta!
	bás-ta
I have forgotten the word.	He olvidado la palabra.
	ay ol-vee-dá-dho la pa-lá-bra
What does it mean?	¿ Qué quiere decir ?
	kay kee-áy-ray day-thēēr
What have I done?	¿ Qué he hecho ?
	kay ay áy-cho
I didn't know.	No sabía.
	no sa-bēē-a
Please explain to me.	Explíqueme por favor.
	es-plēē-kay-may por fa-vór
It wasn't me.	No fui yo.
	no fwee yo
It's not my fault.	No es culpa mía.
	no es kōōl-pa mēē-a
I'll give you nothing.	No le daré nada.
	no lay da-ráy ná-dha
Go away!	¡Márchese!
	már-chay-say
It has nothing to do with me.	No tiene nada que ver conmigo.
	no tee-áy-nay ná-dha kay ver kon-mēē-go
To whom does one apply?	¿A quién se dirige ?
	a kee-én say dee-rēē-hay
What must I do?	¿ Qué debo hacer ?
	kay dáy-bo a-thér
It is already paid for.	Ya está pagado.
	ya es-tá pa-gá-dho
I have paid enough.	He pagado bastante.
	ay pa-gá-dho bas-tán-tay
Let me pass.	Déjeme pasar.
	dáy-hay-may pa-sár

Listen to me a moment. Escúcheme un momento.
es-kōō-chay-may oon mom-én-to

Stop him! ¡Deténgale!
day-tén-ga-lay

Call the police (a doctor). Llame la policía (un médico).
lyá-may la po-lee-thēē-a (oon máy-dhee-ko)

I am a foreigner. Soy extranjero.
soy es-tran-háy-ro

I am a stranger. Soy forastero.
soy fo-ras-táy-ro

I am (not) in a hurry. (No) tengo prisa.
(no) tén-go prēē-sa

How long must I wait? ¿ Cuánto tengo que esperar ?
kwán-to tén-go kay es-pay-rár

I am busy. Estoy ocupado.
es-tóy o-koo-pá-dho

I insist on it. Insisto en ello.
een-sēēs-to en él-yo

I promise you. Se lo prometo.
say lo pro-máy-to

I will give you my address. Le daré mis señas.
lay da-ráy mees sáyn-yas

Open the door! ¡Abra la puerta!
á-bra la poo-áyr-ta

Wait one moment. Espere un momento.
es-páy-ray oon mo-mén-to

What is the Spanish for that? ¿ Cómo se dice eso en español ?
kó-mo say déé-thay áy-so en es-pan-yól

Why not? ¿ Por qué no ?
por kay no

Where is the lavatory? ¿ Dónde están los retretes ?
dón-day es-tán los ray-tráy-tays

Where is the nearest police station? ¿ Dónde está la comisaría más cercana ?
dón-day es-tá la ko-mee-sa-rēē-a mas ther-ká-na

Where is the British (American) consulate?
¿Dónde está el consulado británico (americano)?
dón-day es-tá el kon-soo-lá-dho bree-tá-nee-ko (a-may-ree-ká-no)

You do not understand.
Usted no entiende.
oos-táydh no en-tee-én-day

I am angry.
Estoy enfadado.
es-toy en-fa-dá-dho

I don't want it.
No lo quiero.
no lo kee-áy-ro

I've lost . . .
He perdido . . .
ay per-dēē-dho

Can you tell me . . ?
¿Puede usted decirme . . . ?
poo-áy-dhay oos-táydh day-thēēr-may . . .

Tell him to wait.
Dígale que espere.
dēē-ga-lay kay es-páy-ray

What do I owe you?
¿Qué le debo?
káy lay dáy-bo

POPULAR IDIOMS

It's terribly funny.
Me hace mucha gracia.
may á-thay mōō-cha grá-thee-a

You're pulling my leg.
Me toma el pelo.
may to-ma el páy-lo

Really?
¿De veras?
day váy-ras

Never in your life.
Ni hablar.
nee a-blár

I say!
¡Oiga!
óy-ga

Let's get to the point.
Vamos al caso.
vá-mos al ká-so

You're joking of course.
Naturalmente lo dice en broma.
na-too-ral-mén-tay lo dēē-thay en bró-ma

S.P.B.---B

No kidding.   Sin mentira.
seen men-tēē-ra

Likeable, nice (personality).   Simpático.
seem-pá-tee-ko

Agreed. O.K.   Convenido.
kon-vayn-ēē-dho

It is wonderful!   ¡Es estupendo!
es es-too-páyn-do

Encore!   ¡Otra vez!
ó-tra veth

How nice (of a person).   ¡Qué simpático!
kay seem-pá-tee-ko

How nice (of a thing).   ¡Qué bonito!
kay bo-nēē-to

Absolutely not!   ¡En absoluto!
en ab-so-lōō-to

Of course.   Desde luego.
dés-day loo-áy-go

Of course not.   Claro que no.
klá-ro kay no

It's not necessary.   No hace falta.
no á-thay fál-ta

Good luck!   ¡Mucha suerte!
mōō-cha soo-áyr-tay

What bad luck!   ¡Qué mala suerte!
kay má-la soo-áyr-tay

So much the better (worse).   Tanto mejor (peor).
tán-to may-hór (pay-ór)

Thank goodness!   ¡Menos mal!
máy-nos mal

What a nuisance!   ¡Qué fastidio!
kay fas-tēē-dhee-o

What a bore!   ¡Qué aburrido!
kay a-boo-rēē-dho

How awful!   ¡Qué barbaridad!
kay bar-ba-ree-dádh

How odd!	¡Qué raro!
	kay rá-ro
It doesn't matter.	No importa.
	no eem-pór-ta
What's on?	¿Qué echan?
	kay áy-chan
He is reliable.	Es muy formal.
	es mwee for-mál
He has the cheek of the devil.	Es una cara dura.
	es ōō-na ká-ra dōō-ra
My goodness!	¡Dios mío!
	dee-ós mēē-o
He is a rake.	Es un juerguista.
	es oon hoo-áyr-gēēs-ta
How stupid!	¡Qué disparate!
	kay dees-par-rá-tay
I couldn't care less.	No me da un bledo.
	no may da oon bláy-dho
Bless you! (*when someone has sneezed*)	¡Jesús!
	hay-sōōs
He is a tough.	Es un chulo.
	es oon chōō-lo
He is a pansy.	Es un maricón.
	es oon ma-ree-kón

PUBLIC NOTICES

Abierto = Open.
Aviso = Notice.
Caballeros = Gentlemen.
Caja = Cash Desk.
Carteles no = Stick no bills.
Cerrado = Closed.

Cuidado con la pintura=Wet Paint.
Empujad=Push.
Entrada=Way in.
Es peligroso asomarse=It is dangerous to lean out of the window
Es propiedad=Private.
Libre=Vacant.
Ocupado=Engaged.
Oficina=Office.
Salida=Way out.
Salida de urgencia=Emergency Exit.
Se alquila=To Let.
Señoras=Ladies.
Se prohibe . . .=It is forbidden to . . .
Se prohibe aparcar=No parking.
Se prohibe el cante=No singing.
Se prohibe escupir=No spitting.
Se prohibe fumar=No smoking.
Se prohibe la entrada=No entry.
Se prohibe pisar la hierba=Keep off the grass.
Se vende=For sale.
Tirad=Pull.

NATIONAL HOLIDAYS

National holidays.   Días festivos nacionales.
<small>dēē-as fes-tēē-vos na-thee-on-a-láys</small>

The list below may seem extensive, but many an unwary traveller has been dismayed to find banks and shops closed when he had most need of them. It includes political holidays established by the present régime which may not be permanent. On one's saint's day it is customary to treat one's friends. Children are often given presents at Epiphany (6th January, el día de Reyes) rather than Christmas.

New Year's Day.   El día del Año Nuevo.
<small>el dēē-a del án-yo nwáy-vo</small>

St. Joseph (19th March).	El San José.
	el san ho-sáy
Victory Day (1st April).	El día de la Victoria.
	el dēē-a day la veek-tó-ree-a
Holy Week.	Semana Santa.
	say-má-na sán-ta
Good Friday.	Viernes Santo.
	vee-ér-nays sánto
Easter.	Pascua.
	pás-kwa
Ascension Day (40 days after Easter).	La Ascensión.
	la as-then-sēē-on
Whitsun.	El Pentecostés.
	el pen-tay-kos-táys
Corpus Christi (Thurs. after Whitsun).	El Corpus.
	el kór-poos
Anniversary of Nationalist Rising (18th July).	El día del Alzamiento.
	el dēē-a del al-tha-mee-én-to
St. James (25th July).	El día de Santiago.
	el dēē-a day san-tee-á-go
Assumption (15th Aug.)	La Asunción.
	la a-soon-thee-ón
General Franco's birthday (1st Oct.)	El día del Caudillo.
	el dēē-a del cow-dhēēl-yo
The Virgin of the Pillar (12th Oct.)	El día de la Virgen del Pilar.
"America" Day	El día de la Hispanidad.
el dēē-a day la veér-hen del pee-lár.	day la ees-pa-nee-dádh
All Saints' Day (1st Nov.)	El día de Todos los Santos.
	el dēē-a day tó-dhos los sán-tos
The Immaculate Conception. Mother's Day.	(8th Dec.) } La Concepción.
	la kon-thep-thee-ón

Christmas Eve.	La Noche Buena.
	la nó-chay bwáy-na
Christmas.	La Navidad.
	la na-vee-dádh
A Merry Christmas.	Felices Pascuas.
	fay-lēē-thays pás-kwas
A Good New Year.	Feliz Año Nuevo.
	fay-lēēth án-yo nwáy-vo
My birthday.	Mi cumpleaños.
	mee koom-play-án-yos
My saint's day.	Mi santo.
	mee sán-to

TIME

VOCABULARY

afternoon, la tarde (tár-day)
evening (from about 6 p.m.), la noche (nó-chay)
hour, la hora (ó-ra)
midday, mediodía (may-dee-o-dēē-a)
midnight, medianoche (may-dee-a-nó-chay)
minute, el minuto (mee-nōō-to)
morning, la mañana (man-yá-na)
second, el segundo (say-gōōn-do)

CLOCK TIME

What time is it?	¿Qúe hora es?
	kay ó-ra es
It is one o'clock.	Es la una.
	es la ōō-na
It is two, three, etc., o'clock.	Son las dos, tres. . .
	son las dos, tres . . .
It is a quarter to two.	Son las dos menos cuarto.
	son las dos máy-nos kwár-to

It is half past two.	Son las dos y media.
	son las dos ee máy-dee-a
At 2 a.m.	A las dos de la mañana.
	a las dos day la man-yá-na
At 2 p.m.	A las dos de la tarde.
	a las dos day la tár-day
At twenty past six.	A las seis y veinte.
	a las sáy-ees ee váy-een-tay
At about six.	A eso de las seis.
	a áy-so day las sáy-ees
It is early (late).	Es temprano (tarde).
	es taym-prá-no (tár-day)
We are early (late).	Llegamos temprano (tarde).
	lyay-gá-mos taym-prá-no (tár-day)

DAYS OF THE WEEK

day, el día (dēē-a)
week, la semana (say-má-na)
fortnight, quince días (kēēn-thay dēē-as)
Sunday, el domingo (do-mēēn-go)
Monday, el lunes (lōō-nays)
Tuesday, el martes (már-tays)
Wednesday, el miércoles (mee-ér-ko-lays)
Thursday, el jueves (hoo-áy-vays)
Friday, el viernes (vee-ér-nays)
Saturday, el sábado (sá-ba-dho)

On Sunday.	El domingo.
	el do-mēēn-go
This morning (afternoon, evening).	Esta mañana (tarde, noche).
	és-ta man-yá-na, (tár-day, nó-chay)
In the morning.	Por la mañana.
	por la man-yá-na
Tomorrow.	Mañana.
	man-yá-na

Today.	Hoy.
	oy
Yesterday.	Ayer.
	a-yér
All day.	Todo el día.
	tó-dho el dēē-a
Every day.	Todos los días.
	tó-dhos los dēē-as
The day after tomorrow.	Pasado mañana.
	pa-sá-dho man-yá-na
Next day.	El día siguiente.
	el dēē-a see-gee-én-tay
The day before yesterday.	Anteayer.
	an-tay-a-yér
Last week.	La semana pasada.
	la say-má-na pa-sá-dha
Next week.	La semana próxima.
	la say-má-na próx-ee-ma
Last Monday.	El lunes pasado.
	el lōō-nays pa-sá-dho
A working day.	Un día de trabajo.
	oon dēē-a day tra-bá-ho
Holidays.	Días festivos.
	dēē-as fes-tēē-vos

MONTHS, SEASONS AND DATES

January, enero (ay-náy-ro)
February, febrero (fay-bráy-ro)
March, marzo (már-tho)
April, avril (av-rēēl)
May, mayo (má-yo)
June, junio (hōōn-yo)
July, julio (hōōl-yo)
August, agosto (a-gós-to)
September, septiembre (sep-tee-ém-bray)
October, octubre (ok-tōō-bray)
November, noviembre (no-vee-ém-bray)
December, diciembre (dee-thee-ém-bray)

spring, la primavera (pree-ma-váy-ra)
summer, el verano (vay-rá-no), el estío (es-tēē-o)
autumn, el otoño (o-tón-yo)
winter, el invierno (een-vee-ér-no)
year, el año (án-yo)
month, el mes (mes)
season (of year), la estación (es-ta-thee-ón)
season (football), la temporada (tem-po-rá-dha)
holidays, las vacaciones (va-ka-thee-ó-nays)

On 1st June.	El primero de junio.
	el pree-máy-ro day hōōn-yo
2nd June.	El dos de junio.
	el dos day hōōn-yo
3rd June, 1965.	El tres de junio de mil novecientos sesenta y cinco.
	el tres day hōōn-yo day meel no-vay-thee-én-tos say-sén-ta ee thēēn-ko
How long have you been here?	¿ Hace cúanto tiempo que está usted aquí ?
	á-thay kwán-to tee-ém-po kay es-tá oos-táydh a-kēē
I have been here a few days.	Hace unos pocos días que estoy aquí.
	á-thay ōō-nos pó-kos dēē-as kay es-tóy a-kēē
How long are you staying?	¿ Cuánto tiempo queda usted ?
	kwán-to tee-ém-po káy-dha oos-táydh
When are you leaving?	¿ Cuándo se marcha ?
	kwán-do say már-cha

CORRESPONDENCE

Four model letters are provided. The first is to a Tourist Information Bureau (to be found in many Spanish towns) requesting a list of hotels. The second is to a hotel asking for accommodation to be reserved. Many holiday makers, of course, do this through a travel agency. The third is such as one might send to friends one has made in Spain. The fourth is a short business letter. An International Reply Coupon may be bought for one shilling at any Branch Post Office.

VOCABULARY

address, las señas (sáyn-yas), la dirección (dee-rek-thee-ón)
boarding-house, la pensión (pen-see-ón)
c/o, c./de (cá-sa day)
from, desde (dés-day)
greetings, saludos (sa-lōō-dhos)
hotel, el hotel (o-tél)
inn, la posada (po-sá-dha)
management, la dirección (dee-rek-thee-ón)
manager (ess) el(la) gerente (hay-rén-tay)
Mr. (Mrs., Miss), González Sr. (Sra., Srta.) González (sen-yór,
     sen-yó-ra, sen-yo-rée-ta gon-thá-leth)
Mr. John (Mrs. Mary) González Sr. D. Juan (Sra. Da. María)
     González (don, dón-ya)
price, el precio (práy-thee-o)
proprietor (tress), el(la) dueño(a) (doo-áyn-yo(ya)
Smith & Co. Ltd., Compañía Smith, S.A.
State tourist hotel, el parador (pa-ra-dhór)
tax, el impuesto (eem-pwés-to)
tourist bureau, la oficina de turismo (o-fee-thēē-na day too-
     rēēs-mo)

EXAMPLES OF LETTERS

1   THE TOURIST BUREAU
     TARRAGONA
     Dear Sirs,
         Would you be so kind as to send me a list of good hotels which
are central (near the beach). I enclose an International Reply Coupon.
                                   Yours faithfully,

     LA OFICINA DE TURISMO
     TARRAGONA
     Muy señores míos,
         Les ruego hagan el favor de mandarme una lista de buenos
hoteles en Tarragona que estén céntricos (cerca de la playa). Va
incluso con la presente un cupón de respuesta internacional.
                                   Su seguro servidor,

2   THE MANAGEMENT
     THE PLAYA HOTEL
     17 ST. ANTONY STREET
     MÁLAGA
     Dear Sirs,
         I should like to reserve one (two) single (double) room(s)
(with bathroom) for 6 nights from the evening of Sunday 20th August

to the morning of Saturday 26th August, 1965. Please let me know your prices for full board (half board, accommodation only) and whether breakfast is included. I enclose an International Reply Coupon.

Yours faithfully,

LA DIRECCIÓN
HOTEL PLAYA
SAN ANTONIO 17
MÁLAGA
Muy señores míos,
    Desearía reservar una (dos) habitación (-iones) con una (dos) cama(s) por 6 noches desde el domingo, 20 de agosto hasta la mañana del sábado 26 de agosto de 1965. Hagan el favor de decirme el precio de la pensión completa (la media pensión, la habitación sola) y si está incluido el desayuno. Va incluso con la presente un cupón de respuesta internacional.

Su seguro servidor,

3 My dear friend(s),
    We have arrived home safely. Thank you very much for your hospitality during your stay. We shall have very pleasant memories of. . . . We hope you are all well. Give our greetings to the children. Till some other year.

Yours sincerely,

Muy estimado(s) amigo(s) mío(s),
    Hemos vuelto sanos y salvos a casa. Le(s) agradecemos much-ísimo su hospitalidad durante nuestra estancia. Conservaremos un muy grato recuerdo de. . . . Esperamos que estén todos bien. Salude(n) de nuestra parte a sus hijos. Hasta otro año.

Muy cordialmente, su amigo,

4 GARCÍA Cía. S. A.,
CATEDRAL 127,
MADRID.
Dear Sirs,
    With reference to our conversation of . . . (Refiriéndonos a nuestra conversación del . . .) We thank you for your letter (enquiry, order, offer) (Les agradecemos su carta (pregunta, pedido, ofreci-miento del . . .) We can offer you (Podemos ofrecerles). We are interested in (Nos interesa). We wish to buy (Deseamos comprar). What is the price of . . .? (¿ Qué es el precio de . . .?) Our price is . . . (El precio es de . . .) We hope this will suit you (Esperamos que esto les convenga). Always at your service (Siempre a sus órdenes).

Yours faithfully,
(Su atento y seguro servidor,) or S.A.S.S.

FOOD, DRINKS AND RESTAURANTS

Breakfast in Spain consists of coffee or chocolate, and a bun or fritters or toasted roll with butter. Lunch time varies from about 1 p.m. in the north to 3 p.m. in the south; dinner is from about 9 p.m. in the north to 11 p.m. in the south. Should these somewhat late hours prove trying to the Anglo-Saxon stomach any tavern will provide a variety of appetisers such as prawns, squid, anchovies, eggs, cheese, crisps, olives, peanuts and roasted thrushes to see you through. Olive oil is the basis of most Spanish cooking, but only when of inferior quality need it have the alarming results sometimes reported. Those of delicate constitution may specify *con mantequilla* (kon man-tay-kēēl-ya) if they wish their meals done in butter. Spanish cooking, if sometimes a little plainer than French, is in general excellent. Here are a few well-known typical dishes:

> *Bacalao a la vizcaína* (ba-ka-lá-o a la veeth-ka-ēē-na), cod steaks in rich tomato sauce.
>
> *Cocido madrileño* (ko-thēē-do ma-dree-láyn-yo), boiled meat, chick-peas and potatoes
>
> *Cochinillo* (ko-chee-nēēl-yo), roast sucking pig
>
> *Gazpacho andaluz* (gath-pá-cho an-da-lōōth), cold soup: which sounds off-putting but is very refreshing
>
> *Paella* (pa-él-ya), fried rice, saffron, chicken, shrimps
>
> *Pinchitos árabes* (peen-chēē-tos á-ra-bays), highly seasoned cubes of mutton grilled over a charcoal fire

Vegetables with the exception of French fries and lettuce are normally served as a separate course, but Spaniards are noticeably unenthusiastic about greens. On the other hand a plentiful supply of delicious fruit according to season is always provided as a dessert. Contrary to common belief water is a safe and common drink with meals in Spain; it is best in the north, in Madrid and Granada. Table wines are cheap and a good local one is usually to be had. Among the better-known wine-growing districts are Rioja and Valdepeñas (ree-ó-ha; val-day-páyn-yas). On rising from table it is polite to say "*Que aproveche*" (kay a-pro-váy-chay), "Enjoy your meal" to anyone nearby still eating. The appropriate reply is "*Gracias*" (grá-thee-as): "Thank you". Finally, if wishing to sit at a table already occupied, ask permission with "*Con su permiso*" (kon soo per-mēē-so).

Spain still retains some of the vast nineteenth century cafés with mirrors, marble and venerable waiters that are unknown in Britain or the U.S.A. Here you will be served black coffee: *café solo* (ka-fáy so-lo) unless you ask for white: *con leche* (kon láy-chay), and a glass of water. Should your shoes require cleaning a shoeblack: *limpiabotas* (leem-pee-a-bó-tas) attached to the café is at your service. You may buy a lottery ticket: those on behalf of the blind: *pro ciegos* (pro thee-áy-gos) are for modest sums and are drawn every day, while the more ambitious may buy a *décimo* (dáy-thee-mo), tenth part of a ticket in the hope of winning a bigger prize. Spanish waiters are quick to spot a client, but if you wish to attract the attention of one you may either hiss or clap your hands. In the old-fashioned taverns *bodegas* (bo-dháy-gas) with their tiled walls, oak beams, copper ornaments, wineskins and vats, one feels for once an atmosphere more akin to England than to France. Try a glass of draught sherry at sixpence! Spanish brandies are good and very reasonably priced, as are all drinks except in night-clubs. Beer is light but pleasant.

VOCABULARY

GENERAL

aperitif, el aperitivo (a-pay-ree-tēē-vo)
appetiser, la tapa (tá-pa)
ashtray, el cenicero (thay-nee-tháy-ro)
bar, el bar (bar), el mostrador (mos-tra-dhór)
barman, el mozo del mostrador (mó-tho del mos-tra-dhór)
beer-glass, la caña (kán-ya)
bill, la cuenta (kwén-ta)
blind man, el ciego (thee-áy-go)
bottle, la botella (bo-tél-ya)
bottle, half, la media botella (máy-dhee-a bo-tél-ya)
chair, la silla (sēēl-ya)
cigar, el puro (pōō-ro)
cigarette, el cigarillo (thee-ga-rēēl-yo), el pitillo (pee-tēēl-yo)
coffee-pot, la cafetera (ka-fay-táy-ra)
cork, el corcho (kór-cho)
cork-screw, el sacacorchos (sa-ka-kór-chos)
course, el plato (plá-to)
cruet, la vinagrera (vee-na-gráy-ra)
cup, la taza (tá-tha)
dessert, el postre (pós-tray)
fork, el tenedor (tay-nay-dhór)
glass, el vaso (vá-so)
grilled, a la plancha (a la plán-cha)
hat-stand, el perchero (per-cháy-ro)
hors d'oeuvre, los entremeses (en-tray-máy-says)
hungry, to be, tener hambre (te-nér ám-bray)
jug, el jarrito (ha-rēē-to)
knife, el cuchillo (koo-chēēl-yo)
matches, las cerillas (thay-rēēl-yas)
meal, la comida (ko-mēē-dha)
medium done, regular (ray-goo-lár)
menu, el menú (may-nōō), la lista de platos (lēēs-ta day plá-tos)
plate, el plato (plá-to)
portion, la ración (ra-thee-ón)
price, fixed, el precio fijo (pray-thēē-o fēē-ho)
restaurant, el restaurante (res-tow-rán-tay)
salad bowl, la ensaladera (en-sa-la-dháy-ra)
saucer, el platillo (pla-tēēl-yo)
self-service restaurant, el restaurante para servirse uno mismo (el res-tow-rán-tay pá-ra ser-vēēr-say ōō-no mēēs-mo)

serviette, la servilleta (ser-veel-yáy-ta)
shoeblack, el limpiabotas (leem-pee-a-bó-tas)
spoon, la cuchara (koo-chá-ra)
stew, el estofado (es-to-fá-dho), el cocido (ko-thēē-dho)
table-cloth, el mantel (man-tél)
tavern, la bodega (bo-dháy-ga)
tea-pot, la tetera (tay-táy-ra)
teaspoon, la cucharita (koo-cha-rēē-ta)
thirsty, to be, tener sed (te-nér sed)
tip, la propina (pro-pēē-na)
toothpick, el palillo (pa-lēēl-yo)
tray, la bandeja (ban-dáy-ha)
underdone, poco hecho (pó-ko áy-cho)
waiter, el camarero (ka-ma-ráy-ro)
waiter (head), el jefe de camareros (háy-fay day ka-ma-ráy-ros)
waiter(wine), el camarero de vinos (ka-ma-ráy-ro day vēē-nos)
waitress, la camarera (ka-ma-ráy-ra)
water-jug, la garrafa (ga-rá-fa)
well done, muy hecho (mwee áy-cho)
wine-glass, la copa (kó-pa)
wine-list, la lista de vinos (lēēs-ta day vēē-nos)

DRINKS

aerated water, la gaseosa (ga-say-ó-sa)
alcohol, el alcohol (al-ko-ól)
beer, la cerveza (ther-váy-tha)
brandy, el coñac (kon-yák)
burgundy, el vino de Borgoña (vēē-no day bor-gón-ya)
chocolate, el chocolate (cho-ko-lá-tay)
cider, la sidra (sēēd-ra)
claret, el clarete (kla-ráy-tay)
cocktail, el coctel (kok-tél)
coffee, black, el café solo (ka-fáy só-lo)
coffee, white, el café con leche (ka-fáy kon láy-chay)
drink, la bebida (bay-bēē-dha)
gin, la ginebra (hee-náy-bra)
ice, el hielo (ee-áy-lo)
lemonade, la limonada (lee-mo-ná-dha)
liqueurs, los licores (lee-kó-rays)
milk, la leche (láy-chay)
mineral water, el agua mineral (á-gwa mee-nay-rál)
orangeade, la naranjada (na-ran-há-dha)
port, el oporto (o-pór-to)
refreshment, el refresco (ray-frés-ko)
rum, el ron (ron)
rum and "coke", el cubalibre (koo-ba-lēē-bray)
sherry, el jerez (hay-réth)
   very dry, la manzanilla (man-than-ēēl-ya)
   dry, el jerez seco (hay-réth sáy-ko)
   medium, el amontillado (a-mon-teel-yá-dho)

brown, la solera (so-láy-ra)
siphon, el sifón (see-fón)
soda-water, el agua de seltz (ág-wa day seltz)
tea, el té (tay)
vendor, el vendedor (ven-day-dhór)
vermouth, el vermut (ver-mōōt)
water, el agua (á-gwa)
whisky, el whisky (wēēs-kay)
wine, el vino (vée-no)
   red, el vino tinto (tēēn-to)
   white, el vino blanco (blán-ko)

FOOD

anchovies, anchoas (an-chó-as)
apple, la manzana (man-thá-na)
apricot, el albaricoque (al-bar-ee-kó-kay)
artichoke, la alcachofa (al-ka-chó-fa)
asparagus, el espárrago (es-pár-ra-go)
bacon, el tocino (to-thēē-no)
banana, el plátano (plá-ta-no)
beans, French, judías (hoo-dhēē-as)
beef, la carne de vaca (kár-nay day vá-ka)
beef, roast, el rosbif (ros-bēēf)
biscuit, la galleta (gal-yáy-ta), el bizcocho (beeth-kó-cho)
brains, sesos (sáy-sos)
bread, el pan (pan)
broth, el caldo (kál-do)
butter, la mantequilla (man-tay-kēēl-ya)
cabbage, la col (kol)
cake, el pastelillo (pas-tel-ēēl-yo), la tórta (tór-ta)
carrot, la zanahoria (tha-na-ó-ree-a)
cauliflower, la coliflor (ko-lee-flór)
celery, el apio (á-pee-o)
cheese, el queso (káy-so)
chicken, el pollo (pól-yo)
chick-peas, garbanzos (gar-bán-thos)
chips, patata frita (pa-tá-ta frēē-ta)
chop, la chuleta (choo-láy-ta)
cream, la crema (kráy-ma), la nata (ná-ta)
custard, las natillas (na-tēēl-yas)
custard, cold, el flan (flan)
duck, el pato (pá-to)
egg:
   fried, un huevo al plato (oon wáy-vo al plá-to)
   boiled, un huevo pasado por agua (oon wáy-vo pa-sá-dho por
     á-gwa)
   hard-boiled, un huevo duro (oon wáy-vo dōō-ro)
   poached, un huevo escalfado (oon wáy-vo es-kal-fá-dho)

fish, el pescado (pes-ká-dho)
fritters, churros (chōō-ros)
fruit, la fruta (frōō-ta)
game, la caza (ká-tha)
garlic, el ajo (á-ho)
grapes, uvas (ōō-vas)
hake, la merluza (mer-lōō-tha)
ham, el jamón (ha-món)
herring, el arenque (a-rén-kay)
ice-cream, el helado (ay-lá-dho)
jam, la conserva (kon-sér-va), la mermelada (mer-may-lá-dha)
lamb, el cordero (kor-dáy-ro)
lemon, el limón (lee-món), el citrón (thee-trón)
lettuce, la lechuga (lay-chōō-ga)
lobster, la langosta (lan-gós-ta)
marmalade, la mermelada de naranja (mer-may-lá-dha day na-rán-ha)
mayonnaise, la mayonesa (ma-yo-náy-sa)
melon, el melón (may-lón)
mushrooms, setas (sáy-tas)
mussels, almejas (al-máy-has)
mustard, la mostaza (mos-tá-tha)
mutton, el carnero (kar-náy-ro)
oil, el aceite (a-tháy-ee-tay)
olives, aceitunas (a-thay-ee-tōō-nas), olivas (o-lēē-vas)
omelette: Spanish, tortilla española (tor-tēēl-ya es-pan-yó-la)
          plain, tortilla francesa (tor-tēēl-ya fran-tháy-sa)
orange, la naranja (na-rán-ha)
oysters, ostras (ós-tras)
parsley, el perejil (pay-ray-hēēl)
pastry, la pastelería (pas-tay-lay-rēē-a)
peach, el melocotón (mel-o-ko-tón)
pear, la pera (páy-ra)
peas, guisantes (gee-sán-tays)
pepper, la pimienta (pee-mee-én-ta)
pie, el pastel (pas-tél)
pimentos, pimientos (pee-mee-én-tos)
pineapple, el ananás (a-na-nás)
plums, ciruelas (thee-roo-áy-las)
pork, el cerdo (thér-do)
potato, la patata (pa-tá-ta), (la papa (pá-pa) in S. America)
  crisps, patata inglesa (pa-tá-ta een-gláy-sa)
  French fried, patata frita (pa-tá-ta frēē-ta)
poultry, la volatería (vo-la-tay-rēē-a), las aves (á-vays)
prawns, gambas (gám-bas)
radishes, rábanos (rá-ba-nos)
rice, el arroz (a-róth)
roll, el panecillo (pa-nay-thēēl-yo)
salad, la ensalada (en-sa-lá-dha)
salmon, el salmón (sal-món)

salt, la sal (sal)
sandwich, el bocadillo (bo-ka-dhēēl-yo)
sardines, sardinas (sar-dēē-nas)
    fried, boquerones (bo-kay-ró-nays)
sauce, la salsa (sál-sa)
sausage: spiced, el chorizo (cho-rēē-tho), salchichón (sal-chee-chón)
        small, la salchicha (sal-chēē-cha)
seafood, mariscos (ma-rēēs-kos)
shrimps, camarones (ka-ma-ró-nays)
snails, caracoles (ka-ra-kó-lays)
sole, el lenguado (len-gwá-dho)
soup, la sopa (só-pa)
soup, clear, el consomé (kon-so-máy)
spinach, la espinaca (es-pee-ná-ka)
squid, calamares (ka-la-má-rays)
steak, el filete (fee-láy-tay)
strawberries, fresas (fráy-sas)
sugar, el azúcar (a-thōō-kar)
tart, la tarta (tár-ta)
toast, el pan tostado (tos-tá-dho)
tomato, el tomate (to-má-tay)
trout, la trucha (trōō-cha)
vanilla, la vainilla (va-ee-nēēl-ya)
veal, la ternera (ter-náy-ra)
vegetable, la legumbre (lay-gōōm-bray), la hortaliza (or-ta-lēē-tha)
vegetable, green, la verdura (ver-dōō-ra)
vermicelli, fideos (fee-dháy-os)
whiting, el merlan (mer-lán)

Let's go for a drink.	Vamos a tomar algo. vá-mos a to-már ál-go
Let's sit down here.	Sentémonos aquí. sen-táy-mo-nos a-kēē
I am very thirsty.	Tengo mucha sed. tén-go mōō-cha sed
Be my guest.	Le convido. lay kon-vēē-dho
Two glasses of beer.	Dos cañas de cerveza. dos kán-yas day ther-váy-tha
Two glasses of brandy (sherry).	Dos copas de coñac (jerez). dos kó-pas day kon-yák (hay-réth)

Draught (bottled) beer.
Cerveza a la presión (embot-
ellada).
ther-váy-tha a la pray-see-ón (em-bo-tel-yá-dha)

Stout.
Cerveza negra.
ther-váy-tha náy-gra

Your health!
¡Salud!
sa-lõõdh

Waiter!
¡Camarero!
ka-ma-ráy-ro

Coming!
¡Ya voy!
ya voy

I'll buy one.
Le compro uno.
lay kóm-pro õõ-no

Clean my shoes, please.
Límpieme los zapatos, por
favor.
lẽẽm-pee-ay-may los tha-pá-tos por fa-vór

Two black (white) coffees.
Dos cafés solo (con leche).
dos ca-fáys só-lo (kon láy-chay)

Buttered toast.
Tostadas con mantequilla.
tos-tá-dhas kon man-tay-kẽẽl-ya

We are looking for a good (cheap) restaurant.
Buscamos un buen restaurante (un restaurante económico).
boos-ká-mos oon boo-én res-tow-rán-tay (oon res-tow-rán-tay ay-ko-nó-mee-ko)

Can you recommend one to us?
¿Puede usted recomendarnos uno?
poo-áy-dhay oos-táydh ray-ko-men-dár-nos õõ-no

At what time do you serve lunch (dinner)?
¿A qué hora sirven el almuerzo (la cena)?
a kay ó-ra sẽẽr-ven el al-moo-ér-tho (la tháy-na)

We wish to eat.
Deseamos comer.
day-say-á-mos ko-mér

Are you serving lunch (dinner) now?
¿Sirven ustedes el almuerzo (la cena) ahora?
sẽẽr-ven oos-táy-dhays el al-moo-ér-tho (la tháy-na) a-ó-ra

There are six of us.
Somos seis.
só-mos sáy-ees

We want to sit together.
Deseamos sentarnos juntos.
day-say-á-mos sen-tár-nos hōōn-tos

We would like to sit near the window.
Quisiéramos sentarnos junto a la ventana.
kee-see-áy-ra-mos sen-tár-nos hōōn-to a la vayn-tá-na

We do not want to sit here.
No queremos sentarnos aquí.
no kay-ráy-mos sen-tár-nos a-kēē

Where can I wash my hands?
¿Dónde puedo lavarme las manos?
dón-day poo-áy-dhay la-vár-may las mán-os

Over there. Downstairs.
Por allá. Abajo.
por al-yá. a-bá-ho

What is today's main dish?
¿Qué es el plato del día?
kay es el plá-to del dēē-a

Give me the menu, please.
Déme el menú, por favor.
dáy-may el may-nōō por fa-vór

We shall have a fixed-price meal.
Tomaremos una comida al precio fijo.
to-ma-ráy-mos ōō-na ko-mēē-dha al práy-thee-o fēē-ho

We shall order à la carte.
Pediremos a la carta.
pay-dhee-ráy-mos a la kár-ta

This . . . is dirty.
Este (esta) . . . está sucio(a).
és-tay (és-ta) . . . es-tá sōō-thee-o(a)

I haven't a . . .
No tengo . . .
no tén-go . . .

I do not feel like eating.
No tengo ganas de comer.
no tén-go gá-nas day ko-mér

I only want a snack.
Quiero solamente algo ligero.
kee-áy-ro so-la-mén-tay ál-go lee-háy-ro

Serve us quickly: we have to catch a train (go to the theatre).
Por favor sírvanos de prisa: tenemos que coger el tren (vamos al teatro).
por fa-vór sēēr-va-nos day prēē-sa: te-náy-mos kay ko-hér el tren (vá-mos al tay-á-tro)

We are (not) in a hurry.
(No) tenemos prisa.
no te-náy-mos prēē-sa

We want to eat right away.   Deseamos comer en seguida.
day-say-á-mos ko-mér en say-gēē-dha

What will you have to drink (as   ¿ Qúe tomará usted de bebida
hors d'oeuvre, for dessert)?   (de entremeses, de postre)?
kay to-ma-rá oos-táydh day bay-bēē-dha (day en-tray-máy-says, day pós-tray)

I shall start with . . .   Para empezar tomaré . . .
pá-ra em-pe-thár to-ma-ráy

And to follow, sir?   ¿ Y para seguir, señor?
ee pá-ra say-geer, sayn-yór

Then I shall have . . .   Luego tomaré . . .
loo-áy-go to-ma-ráy . . .

What do you have in the way   ¿ Qué hay de . . .?
of . . .?
kay á-ee day . . .

I don't like . . .   No me gusta . . .
no me gōōs-ta . . .

I want something very simple.   Deseo algo muy sencillo.
day-sáy-o ál-go mwee sen-thēēl-yo

I'm on a diet.   Estoy al regimén.
es-tóy al ray-hee-mén

I'm not allowed to eat . . .   Me está prohibido comer . . .
may es-tá pro-ee-bēē-dho ko-mér . . .

Bring me . . .   Tráigame . . .
trá-ee-ga-may . . .

I would like steak and chips   Deseo un filete con patata frita
(ham and eggs).   (jamón y huevos al plato).
day-sáy-o oon fee-láy-tay kon pa-tá-ta frēē-ta (ha-món ee wáy-vos al plá-to)

How do you want it done?   ¿ Cómo lo quiere usted?
kó-mo lo kee-áy-ray oos-táydh

Well done (medium, underdone).   Muy hecho (regular, poco
        hecho).
mwee áy-cho, (ray-goo-lár, pó-ko áy-cho)

A little more . . .   Un poco más . . .
oon pó-ko mas . . .

We are waiting to be served for the next course (for the bill, for the change).
Esperamos que nos sirvan el plato siguiente (la cuenta, el cambio).
es-pay-rá-mos kay nos sēēr-van el plá-to see-gēē-en-tay (la cwén-ta, el kám-bee-o)

I'd like a named (cheap, local) wine.
Quisiera un vino de marca (corriente, del país).
kee-see-áy-ra oon vēē-no day már-ka (ko-ree-én-tay, del pa-ēēs)

Show me the label.
Enséñeme la etiqueta.
en-sáyn-yay-may la ay-tee-káy-ta

What do you recommend?
¿ Qué recomienda usted?
kay ray-ko-mee-én-da oos-táydh

This wine is corked.
Este vino está agrio.
és-tay vēē-no es-tá ág-ree-o

It doesn't smell nice.
No huele bien.
no wáy-lay bee-én

It is not very fresh.
No está muy fresco.
no es-tá mwee fráys-ko

There is too much fat.
Tiene demasiado grasa.
tee-áy-nay dee-ma-see-á-dho grá-sa

Give me a lean piece.
Démelo más magro.
dáy-may-lo mas má-gro

Do we pay you or at the desk?
¿ Se lo pagamos o a la caja?
say lo pa-gá-mos o o la ká-ha

Is the service charge included?
¿ Está incluido el servicio?
es-tá een-kloo-ēē-dho el ser-vēē-thee-o

Isn't there a mistake?
¿ No hay error?
no á-ee ay-rór

Please check the bill again.
Sírvase volver a hacer la cuenta.
sēēr-va-say vol-vér a a-thér la kwén-ta

We didn't order . . .
No pedimos . . .
no pay-dhēē-mos ..

That is right now.
Ahora está bien.
a-ó-ra es-tá bee-én

While I was eating someone took my . . .	Mientras comía alguien tomó mi . . .

mee-én-tras ko-mēē-a ál-gee-en to-mó mee . . .

I've left my glasses (hat, coat).	He dejado mis lentes (mi sombrero, mi abrigo).

ay day-há-dho mees lén-tays (mi som-bráy-ro, mee a-brēē-go)

We enjoyed the meal.	Nos gustó la comida.

nos goos-tó la co-mēē-dha

MOTORING

While main trunk roads (*carreteras del Estado*; *carreteras de primer orden*) are well-maintained, this is achieved at the expense of secondary roads (*carreteras de segundo, de tercer orden*) which in some places are in a bad state and indicated as such on maps (*en mal estado*). Hair-pin bends must be expected when crossing the sierras. It is advisable to subscribe to the A.A. or R.A.C. as they provide expert advice and service to motorists intending to drive abroad, including ferry reservations, documents, repair vouchers, information on continental road signs and a manual providing detailed technical vocabulary. In any case the following documents are essential: Green Card from your Insurance Company; Temporary Exportation Certificate; International Driving Permit (for Spain, the Canaries and Balearics). Early booking is necessary for summer car ferries. There is now one operating between Southampton and Algeciras. There are no concessions in the form of petrol coupons in Spain. It is advisable to fit amber light bulbs for night driving. Police are empowered to impose fines on the spot for traffic offences. Petrol is normally sold in units of five litres (just over a gallon) and the price is about the same as in Britain at present.

ROAD SIGNS

Most of these are pictorial and used internationally, but here is an explanation of some of the worded signs:

¡Alto!=Halt!
Autoruta=Motorway

Calzada estrecha = Road narrows
Calzada irregular = Uneven surface
Calzada resbaladiza = Slippery surface
Ceda el paso = Give way
Cruce = Crossroads
Cuidado = Take care
Despacio = Slow
Desviación = Diversion
Dirección obligatoria = One-way traffic
Escuela = School
Estacionamiento = Parking
Glorieta = Roundabout
Obras = Road up
¡Pare! = Stop
Paso a nivel = Level crossing
Peligro = Danger
Prohibido adelantar = No overtaking
Prohibido el paso = No entry
Redondel = Roundabout
Salida de fábrica = Factory exit
Se prohibe estacionar = No parking

VOCABULARY

GENERAL

back, atrás (a-trás)
bend, la curva (kōōr-va)
breakdown, la avería (a-vay-rēē-a)
breakdown lorry, el coche-grúa (kó-chay-grōō-a)
bridge, el puente (pwáyn-tay)
can (petrol), el bidón (bee-dhón)
car, el coche (kó-chay), el automóvil (ow-to-mó-veel)
caravan, el coche-vivienda (kó-chay-vee-vee-én-da)
civil guard, el guardia civil (gwár-dee-a thee-vēēl)
dangerous, peligroso (pay-lee-gró-so)
drive, to, conducir (kon-dōō-theer)
driver, el conductor (kon-dook-tór)
fine, la multa (mōōl-ta)

frontier, la frontera (fron-táy-ra)
garage, el garaje (ga-rá-hay)
garage hand, el encargado (en-kar-gá-dho)
highway, la carretera (ka-ray-táy-ra)
insurance policy, la póliza de seguro (pó-lee-tha day say-gōō-ro)
left, la izquierda (eeth-kee-áyr-da)
licence, la licencia (lee-thén-thee-a)
lorry, el camión (ka-mee-ón)
mechanic, el mecánico (may-ká-nee-ko)
milestone, la piedra kilométrica (pee-áy-dra kee-lo-máy-tree-ka)
motor-cycle, la motocicleta (mo-to-thee-kláy-ta)
motorist, el motorista (mo-to-rēēs-ta), automovilista (ow-to-mo-veel-ēēs-ta)
narrow, estrecho (es-tráy-cho)
number (car), la matrícula (ma-trēē-koo-la)
oil, el aceite (a-tháy-ee-tay)
patrol, la patrulla (pa-trōōl-ya)
pedestrian, el peatón (pay-a-tón)
permit, el permiso (per-mēē-so)
petrol, la gasolina (ga-so-lēē-na)
policeman, el guardia (gwár-dee-a), el policía (po-lee-thēē-a)
police-station, la comisaría (ko-mee-sa-rēē-a)
pressure, la presión (pray-see-ón)
pump (air), la bomba de aire (bóm-ba day á-ee-ray)
pump (petrol), el surtidor (soor-tee-dhór)
reverse, marcha atrás (már-cha a-trás)
right, la derecha (day-ráy-cha)
river, el río (rēē-o)
road, el camino (ka-mēē-no), la ruta (rōō-ta)
scooter, el escúter (es-kōō-ter)
service station, la estación de servicio (es-ta-thee-ón day ser-vēē-thee-o)
signal, sign, la señal (sayn-yál)
signpost, el poste indicador (pós-tay een-dee-ka-dhór)
skid, to, patinar (pa-tee-nár)
spanner, la llave inglesa (lyá-vay een-gláy-sa)
spare parts, las piezas de recambio (pee-áy-thas day ray-kám-bee-o)
speed limit, el límite de velocidad (lēē-mee-tay day vay-lo-thee-dhádh)
straight on, adelante (a-day-lán-tay), todo seguido (tó-dho say-gēē-dho)
swerve, to, desviar (des-vee-ár)
telephone, the, el teléfono (tay-láy-fo-no)
touring saloon, el turismo (too-rēēs-mo)
tow, to, remolcar (ray-mol-kár)
traffic jam, la obstrucción del tráfico (ob-strook-thee-ón del trá-fee-ko)
traffic lights, las luces del tráfico (loó-thays del trá-fee-ko)
traffic policeman, el guardia de la circulación (gwár-dee-a day la theer-koo-la-thee-ón)

trailer, el remolque (ray-mól-kay)
two-stroke mixture, la mezcla de dos tiempos (máyth-kla day dos tee-ém-pos)
vehicle, el vehículo (vay-ēē-koo-lo)
well-surfaced, en buen estado (en boo-én es-tá-dho)
wide, ancho (án-cho)

CAR

accelerator, el acelerador (a-thay-lay-ra-dhór)
battery, la batería (ba-tay-rēē-a)
body, la carrocería (kar-ro-thay-rēē-a)
bonnet, el capó (ka-pó)
boot, el maletón del equipaje (ma-lay-tón del ay-kee-pá-hay)
brake, el freno (fráy-no)
brake (hand), el freno de mano (fráy-no day má-no)
brake-lining, el forro (fór-ro)
bulb, la bombilla (bom-bēēl-ya)
bumper, el parachoques (pa-ra-chó-kays)
choke, el obturador (ob-too-ra-dhór)
clutch, el embrague (em-brá-gay)
door, la puerta (poo-áyr-ta)
exhaust, el escape (es-ká-pay)
gear box, la caja de velocidades (ká-ha day vay-lo-thee-dhá-dhays)
gear lever, la palanca de cambio (pa-lán-ka day kám-bee-o)
handle, la manivela (ma-nee-váy-la)
horn, la bocina (bo-thēē-na)
indicator, el indicador (een-dee-ka-dhór)
inner tube, la cámara de aire (ká-ma-ra day á-ee-ray)
jack, el gato (gá-to)
key, la llave (lyá-vay)
lights (head), los faros (fá-ros)
lights (side), las luces de posición (lōō-thays day po-see-thee-ón)
lights (tail), las luces de posición traseras (tra-sáy-ras)
mirror (rear-view), el espejo (retrovisor) (es-páy-ho /ray-tro-vee-sór)
nationality plate, el indicativo de nacionalidad (een-dee-ka-tēē-vo day na-thee-o-na-lee-dádh)
nut, la tuerca (too-áyr-ka)
radiator, el radiador (ra-dhee-a-dhór)
rear-window, la ventana de atrás (vayn-tá-na day a-trás)
rim, la llanta (lyán-ta)
screw, el tornillo (tor-nēēl-yo)
shock-absorber, el amortiguador (a-mor-tee-gwa-dhór)
spare wheel, la rueda de recambio (roo-áy-dha day ray-kám-bee-o)
speedometer, el cuenta-kilómetros (kwén-ta-kee-ló-may-tros)
spring, la ballesta (bal-yáys-ta)
steering, la dirección (dee-rek-thee-ón)
steering wheel, el volante (vo-lán-tay)
tank, el depósito de gasolina (day-pó-see-to day ga-so-lēē-na)

tubeless, sin cámara (seen ká-ma-ra)
tyre, el neumático (nay-oo-má-tee-ko)
washer, la arandela (a-ran-dáy-la)
wheel, la rueda (roo-áy-dha)
windscreen, el parabrisas (pa-ra-brēē-sas)
windscreen wiper, el limpia parabrisas (lēēm-pee-a pa-ra-brēē-sas)
wing, la aleta (a-láy-ta)

ENGINE

big end, la cabeza de biela (ka-báy-tha day bee-áy-la)
camshaft, el árbol de levas (ár-bol day láy-vas)
carburettor, el carburador (kar-boo-ra-dhór)
crank-case, el cárter del cigüeñal (kár-ter del thee-gwayn-yál)
crank-shaft, el árbol cigüeñal (ár-bol thee-gwayn-yál)
cylinder, el cilindro (thee-lēēn-dro)
dipstick, el indicador de nivel de aceite (een-dee-ka-dhór day nee-vél day a-tháy-ee-tay)
distributor, el distribuidor (dees-tree-bwee-dhór)
dynamo, el dínamo (dēē-na-mo)
engine, el motor (mo-tór)
fan, el ventilador (ven-tee-la-dhór)
fan-belt, la correa del ventilador (ko-ráy-a del ven-tee-la-dhór)
ignition, el encendido (en-then-dēē-dho)
piston, el pistón (pees-tón)
piston rings, los segmentos (seg-mén-tos)
plug, la bujía (boo-hēē-a)
starter, el motor de arranque (mo-tór day a-rán-kay)
valve, la válvula (vál-voo-la)

Is this the road to . . . ? ¿ Es éste el camino de . . . ?
es és-tay el ka-mēē-no day . . .

How far is it to . . . ? ¿ A cuánto de aquí está . . . ?
a kwán-to day a-kēē es-tá . . .

Which is the best road to . . . ? ¿ Cuál es el mejor camino para . . . ?
kwal es el may-hór ka-mēē-no pá-ra . . .

Is it near (far)? ¿ Está cerca (lejos)?
es-tá tháyr-ka (láy-hos)

How long does it take to go to . . . ? ¿ Cuánto se tarda en ir a . . . ?
kwán-to say tár-da en eer a . . .

It is that way.	Está por allá.
	es-tá por al-yá
Go straight on.	Siga adelante. Todo seguido.
	sēē-ga a-dhay-lán-tay. tó-dho say-gēē-dho
Turn left.	Tome por la izquierda.
	tó-may por la eeth-kee-áyr-da
Turn right.	Tome por la derecha.
	tó-may por la day-ráy-cha
Go back.	Vuelva atrás.
	voo-áyl-va a-trás
Slow down.	Ande más despacio.
	án-day mas days-pá-thee-o
Stop!	¡Párese!
	pá-ray-say
Reverse!	¡Póngase en marcha atrás!
	pón-ga-say en már-cha a-trás
What is the name of this place?	¿Cómo se llama este lugar?
	kó-mo say lyá-ma és-tay loo-gár
Where is the nearest garage (telephone, restaurant, hotel)?	¿Dónde está el garaje (teléfono, restaurante, hotel) más próximo?
	dón-day es-tá el ga-rá-hay (tay-láy-fo-no, res-tow-rán-tay, o-tél) mas próx-ee-mo
You (he, she) is (are) a bad driver.	Conduce muy mal.
	kon-dōō-thay mwee mal
You were driving carelessly.	Conducía sin cuidado.
	kon-doo-thēē-a seen kwee-dhá-dho
You were going too fast.	Iba demasiado de prisa.
	ēē-ba day-ma-see-á-dho day prēē-sa
Idiot!	¡Idiota!
	ee-dhee-ó-ta
What is your name?	¿Cómo se llama usted?
	kó-mo say lyá-ma oos-táydh
	or
	¿Cuál es su nombre?
	kwál es soo nóm-bray

What is your address? ¿ Qué son sus señas?
kay son soos sáyn-yas

I didn't see . . . No vi . . .
no vee . . .

I didn't know. No sabía.
no sa-bēē-a

I forgot to keep to the right. Olvidé llevar la derecha.
ol-vee-dáy lyay-vár la day-ráy-cha

I need some petrol (air, water, oil). Necesito gasolina (aire, agua, aceite).
nay-thay-sēē-to ga-so-lēē-na (á-ee-ray, á-gwa, á-tháy-ee-tay)

Fill the tank. Sírvase llenar el depósito.
sēēr-va-say lyay-nár el day-pó-see-to

Give me twenty litres, please. Póngame veinte litros, por favor.
pón-ga-may váy-een-tay lēēt-ros por favór

Check the oil (battery, water). Compruebe el aceite (la batería, el agua).
kom-proo-áy-bay el a-tháy-ēē-tay (la ba-tay-rēē-a, el á-gwa)

Check the tyres at 24 lb. per sq. in. Compruebe los neumáticos a uno punto sesenta y nueve (kilogramos al centímetro cuadrado).
kom-proo-áy-bay los nay-oo-má-tee-kos a ōō-no pōōn-to say-sén-ta ee noo-áy-vay
(kee-lo-grá-mos al then-tēē-may-tro kwa-drá-do)
See CONVERSION TABLES pp. 143-7

Wash the windscreen (car). Lave el parabrisas (el coche).
lá-vay el pa-ra-brēē-sas (el kó-chay)

How much is it to garage here for the night? ¿ Cuánto cobra usted si dejo el coche aquí por la noche?
kwán-to kó-bra oos-táydh see dáy-ho el kó-chay a-kēē por la nó-chay

My car is on the road two kilometres from here. Mi coche está en la ruta a dos kilómetros de aquí.
mee kó-chay es-tá en la rōō-ta a dos kee-ló-may-tros day a-kēē

My car has broken down.   Mi coche está con averías.

mee kó-chay es-tá con a-vay-rēē-as

My car will not start.   Mi coche no arranca.

mee kó-chay no ar-rán-ka

I have had a puncture.   He tenido un pinchazo.

ay tay-nēē-dho oon peen-chá-tho

The battery is run down.   La batería no funciona.

la ba-tay-rēē-a no foon-thee-ó-na

There is something wrong.   Hay algo que no anda.

á-ee ál-go kay no án-da

Can you send someone?   ¿Puede usted mandar a alguien?

poo-áy-dhay oos-táydh man-dár a ál-gee-en

Can you tow it?   ¿Puede usted remolcarlo?

poo-áy-dhay oos-táydh ray-mol-kár-lo

Does the carburettor need cleaning?   ¿Hay que limpiar el carburador?

á-ee kay leem-pee-ár el kar-boo-ra-dhór

What is wrong?   ¿Qué pasa?

kay pá-sa

... is broken (loose).   ... está roto (flojo).

... es-tá ró-to (fló-ho)

The brakes need adjusting.   Hay que ajustar los frenos.

á-ee kay a-hoos-tár los fráy-nos

There is a leak.   Hay un escape.

á-ee oon es-ká-pay

This must be replaced (straightened, repaired).   Hay que reemplazar (enderezar, arreglar) esto.

á-ee kay ray-em-pla-thár (en-dhay-ray-thár, ar-ray-glár) és-to

How long will it take?   ¿Cuánto tiempo necesitará?

kwán-to tee-ém-po nay-thay-see-ta-rá

Can't you do it at once?   ¿No puede usted hacerlo en seguida?

no poo-áy-dhay oos-táydh a-thér-lo en say-gēē-dha

How much will the repair cost?   ¿Cuánto costará arreglarlo?

kwán-to kos-ta-rá ar-ray-glár-lo

When can I collect it?   ¿ Cuándo puedo recogerlo ?
kwán-do poo-áy-dho ray-ko-hér-lo

Can you lend me . . . ?   ¿ Puede usted prestarme . . . ?
poo-áy-dhay oos-táydh pres-tár-may . . .

I want to hire a car.   Deseo alquilar un coche.
day-sáy-o al-kee-lár oon kó-chay

How much is it per hour (per day)?   ¿ Cuánto es por hora (al día)?
kwán-to es por ó-ra (al dēē-a)

TRAVEL

CUSTOMS AND PORTERS

Travellers to Spain should ascertain (from a consulate, passport office or a travel agency) whether a certificate of vaccination against smallpox will be required; if so they should obtain a form from their local health authority to take to their doctor. As a concession small amounts of alcohol and tobacco may be brought in if for personal use, carried in one's hand luggage and declared. It is as well to check on this with, for instance, the duty-free shops at airports. One must be present when the Customs check one's luggage and have keys ready. If a porter is employed, note his number to be sure of identifying him. Personal trolleys may be available at airports. One should make a list of all purchases whether liable to duty or not and declare them when returning to Britain. Here again small concessions are made subject to the same conditions as above. Keep a receipt of purchase of any fairly expensive article.

VOCABULARY

alcohol, el alcohol (al-ko-ól)
bag, el saco (sá-ko)
bank-note, el billete de banco (beel-yáy-tay day bán-ko)
bottle, la botella (bo-táyl-ya)
box, la caja (ká-ha)
camera, la máquina fotográfica (má-kee-na fo-to-grá-fee-ka)
cigar, el puro (pōō-ro)
cigarette, el cigarillo (thee-ga-rēēl-yo)
Customs, la Aduana (ad-wá-na)
customs officer, el aduanero (ad-wa-náy-ro)

key, la llave (lyá-vay)
label, la etiqueta (ay-tee-káy-ta)
luggage, el equipaje (ay-kee-pá-hay)
money, el dinero (dee-náy-ro)
number, el número (nōō-may-ro)
porter, el mozo (mó-tho)
passport, el pasaporte (pa-sa-pór-tay)
present, el regalo (ray-gá-lo)
suitcase, la maleta (ma-láy-ta)
tobacco, el tabaco (ta-bá-ko)
train, el tren (tren)
traveller's cheque, el cheque de viajero (cháy-kay day vee-a-háy-ro)
trunk, el baúl (ba-ōōl)

Carry this please.　　　　　Lléveme esto por favor.
lyáy-vay-may és-to por ta-vór

What is your number?　　　　¿ Qué número tiene?
kay nōō-may-ro tee-áy-nay

That is all.　　　　　　　Es todo.
es tó-dho

I shall take this myself.　　Tomaré esto yo mismo.
to-ma-ráy és-to yo mís-mo

I'll keep my hand luggage.　Voy a guardar mi equipaje de
　　　　　　　　　　　　　　mano.
voy a gwar-dár mee ay-kee-pá-hay day má-no

Careful with that!　　　　¡Cuidado con eso!
kwee-dá-dho con áy-so

There's another bag there.　Hay otro saco allí.
á-ee ó-tro sá-ko al-yēē

Don't leave this!　　　　　¡No deje esto!
No dáy-hay és-to

Don't forget that!　　　　¡No olvide eso!
no ol-vēē-dhay áy-so

I can't find my porter.　　No encuentro a mi mozo.
no en-kwén-tro a mee mó-tho

Have you seen porter number ten?　　¿Ha visto usted al mozo número diez?
a vēēs-to oos-táydh al mó-tho nōō-may-ro dee-éth

What do I owe you for three items?

¿Qué le debo por los tres bultos?

kay lay dáy-bo por los tres bōōl-tos

Have you anything to declare?

¿Tiene usted algo que declarar?

tee-áy-nay oos-táydh ál-go kay day-kla-rár

Only some presents.

Solamente algunos regalos.

so-la-mén-tay al-gōō-nos ray-gá-los

I only have this.

No tengo más que esto.

no tén-go mas kay és-to

No alcohol (tobacco).

Ningún alcohol (tabaco).

neen-gōōn al-ko-ól (ta-bá-ko)

Some alcohol (tobacco).

Algún alcohol (tabaco)

al-gōōn al-ko-ól (ta-bá-ko)

It's for my personal use.

Es para mi uso personal.

es pá-ra mee oó-so per-so-nál

I've nothing to declare.

No tengo nada que declarar.

no tén-go ná-da kay day-kla-rár

Anything else?

¿Otra cosa?

ó-tra kó-sa

It's already marked.

Ya está señalado.

ya es-tá sayn-ya-lá-dho

Open it please!

¡Abralo por favor!

á-bra-lo por fa-vór

You must pay duty.

Usted debe pagar los derechos.

oos-táydh dáy-bay pa-gár los day-ráy-chos

This way please.

Por aquí, haga el favor.

por a-kēē, á-ga el fa-vór

Where is the way out?

¿Dónde está la salida?

dón-day es-tá la sa-lēē-dha

It's been used.

Es usado.

es oo-sá-dho

Have you any Spanish (English) money?

¿Tiene usted dinero español (inglés)?

tee-áy-nay oos-táydh dee-náy-ro es-pan-yól (een-gláys)

I have some notes (traveller's cheques).	Tengo algunos billetes (cheques de viajero).

tén-go al-gōō-nos beel-yáy-tays (chay-káys day vee-a-háy-ro)

Please move on.	Pase usted por favor.

pá-say oos-táydh por fa-vór

TRAINS

Spanish Railways (*la Red Nacional de Ferrocarriles Españoles* or R.N.F.E. for short, pronounced rén-fay) have to contend with mountainous terrain often using ageing rolling stock. This sometimes results in slow travel especially in the case of the *correo* (mail-train) and *ómnibus* (stopping-train). On the other hand the T.A.L.G.O., a fast first-class express on which a supplement is payable, runs on main lines. On ordinary express trains *rápido* or *expreso*, 3rd class is uncomfortable but rich in local colour, 2nd class is quite comfortable and 1st not appreciably more so. Restaurant-cars provide excellent meals at prices which compare well with other European railways. It is customary to take a basket of food for one's journey. This can be supplemented from station buffets and vendors. A variety of food is quite likely to be pressed on the traveller who has not started on his own supply. If such generosity becomes overwhelming a polite refusal would be *Gracias, que aproveche* (grá-thee-as kay ap-ro-váy-chay), No thanks, but may you enjoy it.

Trains are usually full, so one should book a seat in advance. In large towns there is often a central R.N.F.E. office where this may be done. In smaller towns it is advisable, about 1½ hours before the time of departure, to get a porter to buy your ticket and secure your seat. This method is perfectly reliable and will save a tedious wait with uncertain prospects as the ticket office sells tickets for only an hour before departure time. Allow a tip of 10% of the fare. Rail travel in Spain is an excellent way of getting to know the people as they are very ready to take a polite interest in their fellow passengers.

VOCABULARY

arrival, la llegada (lyay-gá-dha)
back to engine, de espalda a la máquina (day es-pál-da a la má-kee-na)
berth, la cama (ká-ma), la litera (lee-táy-ra)
blanket, la manta (mán-ta)
blind, la persiana (payr-see-á-na)
booking-office, el despacho de billetes (days-pá-cho day beel-yáy-tays)
bookstall, el puesto de periódicos (pwáys-to day pay-ree-ó-dhee-kos)
buffet bar, la cantina (kan-tēē-na)
carriage, el coche (kó-chay), el vagón (va-gón)
compartment, el departamento (day-par-ta-mén-to)

S.P.B.---C

communication cord, el timbre de alarma (tēēm-bray day a-lár-ma)
connection, el empalme (em-pál-may)
corner, el rincón (reen-kón)
corridor, el pasillo (pa-sēēl-yo)
delay, el retraso (ray-trá-so)
departure, la salida (sa-lēē-dha)
dining-car, el coche-restaurante (kó-chay-res-tow-rán-tay)
dinner, la cena (tháy-na)
door, la portezuela (por-tay-thoo-áy-la)
draught, la corriente de aire (ko-ree-én-tay day á-ee-ray)
engine, la máquina (má-kee-na), la locomotora (lo-ko-mo-tó-ra)
enquiry office, la oficina de informaciones (o-fee-thēē-na day een-for-ma-thee-ó-nays)
entrance, la entrada (ayn-trá-dha)
exit, la salida (sa-lēē-dha)
facing the engine, de cara a la máquina (day ká-ra a la má-kee-na)
fare, el precio del viaje (práy-thee-o del vee-á-hay)
first class, de primera clase (day pree-máy-ra klá-say)
gentlemen, caballeros (ka-bal-yáy-ros)
guard, el jefe de tren (háy-fay day tren)
guard's van, el furgón de equipajes (foor-gón dey ay-kee-pá-hays)
journey, el viaje (vee-á-hay), el trayecto (tra-yáyk-to)
ladies, señoras (sayn-yó-ras)
lavatory, el retrete (ray-tráy-tay)
left-luggage, la consigna (kon-sēēn-ya)
luggage, el equipaje (ay-kee-pá-hay)
luggage-ticket, el talón (ta-lón)
lunch, el almuerzo (al-moo-ér-tho)
newspaper, el periódico (pay-ree-ó-dhee-ko)
number, el numero (nōō-may-ro)
occupied, ocupado (o-koo-pá-dho)
passenger, el viajero (vee-a-háy-ro)
pillow, la almohada (al-mo-á-dha)
place, el sitio (sēē-tee-o)
platform, el andén (an-dén)
porter, el mozo (mó-tho)
rack, la red (raydh)
railway, el ferrocarril (fay-ro-ka-rēēl)
seat, el asiento (a-see-én-to)
second class, de segunda clase (day say-gōōn-da klá-say)
sleeping-car, el coche-camas (kó-chay-ká-mas)
smokers, fumadores (foo-ma-dhó-rays)
station, la estación (es-ta-thee-ón)
station-master, el jefe de estación (háy-fay day es-ta-thee-ón)
subway, el corredor subterráneo (ko-ray-dhór soob-tay-rá-nay-o)
suitcase, la maleta (ma-láy-ta)
supplement, el suplemento (soo-play-mén-to)
third class, de tercera clase (day ter-tháy-ra klá-say)
ticket, el billete (beel-yáy-tay)
ticket inspector, el revisor (ray-vee-sór)

ticket (return), el billete de ida y vuelta (day ēē-dha ee voo-áyl-ta)
time-table, el horario (o-rá-ree-o)
vacant, libre (lēē-bray)
valid, válido (vá-lee-dho)
waiting-room, la sala de espera (sá-la day es-páy-ra)
window (of carriage), la ventanilla (vayn-ta-nēēl-ya)
window (of booking office), la taquilla (ta-kēēl-ya)

What is the fare to . . . ?	¿ Qué es el precio del viaje a . . ?
	kay es el práy-thee-o del vee-á-hay a . . .

I should like to reserve a first (second) class seat.
Quisiera reservar un asiento de primera (segunda) clase.
kee-see-áy-ra ray-ser-vár oon a-see-én-to day pree-máy-ra (say-gōōn-da) klá-say

I have two seats reserved.
Tengo reservados dos asientos.
tén-go ray-ser-vá-dhos dos a-see-én-tos

Find me a corner seat by the window.
Búsqueme un asiento de rincón junto a la ventanilla.
bōōs-kay-may oon a-see-én-to day reen-kón hōōn-to a la ven-ta-nēēl-ya

Are there any vacant berths in the sleeping-car?
¿ Hay plazas en el coche-camas?
á-ee plá-thas en el kó-chay-ká-mas

Is there a dining-car on this train?
¿ Hay un coche-restaurante en este tren?
á-ee oon kó-chay-res-tow-rán-tay en és-tay tren

I have reserved a sleeper.
He reservado una litera.
ay ray-ser-vá-dho ōō-na lee-táy-ra

Is it free?
¿ Está libre?
es-tá lēē-bray

It is occupied (reserved).
Está ocupado (reservado).
es-tá o-koo-pá-dho (ray-ser-vá-dho)

I believe it is my seat.
Creo que es mi asiento.
kráy-o kay es mee a-see-én-to

Where is the guard (ticket inspector)?
¿ Dónde está el jefe de tren (el revisor)?
dón-day es-tá el háy-fay day tren (el ray-vēē-sor)

Find me another seat!
¡Búsqueme otro asiento!
bōōs-kay-may ó-tro a-see-én-to

Nearer the dining-car.   Más cerca del coche-restaurante.
                            mas thér-ka del kó-chay-res-tow-rán-tay

I shall pay the excess.   Pagaré el suplemento.
                            pa-ga-ráy el soo-play-mén-to

When does the train leave ¿A qué hora sale el tren
for . . . ?   para . . . ?
                            a kay ó-ra sá-lay el tren pá-ra . . .

When does it arrive at . . . ?   ¿Cuándo llega a . . . ?
                            kwán-do lyáy-ga a . . .

Is there a through train to . . . ?   ¿Hay un tren directo a . . . ?
                            á-ee oon tren dee-rék-to a . . .

Must I change for . . . ?   ¿Debo cambiar para . . . ?
                            dáy-bo kam-bee-ár pá-ra . . .

Where must I get off for . . . ?   ¿Dónde debo bajar para . . . ?
                            dón-day dáy-bo ba-hár pá-ra

Where can I buy a platform ¿Dónde puedo comprar un
ticket?   billete de andén?
                            dón-day pwáy-dho kom-prár oon beel-yáy-tay day an-dén

Is there a reduced fare for ¿Hay una tarifa reducida para
children?   los niños?
                            á-ee oó-na ta-rēē-fa ray-doo-theé-dha pá-ra los nēēn-yos

It is not valid.   No vale.
                            no vá-lay

I want to register this for . . .   Deseo facturar esto para . . .
                            day-sáy-o fak-too-rár áys-to pá-ra . . .

Please give me a receipt.   Por favor déme un recibo.
                            por fa-vór dáy-may oon ray-thēē-bo

Is this the right train for . . . ?   ¿Es en efecto el tren para . . . ?
                            es en ay-fék-to el tren pá-ra . . .

May I put my case here?   ¿Permite usted que ponga mi
                                            maleta aquí?
                            per-mēē-tay oos-táydh kay pón-ga mee ma-láy-ta a-kēē

All aboard!   ¡Señores viajeros, al tren!
                            sayn-yó-rays vee-a-háy-ros, al tren

May I open (close) the window?   ¿ Permite usted que abra (cierre) la ventanilla?

per-mĕĕ-tay oos-táydh kay áb-ra (thee-áy-ray) la vayn-ta-nĕĕl-ya

Where is the toilet?   ¿ Dónde está el retrete?

dón-day es-tá el ray-tráy-tay

I have left my ticket in the compartment.   He dejado mi billete en el departamento.

ay day-há-dho mee beel-yáy-tay en el day-par-ta-mén-to

When do we get to . . . ?   Cuándo llegamos a . . . ?

kwán-do lyay-gá-mos a . . .

At what time is the first (second) service?   ¿ A qué hora es el primer (segundo) servicio?

a kay ó-ra es el pree-mér (say-gōōn-do) ser-vĕĕ-thee-o

At the front (back) of the train.   A la cabeza del (a la cola del) tren.

a la ka-báy-tha del (a la kó-la del) tren

How much late are we running?   ¿ Cuánto de retraso llevamos?

kwán-to day ray-trá-so lyay-vá-mos

We are running ten minutes late.   Llevamos diez minutos de retraso.

lyay-vá-mos dee-éth mee-nōō-tos day ray-trá-so

We will arrive on time.   Llegaremos a la hora.

lyay-ga-ráy-mos a la ó-ra

How long does the train stop here?   ¿ Cuánto para el tren aquí?

kwán-to pá-ra el tren a-kĕĕ

Do we pass through . . . ?   ¿ Pasamos por . . . ?

pa-sá-mos por . . .

Do you smoke?   ¿ Fuma usted?

fōō-ma oos-táydh

Would you like to read my paper?   ¿ Desea usted leer mi periódico?

day-sáy-a oos-táydh lay-ér mee pay-ree-ó-dee-ko

Do you mind if I smoke?   ¿ Le molesta que yo fume?

lay mo-lés-ta kay yo fōō-may

Where is the left-luggage office?   ¿ Dónde está la consigna ?
dón-day es-tá la con-sēēn-ya

I want to leave this luggage.   Deseo dejar este equipaje.
day-sáy-o day-hár és-tay ay-kee-pá-hay

I shall come for them this afternoon (evening).   Vendré a cogerlas esta tarde (noche).
ven-dráy a ko-hér-las és-ta tár-day (nó-chay)

I am leaving by the nine o'clock train.   Me marcho con el tren de las nueve.
may már-cho kon el tren day las noo-áy-vay

I want to take out my luggage.   Deseo sacar mi equipaje.
day-sáy-o sa-kár mee ay-kee-pá-hay

Here is my luggage ticket.   Aquí tiene usted mi talón.
a-kēē tee-áy-nay oos-táydh mee ta-lón

This is not mine.   Esto no es mío.
és-to no es mēē-o

Where is the lost property office?   ¿ Dónde está la oficina de objetos perdidos?
dón-day es-tá la o-fee-thēē-na day ob-háy-tos per-dēē-dhos

There is a case missing.   Falta una maleta.
fál-ta ōō-na ma-láy-ta

I've got into the wrong train.   Me he equivocado de tren.
may ay ay-kee-vo-ká-dho day tren

I've missed the train to . . .   He perdido el tren de . . .
ay per-dhēē-dho el tren day . . .

How long shall I have to wait?   ¿ Cuánto tiempo tendré que esperar?
kwán-to tee-ém-po ten-dráy kay es-pay-rár

The last train has gone.   El último tren ha salido.
el ōōl-tee-mo tren a sa-lēē-dho

PLANE

B.E.A. in co-operation with Iberia Air Lines of Spain and Gibair, provide scheduled flights to Madrid, Barcelona, Gibraltar, Málaga, Mallorca, the Canaries, Tangier and Valencia. Other places in Spain are served by Iberia and, in season, by chartered flights. At London airport a service charge is payable when embarking on an international flight. The free baggage allowance is: Tourist class 44 lb. (20 kg.), First class 66 lb. (30 kg.). Excess baggage must be paid for at rates varying with the distance. The London Air Terminal is situated in Cromwell Road, S.W.7.

At the time of going to press B.U.A. plan flights to Madrid, Las Palmas, Buenos Aires, Montevideo and Santiago.

VOCABULARY

aeroplane, el avión (a-vee-ón)
air hostess, la azafata (a-tha-fá-ta)
airline, la línea aérea (lēē-nay-a a-áy-ray-a)
air-pocket, el bache (bá-chay)
airsick, mareado (ma-ray-á-dho)
air terminal, el aeropuerto terminal (a-ay-ro-poo-áyr-to ter-mee-nál)
arm-rest, el brazo (brá-tho)
ashtray, el cenicero (thay-nee-tháy-ro)
cloud, la nube (nōō-bay)
cotton-wool, el algodón (al-go-dhón)
crew, la tripulación (tree-poo-la-thee-ón)
emergency exit, la salida de socorro (sa-lēē-da day so-kó-ro)
engine, el motor (mo-tór)
flight, el vuelo (voo-áy-lo)
fog, la niebla (nee-áy-bla)
jet aircraft, el avión de reacción (a-vee-ón day ray-ak-thee-ón)
land, to, aterrizar (a-tay-ree-thár)
paper bag, el saco de papel (sá-ko day pa-pél)
passenger, el viajero (vee-a-háy-ro)
pill, la píldora (pēēl-do-ra)
pilot, el piloto (pee-ló-to)
propeller, la hélice (áy-lee-thay)
refreshment, el refresco (ray-frés-ko)
runway, la pista de aterrizaje (pēēs-ta day a-tay-ree-thá-hay)
safety-belt, el cinturón de seguridad (theen-too-rón day say-goo-ree-dhádh)
steward, el camarero (ka-ma-ráy-ro)
stewardess, la camarera (ka-ma-ráy-ra)
storm, la borrasca (bo-rás-ka), la tormenta (tor-mén-ta)
sweet, el caramelo (ka-ra-máy-lo)
take off, to, despegar (des-pay-gár)
tray, la bandeja (ban-dáy-ha)
turbo-jet, el turborreactor (toor-bo-ray-ak-tór)
weather forecast, el pronóstico meteorológico (pro-nós-tee-ko may-tay-o-ro-ló-hee-ko)
window, la ventanilla (vayn-ta-nēēl-ya)
wing, el ala (*f.*) (á-la)

Where are the airline offices? ¿Dónde están las oficinas de la línea aérea?

dón-day es-tán las o-fee-thēē-nas day la lēē-nay-a a-áy-ray-a

When is the plane to . . . ? ¿Cuándo hay avión a . . . ?

kwán-do á-ee a-vee-ón a . . .

What is the fare? ¿Cuánto es el billete?

kwán-to es el beel-yáy-tay

Tourist class. De segunda clase.

day say-gōōn-da klá-say

First class. De primera clase.

day pree-máy-ra klá-say

Return. De ida y vuelta.

day ēē-dha ee voo-áyl-ta

How do I get to the airport (air terminal)? ¿Cómo se va al aeropuerto (al aeropuerto terminal)?

kó-mo say va al a-ay-ro-poo-áyr-to (a-ay-ro-poo-áyr-to ter-mee-nál)

I want to reserve a seat on the plane leaving on Thursday for . . . Deseo reservar un asiento en el avión que sale el jueves para . . .

day-sáy-o ray-ser-vár oon a-see-én-to en el a-vee-ón kay sá-lay el hoo-áy-vays pá-ra . . .

Is there a bus to the airport? ¿Hay un autocar hasta el aeropuerto?

á-ee oon ow-to-kár ás-ta el a-ay-ro-poo-áyr-to

Can I change my seat? ¿Puedo cambiar de asiento?

pwáy-do kam-bee-ár day a-see-én-to

Would you like some refreshment? ¿Desea usted algún refresco?

day-sáy-a oos-táydh al-gōōn ray-frés-ko

I should like some coffee (brandy). Quisiera café (coñac).

kee-see-áy-ra ka-fáy (kon-yák)

I am feeling sick. Estoy mareado.

es-tóy ma-ray-á-dho

Give me a paper bag (glass of water).

Déme un saco de papel (un vaso de agua).

dáy-may oon sá-ko day pa-pél (oon vá-so day á-gwa)

Where is the toilet?

¿Dónde está el excusado?

dón-day es-tá el ex-koo-sá-dho

Welcome aboard.

Sean los bienvenidos a bordo.

sáy-an los bee-en-ven-ēē-dos a bór-do

The sky is clear (cloudy).

El cielo está despejado (nublado).

el thee-áy-lo es-tá days-pay-há-dho (noo-blá-dho)

We shall be flying at a height of 12,000 feet.

Volaremos a una altura de cuatro mil metros.

vo-la-ráy-mos a ōō-na al-tōō-ra day kwá-tro meel máy-tros

We shall run into some disturbance.

Encontraremos una borrasca.

en-kon-tra-ráy-mos ōō-na bo-rás-ka

There is fog at Barcelona.

Hay niebla en Barcelona.

á-ee nee-áy-bla en bar-thay-ló-na

Would passengers on flight 10 to Barcelona please go to door A.

Se ruega a los viajeros del vuelo número diez a Barcelona que pasen a la puerta A.

say roo-áy-ga a los vee-a-háy-ros del voo-áy-lo nōō-may-ro dee-éth a bar-thay-ló-na kay pá-sen a la pwáyr-ta a

The plane from Palma is arriving.

Se anuncia la llegada del vuelo de Palma.

say a-nōōn-thee-a la lyay-gá-dha del voo-áy-lo day pál-ma

We are crossing over the Spanish coast.

Estamos cruzando por encima de la costa española.

es-tá-mos kroo-thán-do por en-thēē-ma day la kós-ta es-pan-yó-la

We shall be landing in five minutes.

Aterrizaremos dentro de cinco minutos.

a-tay-ree-tha-ráy-mos dén-tro day thēēn-ko mee-nōō-tos

Please fasten your safety-belts and put out your cigarettes.

Sírvanse abrochar su cinturón de seguridad y apagar los cigarillos.

sēēr-van-say a-bro-chár soo theen-too-rón day say-goo-ree-dhádh ee a-pa-gár los thee-ga-rēēl-yos

You may smoke if you wish but   Pueden fumar si quieren, pero
cigarettes only please.   solamente los cigarillos por
                                favor.

poo-áy-den foo-már see kee-áy-ren, pé-ro so-la-mén-tay los thee-ga-réēl-yos
por fa-vór

COACH, BUS, TRAM, TAXI

In some areas travel by long-distance coach is faster and more comfortable than by train. One disadvantage is the early hour of departure, often 6 a.m. Bus and tram fares in town are cheap. Sometimes the driver collects fares, sometimes the conductor sits at a ticket machine. Often one boards the vehicle at one end and gets off at the other. Spaniards, who are polite people on other occasions, have an aversion to queueing. Taxi fares are very reasonable, but there are the usual extra charges for luggage, for travel outwith town boundaries or for journeys late at night.

VOCABULARY

bus (town), el autobús (ow-to-bōōs)
bus (touring), el autocar (ow-to-kár)
bus stop, la parada (pa-rá-dha)
change, el dinero suelto (dee-náy-ro swáyl-to)
change, to, cambiar (kam-bee-ár)
coach, el coche de línea (kó-chay day lēē-nay-a)
conductor, el cobrador (ko-bra-dhór)
driver, el conductor (kon-dook-tór), el chófer (chó-fer)
front-seat, la delantera (day-lan-táy-ra)
half-fare, el medio billete (máy-dee-o beel-yáy-tay)
platform, la plataforma (pla-ta-fór-ma)
route, el recorrido (ray-ko-rēē-dho)
taxi, el taxi (ták-see)
taxi-driver, el chófer de taxi (chó-fer day ták-see)
terminus, el fin del recorrido (feen del ray-ko-rēē-dho)
tip, la propina (pro-pēē-na)
tram, el tranvía (tran-bēē-a)
trolleybus, el trolebús (tro-lay-bōōs)

Where can I catch a bus to . . . ?   ¿Dónde puedo coger un auto-
                                  bús a . . . ?

dón-day pwáy-dho ko-her oon ow-to-bōōs a . . .

I want to buy a bus ticket to . . . Deseo comprar un billete de autocar para . . .
day-sáy-o kom-prár oon beel-yáy-tay day ow-to-kár pá-ra . . .

Where does the coach to . . . leave from? ¿De dónde sale el coche de . . . ?
day dón-day sá-lay el kó-chay day . . .

At what time does it leave? ¿A qué hora sale?
a kay ó-ra sá-lay

I haven't any change. No tengo dinero suelto.
no tén-go dee-náy-ro swáyl-to

Move right forward please! ¡Pasen adelante por favor!
pá-sen a-dhay-lán-tay por fa-vór

Everybody off (all change)! ¡Que baje (cambie) todo el mundo!
kay bá-hay (kám-bee-ay) tó-dho el mōōn-do

Can you tell me where to get off for . . . ? ¿Puede usted decirme dónde bajar para . . . ?
pwáy-dhay oos-táydh day-thēēr-may dón-day ba-hár pá-ra . . .

Don't forget to tell me. No olvide decírmelo.
no ol-vēē-dhay day-thēēr-may-lo

Get off at the next stop. Baje usted a la parada siguiente.
bá-hay oos-táydh a la pa-rá-dha see-gee-én-tay

I should like a front seat (seat near the window). Quisiera una delantera (un asiento cerca de la ventana).
kee-see-áy-ra ōō-na day-lan-táy-ra (oon a-see-én-to tháyr-ka day la vayn-tá-na)

The bus will stop here for half an hour. El coche parará aquí por media hora.
el kó-chay pa-ra-rá a-kēē por máy-dee-a ó-ra

Take me to the station! ¡Lléveme a la estación!
Lyáy-vay-may a la es-ta-thee-ón

I'm in a hurry. Tengo prisa.
tén-go prēē-sa

I've a train to catch. Tengo que coger un tren.
tén-go kay ko-hér oon tren

Don't go so fast! ¡No vaya tan de prisa!
no vá-ya tan day prēē-sa

Stop here!   ¡Párese aquí!
pá-ray-say a-kēē

Wait here!   ¡Espere aquí!
es-páy-ray a-kēē

Come and collect us at eight Venga a recogernos a las ocho
o'clock tomorrow morning. mañana por la mañana.
váyn-ga a ray-ko-hér-nos a las óch-o man-yá-na por la man-yá-na

SHIP

aft, hacia popa (á-thee-a pó-pa)
berth, la litera (lee-táy-ra)
boat, el barco (bár-ko)
bridge, el puente de mando (poo-én-tay day mán-do)
cabin, el camarote (ka-ma-ró-tay)
crossing, la travesía (tra-vay-sēē-a)
deck, la cubierta (koo-bee-áyr-ta)
deck-chair, la silla de cubierta (sēēl-ya)
disembark, to, desembarcar (des-em-bar-kár)
embark, to, embarcarse (em-bar-kár-say)
ferry, el pasaje (pa-sá-hay)
forward, hacia proa (á-thee-a pró-a)
gangway, el pasamano (pa-sa-má-no)
harbour, el puerto (poo-áyr-to)
ladder, la escalera (es-ka-láy-ra)
landing ticket, el billete de desembarco (beel-yáy-tay day
   des-em-bár-ko)
lifeboat, el bote salvavidas (bó-tay sal-va-vēē-dhas)
life-jacket, el chaleco salvavidas (cha-láy-ko sal-va-vēē-dhas)
port (side), babor (bá-bor)
port (harbour), el puerto (poo-áyr-to)
purser's office, la oficina del contador (o-fee-thēē-na del
   kon-ta-dhór)
quay, el muelle (moo-él-yay)
starboard, estribor (es-trēē-bor)
yacht, el yate (yá-tay)

Which is the way to the harbour ¿ Por dónde está el puerto (el
(wharf)? muelle)?
por dón-day es-tá el poo-áyr-to (el moo-áyl-yay)

How long does the crossing take? ¿ Cuánto dura la travesía?
kwán-to dōō-ra la tra-vay-sēē-a

I want a first (second) class cabin (berth). Deseo un camarote (una litera) de primera (segunda) clase.
day-sáy-o oon ka-ma-ró-tay (ōō-na lee-táy-ra) day pree-máy-ra (say-gōōn-da) klá-say

When does the boat leave for . . . ? ¿ Cuándo sale el barco para . . . ?
kwán-do sá-lay el bár-ko pá-ra . . .

When does the boat arrive at . . . ? ¿ Cuándo llega el barco a . . . ?
kwán-do lyáy-ga el bár-ko a . . .

Does it call at . . . ? ¿ Hace escala en . . . ?
á-thay es-ká-la en . . .

Where is the saloon (bar)? ¿ Dónde está el salón (bar)?
dón-day es-tá el sa-lón (bar)

Where do I get a landing-ticket? ¿ Dónde se sacan los billetes de desembarco?
dón-day say sá-kan los beel-yáy-tays day des-em-bár-ko

I want a deck-chair. Deseo una silla de cubierta.
day-sáy-o ōō-na sēēl-ya day koo-bee-áyr-ta

I am sea-sick. Estoy mareado.
es-tóy ma-ray-á-dho

Have you any sea-sickness pills? ¿ Tiene usted píldoras contra el mareo?
tee-áy-nay oos-táydh pēēl-do-ras kón-tra el ma-ráy-o

Bring me a basin! ¡Tráigame una jofaina!
trá-ee-ga-may ōō-na ho-fá-ee-na

How long can we stay ashore? ¿ Cuánto tiempo podemos quedar en tierra?
kwán-to tee-ém-po po-dháy-mos kay-dár en tee-áyr-ra

Hold on tight! ¡Agárrese bien!
a-gár-ray-say bee-én

Mind your head! ¡Cuidado con la cabeza!
kwee-dhá-dho kon la ka-bé-tha

HOTELS

These are classified by the Ministry of Tourism from Luxury to Third
Class. There are also *paradores* often in renovated buildings of historical
interest and *albergues* similar to motels, which are government-owned
and lists of which may be obtained from the National Tourist Office.
Higher rates are charged for a stay of only two days than for a longer period
and also at busy times, for example Holy Week in Seville. Meals are served
progressively later as one goes south: lunch in the north at about 1 p.m.
but as late as 3 p.m. in the south; dinner in the north about 9 p.m. but
as late as 11 p.m. in the south. Establishments accustomed to a British
clientele may serve dinner earlier. The light Spanish breakfast is a natural
consequence of late dinner. In smaller southern hotels it may not be
served at all, which is not a great disadvantage as it will be easily available
in a local *cafetería*—as late as one likes! Standards of cleanliness are high.
Hot water, however, is not always available and in some areas subject
to drought, water may be cut off for a few hours each day in summer.
Showers are more common than baths which are charged extra. Soap
is not provided. Electric shavers may have to be adapted to a voltage of
125 volts.

VOCABULARY

armchair, la butaca (boo-tá-ka)
ashtray, el cenicero (thay-nee-tháy-ro)
bath, el baño (bán-yo)
bathroom, el cuarto de baño (kwár-to day bán-yo)
bed, la cama (ká-ma)
bedroom, la habitación (a-bee-ta-thee-ón), la alcoba (al-kó-ba)
bell, el timbre (tēēm-bray)
bill, la cuenta (kwén-ta)
blanket, la manta (mán-ta)
blind, la persiana (per-see-á-na)
boarding-house, la pensión (pen-see-ón), la casa de huéspedes
     (ká-sa day wáys-pay-dhays)
board (full/half), la pensión (completa/media) (kom-pláy-ta/
     máy-dhee-a)
breakfast, el desayuno (day-sa-yōō-no)
chair, la silla (sēēl-ya)
chamber-pot, el orinal (o-ree-nál)
clean, limpio (lēēm-pee-o)
coat-hanger, la percha (pér-cha)
cold, frío (frēē-o)
curtain, la cortina (kor-tēē-na)

damp, húmedo (ōō-may-dho)
dining-room, el comedor (ko-may-dhór)
dinner, la cena (tháy-na)
dirty, sucio (sōō-thee-o)
floor, ground (first), el piso bajo (el primer piso) (pēē-so bá-ho /pree-mér pēē-so)
head-waiter, el maître d'hotel (mé-tray do-tél)
heating, la calefacción (ka-lay-fak-thee-ón)
hot, caliente (ka-lee-én-tay)
hotel, el hotel (o-tél)
hot-water bottle, la botella de agua caliente (bo-tél-ya day á-gwa ka-lee-én-tay)
inn, la posada (po-sá-dha)
key, la llave (lyá-vay)
lamp, la lámpara (lám-pa-ra)
lift, el ascensor (as-then-sór)
light, la luz (looth)
lounge, el salón (sa-lón)
lunch, el almuerzo (al-moo-ér-tho)
management, la dirección (dee-rek-thee-ón)
manager, el gerente (hay-rén-tay), el director (dee-rek-tór)
mattress, el colchón (kol-chón)
message, el mensaje (men-sá-hay)
meter, el contador (kon-ta-dhór)
mirror, el espejo (es-páy-ho)
office, la oficina (o-fee-thēē-na)
page-boy, el botones (bo-tó-nays)
pillow, la almohada (al-mo-á-dha)
plug, el enchufe (en-chōō-fay)
porter, el mozo (mó-tho)
proprietor, el dueño (dwén-yo)
receptionist, el (la) recepcionista (ray-thep-thee-on-ēēs-ta)
register, el libro de registro (leé-bro day ray-hēēs-tro)
sheet, la sábana (sá-ba-na)
shower, la ducha (dōō-cha)
shutter, la contraventana (kon-tra-vayn-tá-na)
soap, el jabón (ha-bón)
staircase, la escalera (es-ka-láy-ra)
switch, el interruptor (een-ter-roop-tór)
table (bedside), la mesilla de noche (may-sēēl-ya day nó-chay)
tap, el grifo (grēē-fo)
towel, la toalla (to-ál-ya)
tumbler, el vaso (vá-so)
valet, el criado (kree-á-dho)
wardrobe, el armario (ar-má-ree-o)
washhand basin, el lavabo (la-vá-bo)
window, la ventana (vayn-tá-na)
writing materials, el recado de escribir (ray-ká-do day es-kree-bēēr)

I am Mr. (Mrs., Miss) . . .   Soy el Señor (la Señora, la Señorita) . . .
soy el sayn-yór (la sayn-yó-ra, la sayn-yo-rēē-ta) . . .

I wrote to you reserving a room.   Le escribí para reservar una habitación.
lay es-kree-bēē pá-ra ray-ser-vár ōō-na a-bee-ta-thee-ón

I wrote three weeks ago.   Escribí hace tres semanas.
es-kree-bēē á-thay tres say-má-nas

Did you not get my letter?   ¿No recibió usted mi carta?
no ray-thee-bee-ó oos-táydh mee kár-ta

I asked for a second floor room.   Pedí una habitación del segundo piso.
pay-dēē ōō-na a-bee-ta-thee-ón del say-gōōn-do pēē-so

I want a room looking on to the street.   Deseo una habitación que dé a la calle.
day-sáy-o ōō-na a-bee-ta-thee-ón kay day a la kál-yay

I am looking for a good hotel.   Busco un buen hotel.
bōōs-ko oon boo-én o-tél

Can you give me a room for the night?   ¿Puede usted darme una habitación para esta noche?
poo-áy-day oos-táydh dár-may ōō-na a-bee-ta-thee-ón pá-ra és-ta nó-chay

Do you want to see the room?   ¿Quiere usted ver la habitación?
kee-áy-ray oos-táydh ver la a-bee-ta-thee-ón

I don't like it.   No me gusta.
no may gōōs-ta

If there is not anything better I shall have to look elsewhere.   Si no hay nada mejor tendré que buscar en otra parte.
see no á-ee ná-dha may-hór ten-dráy kay boos-kár en ó-tra pár-tay

I'll take it.   La tomaré.
la to-ma-ráy

Have my luggage taken up, please.   Sírvase hacer subir mi equipaje.
sēēr-va-say a-thér soo-bēēr mee ay-kee-pá-hay

I am staying for only two or three days.   Me quedo sólo dos o tres días.
dhomay káy- só-lo dos o tres dēē-as

I am staying for a week (fortnight) at least. Me quedo por ocho (quince) días por lo menos.
may káy-dho por ó-cho (kēēn-thay) dēē-as por lo máy-nos

How much do you charge per day with (without) meals? ¿Cuánto cobra usted al día con (sin) las comidas?
kwán-to kó-bra oos-táydh al dēē-a kon (seen) las ko-mēē-dhas

I want a quiet room. Deseo una habitación tranquila.
day-say-o ōō-na a-bee-ta-thee-ón tran-kēē-la

Is there a lift? ¿Hay ascensor?
á-ee as-then-sór

I cannot sleep; there is too much noise. No puedo dormir; hay demasiado ruido.
no poo-áy-dho dor-mēēr; á-ee day-ma-see-á-dho roo-ēē-dho

There is no . . . in my room. No hay . . . en mi habitación.
no á-ee . . . en mee a-bee-ta-thee-ón

The . . . does not work in my room. El(la) . . . no funciona en mi habitación.
el(la) . . . no foon-thee-ó-na en mee a-bee-ta-thee-ón

The sheets are dirty (damp). Las sábanas están sucias (húmedas).
las sá-ba-nas es-tán sōō-thee-as (ōō-may-dhas)

The . . . is broken. El(la) . . . está roto(a).
el(la) . . . es-tá ró-to(a)

Nobody comes when I ring. Nadie viene cuando llamo.
ná-dee-áy vee-áy-nay kwán-do lyá-mo

I need . . . Necesito . . .
nay-thay-sēē-to . . .

Bring me . . . ! ¡Tráigame . . . !
trá-ee-ga-may . . .

I want to have a bath. Deseo tomar un baño.
day-sáy-o to-már oon bán-yo

Please open . . . ¡Abra el(la) . . . por favor!
á-bra el(la) por fa-vór

You have not given me . . . No me ha dado . . .
no may a dá-dho . . .

The light is poor. No hay bastante luz.
no á-ee bas-tán-tay looth

The bed is not made. La cama no está hecha.
la ká-ma no es-tá áy-cha

I am going to bed at once. Me acuesto en seguida.
may a-kwáys-to en say-gēē-dha

Is the tapwater drinkable? ¿Se puede beber el agua del grifo?
say poo-áy-dhay bay-bér el á-gwa del grēē-fo

At what time do we have lunch (dinner)? ¿A qué hora almorzamos (cenamos)?
a kay ó-ra al-mor-thá-mos (thay-ná-mos)

I wish to eat earlier. Deseo comer más temprano.
day-sáy-o ko-mér mas tem-prá-no

I am expecting a visitor. Espero una visita.
es-páy-ro ōō-na vee-sēē-ta

Is there a letter (message) for me? ¿Hay una carta (un mensaje) para mí?
a-ee ōō-na kár-ta (oon men-sá-hey) pá-ra mee

Did anyone call for me? ¿Vino alguien a buscarme?
vēē-no ál-gee-en a boos-kár-may

I shall be back at three o'clock. Estaré de vuelta a las tres.
es-ta-ráy day voo-él-ta a las tres

Please send him (her) up. Sírvase decirle que suba.
sēēr-va-say day-thēēr-lay kay sōō-ba

What is the voltage? ¿Qué es el voltaje?
kay es el vol-tá-hay

Have these clothes dried. Haga secar esta ropa.
á-ga say-kár és-ta ró-pa

Can you sew on this button? ¿Puede usted coser este botón?
poo-áy-day oos-táydh ko-sér és-tay bo-tón

Can you press my trousers? ¿Puede usted planchar mi pantalón?
poo-áy-dhay oos-táydh plan-chár mee pan-ta-lón

When does the postman come? ¿A qué hora viene el cartero?
A kay ó-ra vee-áy-nay el kar-táy-ro

May I use your telephone?   ¿ Puedo usar su teléfono?
poo-áy-dho oo-sár soo tay-láy-fo-no

Have you a map of the town?   ¿ Tiene usted un mapa de la ciudad?
tee-áy-nay oos-táydh oon má-pa day la thee-oo-dhádh

Will you get me tickets for . . . ?   ¿ Quiere usted sacarme entradas para . . . ?
kee-áy-ray oos-táydh sa-kár-may en-trá-dhas pá-ra . . .

Where can I buy . . . ?   ¿ Dónde puedo comprar . . . ?
dón-day poo-áy-dho kom-prár . . .

I want to post a letter.   Deseo echar una carta al correo.
day-sáy-o ay-chár ōō-na kár-ta al ko-ráy-o

Give me key number six, please.   Déme la llave número seis por favor.
dáy-may la lyá-vay nōō-may-ro sáy-ees por fa-vór

I'm leaving tomorrow.   Me marcho mañana.
may már-cho man-yá-na

I shall have to get up early.   Tendré que madrugar.
ten-dráy kay ma-droo-gár

Order me a taxi for . . .   Mándeme un taxi para las . . .
mán-day-may oon táx-ee pá-ra las . . .

Please forward my letters to this address.   Sírvase remitir mis cartas a esta dirección.
sēēr-va-say ray-mee-tēēr mees kár-tas a és-ta dee-rek-thee-ón

Waken me at. . .   Despiérteme a las . . .
des-pee-ér-tay-may a las . . .

Knock until I answer.   Llame hasta que conteste.
lyá-may á-sta kay kon-tés-tay

Don't disturb me in the morning.   No me moleste por la mañana.
no may mo-lés-tay por la man-yá-na

Who is there?   ¿ Quién está allí?
kee-én es-tá al-yēē

Wait a moment.   Espere un momento.
es-páy-ray oon mo-mén-to

Come in!   ¡Adelante!
a-dháy-lán-tay

Make out my bill.   Prepare mi cuenta.
pray-pá-ray mee kwén-ta

I think there is a mistake.   Creo que se ha equivocado.
kráy-o kay say a ay-kee-vo-ká-dho

You said the room cost only ...   Usted dijo que la habitación costaba solamente ...
oos-táydh dēē-ho kay la a-bee-ta-thee-ón kos-tá-ba so-la-mén-tay ...

Is the service included?   ¿Está incluido el servicio?
es-tá een-kloo-ēē-dho el ser-vēē-thee-o

This is for you.   Esto es para usted.
és-to es pá-ra oos-táydh

I want a room to change in.   Deseo una habitación para cambiarme.
day-sáy-o ōō-na a-bee-ta-thee-ón pá-ra kám-bee-ár-may

Please bring down my luggage.   Sírvase bajar mi equipaje.
sēēr-va-say ba-hár mee ay-kee-pá-hay

I have left my ...   He dejado mi ...
ay day-há-dho mee ...

Will you take a cheque?   ¿Aceptará usted un cheque?
a-thayp-ta-rá oos-táydh oon cháy-kay

I shall be in late.   Volveré tarde.
vol-ver-áy tár-day

Will someone let me in?   ¿Me abrarán?
may a-bra-rán

Do you serve English breakfast?   ¿Sirve usted el desayuno inglés?
sēēr-vay oos-táydh el day-sa-yōō-no een-gláys

Will you give us a packed meal?   ¿Quiere usted darnos una merienda empaquetada?
kee-áy-ray oos-táydh dár-nos ōō-na may-ree-én-da em-pa-kay-tá-dha

Bring me hot water for shaving.   Tráigame agua caliente para afeitarme.
trá-ee-ga-may á-gwa ka-lee-én-tay pá-ra a-fáy-ee-tár-may

LAUNDRY

For washing list see vocabulary under SHOPPING *pp. 125-7.*

I have some things to be washed.   Tengo algunas cosas para lavar.
tén-go al-gōō-nas kó-sas pá-ra la-vár

When can I have them back?   ¿ Cuándo me las devolverán ?
kwán-do me las day-vol-vay-rán

I must have them back by . . .   Importa que las tenga para . . .
eem-pór-ta kay las tén-ga pá-ra . . .

How long will it take?   ¿ Cuánto tardará ?
kwán-to tar-da-rá

There is a button missing.   Falta un botón.
fál-ta oon bo-tón

I (do not) like my collars **(No)** me gustan los cuellos
starched.   almidonados.
(no) may gōōs-tan los koo-áyl-yos al-mee-do-ná-dhos

Can you have a shirt ironed for ¿ Puede usted planchar una
tonight?   camisa para esta noche ?
poo-áy-dhay oos-táydh plan-chár ōō-na ka-mēē-sa pá-ra és-ta nó-chay

There are two handkerchiefs Faltan dos pañuelos.
missing.
fál-tan dos pan-yoo-áy-los

This is not mine.   No es mío.
no es mēē-o

My suit (dress) is stained.   Mi traje está manchado.
mee trá-hay es-tá man-chá-dho

Can you clean it?   ¿ Puede limpiarlo ?
poo-áy-dhay leem-pee-ár-lo

Press it (them) please.   Plánchemelo por favor.
plán-chay-may-lopor fa-vór

POLICE, PASSPORTS, FORMS

Hotel and boarding-house proprietors are required to fill in a form for the police giving brief details of foreigners' passports and movements. A visa is not necessary for a stay in Spain not exceeding three months. A visa when granted may have to be confirmed after a stated time at the local offices of the *gobierno civil* (go-bee-áyr-no thee-véēl). When obtaining any kind of licence from the authorities it may be necessary to pay in addition to the usual fee a small tax to charity, receipt of which is usually indicated by a special stamp. There are four bodies of police with whom the traveller may come in contact: the *guardia civil* (gwár-dee-a thee-véēl) recognisable by their tricorne hats and green uniform; the *policía armada* who wear a grey uniform and red cap-band. These two corps perform the usual duties of uniformed police, but traffic on the roads is the special care of the *guardia de la circulación* (gwár-dee-a day la theer-koo-la-thee-ón) who wear a blue uniform with white tunic, helmet and baton. There are also plain-clothes police whom the traveller will meet during the examination of passports. At present the Spanish police are empowered to impose fines on the spot in certain cases and to hold charged persons longer without proceedings than would be the case in Britain or other countries.

VOCABULARY

address (permanent), domicilio (fijo) (do-mee-thēē-lee-o fēē-ho)
birth, el nacimiento (na-thee-mee-én-to)
city chambers, el ayuntamiento (a-yoon-ta-mee-én-to)
date, la fecha (fáy-cha)
fine, la multa (mōōl-ta)
first name, nombre (nóm-bray)
foreign money, divisas extranjeras (dee-vēē-sas ex-tran-háy-ras)
form, la ficha (fēē-cha)
married, casado (kas-sá-dho)
passport, el pasaporte (pa-sa-pór-tay)
police, la policía (po-lee-thēē-a)
police station, la comisaría (ko-mee-sa-rēē-a)
purpose of journey, motivo del viaje (mo-tēē-vo del vee-á-hay)
   note: the answer is usually *turismo* (too-rēēs-mo) or business *negocios* (nay-gó-thee-os)
residence (temporary), paradero (pa-ra-dháy-ro)
single, soltero (sol-táy-ro)
surname, apellido (a-payl-yēē-dho)
tax, impuesto (eem-pwáys-to)
valid until, válido hasta (vá-lee-dho á-sta)
visa, el visado (vee-sá-dho)
work permit, el permiso de trabajo (per-mēē-so day tra-bá-ho)

May I have your passport? ¿Puede darme su pasaporte?
poo-áy-dhay dár-may soo pa-sa-pór-tay

I intend to stay . . . days. Pienso quedarme . . . días.
pee-én-so kay-dhár-may . . . dēē-as

Are you a foreigner? ¿Es usted extranjero?
es oos-táydh ex-tran-háy-ro

I am a British (American) Soy súbdito británico (ameri-
subject. cano).
soy sōōb-dee-to bree-tá-nee-ko (a-may-ree-ká-no)

Please come with me. Venga conmigo por favor.
vén-ga kon-mēē-go por fa-vór

Please fill up this form. Haga el favor de completar
esta ficha.
á-ga el fa-vór day kom-play-tár és-ta fēē-cha

Where have you come from? ¿De dónde llega usted?
day dón-day lyáy-ga oos-táydh

Where are you going? ¿A dónde va usted?
a dón-day va oos-táydh

I'll give it back to you . . . Se lo devolveré . . .
say lo day-vol-vay-ráy

I must detain you. Debo detenerle.
dáy-bo day-ten-ér-lay

For what reason? ¿Con qúe motivo?
kon kay mo-tēē-vo

I wish to inform the Consul. Deseo informar al consulado.
day-sáy-o een-for-már al kon-soo-lá-dho

I wish to consult a lawyer. Deseo consultar con un
abogado.
day-sáy-o kon-sōōl-tar kon oon a-bo-gá-dho

I have been robbed. Me han robado.
may an ro-bá-dho

Can you describe it? ¿Puede usted describirlo?
poo-áy-dhay oos-táydh des-kree-bēēr-lo

What was in the wallet? ¿Qué contenía la cartera?
kay kon-tayn-ēē-a la kar-táy-ra

What was this man like?	**¿Cómo era este hombre?**
	kó-mo áy-ra és-tay óm-bray
Is that the thief?	**¿Es éste el ladrón?**
	es és-tay el la-drón
I have lost . . .	**He perdido . . .**
	ay per-dēē-dho

VILLAS

There are now many agencies in this country through which one may rent a Spanish villa in summer, obtaining at the same time the services of a maid. Rather than ask the latter to give an account of her shopping for you (such an account being liable to fluctuations due to changes in the price and quality of produce), take an occasional stroll through the market with an eye to these factors and you are unlikely to suffer any gross deception. It is well to be clear about what household goods you expect to find and the extent of your liability for damage or theft. Ascertain whether there is any possibility of water being cut off.

VOCABULARY

armchair, el sillón de brazos (seel-yón day brá-thos)
basket, el cesto (thés-to), la cesta (thés-ta)
bathroom, el cuarto de baño (kwár-to day bán-yo)
bed, la cama (ká-ma)
bedroom, la alcoba (al-kó-ba)
blanket, la manta (mán-ta)
blind, la persiana (per-see-á-na)
blocked, obturado (ob-too-rá-dho)
brazier, el brasero (bra-sáy-ro)
broken, roto (ró-to)
broom, la escoba (es-kó-ba)
bucket, el cubo (kōō-bo)
bulb, la bombilla (bom-bēēl-ya)
chair, la silla (sēēl-ya)
clean, limpio (lēēm-pee-o)
crockery, la loza (ló-tha)
cup, la taza (tá-tha)
detergent, el detergente (day-ter-hén-tay)
dining-room, el comedor (ko-may-dhór)
dinner, la cena (tháy-na)
dirty, sucio (sōō-thee-o)
dish, el plato (plá-to)
dishes, la vajilla (va-hēēl-ya)
drain, el desagüe (day-ság-way)
dustman, el basurero (ba-soo-ráy-ro)
electricity, la electricidad (ay-lek-tree-thee-dádh)

fibre (for washing-up), el estropajo (es-tro-pá-ho)
floor, el suelo (swáy-lo)
food, la comida (ko-mēē-dha)
fork, el tenedor (te-ne-dhór)
frying-pan, la sartén (sar-tén)
glass, el vaso (vá-so)
guest, el huésped (wáys-pedh), el invitado (een-vee-tá-dho)
iron, la plancha (plán-cha)
jug, el jarro (há-ro)
key, la llave (lyá-vay)
knife, el cuchillo (koo-chēēl-yo)
lamp, la lámpara (lám-pa-ra)
landing, el descanso de la escalera (des-kán-so day la es-ka-láy-ra)
landlord (lady), el dueño (dueña) (dwáyn-yo, -ya)
light, la luz (looth)
lunch, el almuerzo (al-moo-ér-tho)
maid, la criada (kree-á-dha)
market, el mercado (mer-ká-dho)
mattress, el colchón (kol-chón)
meal, la comida (ko-mēē-dha)
meter, el contador (kon-ta-dhór)
oven, el horno (ór-no)
pillow, la almohada (al-mo-á-dha)
pipe, el tubo (tōō-bo)
place (at table), el cubierto (koo-bee-ér-to)
plug (electric), el enchufe (en-chōō-fay)
plug (of basin), el tapón (ta-pón)
plumber, el plomero (plo-máy-ro)
power-cut, el apagón (a-pa-gón)
refrigerator, la nevera (nay-váy-ra)
rent, el alquiler (al-kee-lér)
rubbish, la basura (ba-sōō-ra)
saucepan, la cacerola (ka-thay-ró-la)
sheet, la sábana (sá-ba-na)
shopping, las compras (kóm-pras)
shopping-basket, la cesta (tháys-ta)
shower, la ducha (dōō-cha)
shutter, la contraventana (kon-tra-vayn-tá-na)
sink, el fregadero (fray-ga-dháy-ro)
sitting-room, la sala de estar (sá-la day es-tár)
soap, el jabón (ha-bón)
spoon, la cuchara (koo-chá-ra)
stairs, la escalera (ays-ka-láy-ra)
stewpot, la olla (ól-ya)
sun-roof, la terraza (tay-rá-tha), la azotea (a-tho-táy-a)
switch, el interruptor (een-ter-roop-tór)
table, la mesa (máy-sa)
tap, el grifo (grēē-fo)
tea, el té (tay)

teaspoon, la cucharita (koo-cha-rēē-ta)
tea-pot, la tetera (tay-táy-ra)
tin-opener, el abrelatas (a-bray-lá-tas)
toilet, el wáter (vá-ter)
towel, la toalla (to-ál-ya)
washhand basin, el lavabo (la-vá-bo)
waste-paper basket, el cesto para papeles (tháys-to pá-ra pa-páy-lays)
window, la ventana (vayn-tá-na)
yard, el patio (pá-tee-o)

I am looking for rooms to rent.   Estoy buscando habitaciones para alquilar.
es-tóy boos-kán-do a-bee-ta-thee-ón-ays pá-ra al-keel-ár

How much is the rent?   ¿ Cuánto es el alquiler?
kwán-to es el al-keel-ér

What is included in the price?   ¿ Qué va incluido con el precio?
kay va een-kloo-ēē-dho kon el p̃ráy-thee-o

What furniture is there?   ¿ Qué muebles hay?
kay moo-áy-blays á-ee

Write down the conditions, please.   Apunte las condiciones, por favor.
a-pōōn-tay las kon-dee thee-ó-nays por fa-vór

I want a daily maid.   Quiero una sirvienta cada día.
kee-áy-ro ōō-na seer-vee-én-ta ká-dha dēē-a

How much an hour does she get?   ¿ Cuánto recibe por hora?
kwán-to ray-thēē-bay por ó-ra

How much do you ask?   ¿ Cuánto pide usted?
kwán-to pēē-dhay oos-táydh

. . . per hour (day, week).   . . . por hora (al día, por semana).
. . . por ó-ra, (al dēē-a, por say-má-na)

What is your name, miss?   ¿ Cómo se llama usted, señorita?
kó-mo say lyá-ma oos-táydh sayn-yo-rēē-ta

Do the shopping.   Haga las compras.
á-ga las kóm-pras

Tell me what you spend.   Dígame lo que gaste.
dēē-ga-may lo kay gás-tay

Is this enough?   ¿Es bastante?
es bas-tán-tay

Bring me the change.   Tráigame el cambio.
trá-ee-ga-may el kám-bee-o

Make the beds.   Haga las camas.
á-ga las ká-mas

Sweep the rooms.   Barra las habitaciones.
bár-ra las a-bee-ta-thee-ó-nays

Will you prepare the meals?   ¿Quiere usted preparar las comidas?
kee-áy-ray oos-táydh pray-pa-rár las ko-mēē-dhas

Wash and iron these clothes.   Lave y planche esta ropa.
lá-vay ee plán-chay és-ta ró-pa

Clean this.   Limpie esto.
lēēm-pee-ay és-to

Will you wash up?   ¿Quiere usted fregar?
kee-áy-ray oos-táydh fray-gár

The water must be boiling.   El agua tiene que estar hirvi-endo.
el á-gwa tee-áy-nay kay es-tár eer-vee-én-do

At what time can you come?   ¿A qué hora puede usted venir?
a kay ó-ra poo-áy-dhay oos-táydh vay-nēēr

Can you stay and baby sit?   ¿Puede quedarse y cuidar al niño?
poo-áy-dhay kay-dár-say ee kwee-dhár al nēēn-yo

We are going out tonight.   Vamos a salir esta noche.
vá-mos a sa-lēēr és-ta nó-chay

How many hours did you work today?   ¿Cuántas horas trabajó hoy?
kwán-tas ó-ras tra-ba-hó oy

We shall have a guest tonight.   Tendremos un invitado esta noche.
ten-dráy-mos oon een-vee-tá-dho és-ta nó-chay

Lay four places at table.   Ponga cuatro cubiertos.
pón-ga kwá-tro koo-bee-ér-tos

Cook us a local dish.   Háganos un plato típico.
á-ga-nos oon plá-to tēē-pee-ko

The meal was excellent.   La comida era excelente.
la ko-mēē-dha áy-ra ex-thay-lén-tay

Fetch a plumber immediately.   Busque un plomero en seguida.
bōōs-kay oon plo-máy-ro en say-gēē-dha

Give the dustman this tip.   Dé esta propina al basurero.
day és-ta pro-pēē-na al ba-soo-ráy-ro

You have looked after us very   Usted nos ha cuidado muy
well.   bien.
oos-táydh nos a kwee-dá-dho mwee bee-én

SIGHTSEEING AND SEASIDE

There are many guide books which provide information about places of interest in Spanish towns and the excursions which may be made from them, and only a few suggestions are given here. A local map may be obtained from a bookstall or the local tourist information office. The word *museo* (moo-sáy-o) means both a museum and an art gallery. On certain days as an inducement to the local population the entry fee is reduced. One should not go round a church if mass is being said at the high altar, and women are expected to cover their heads and arms. Resist gypsy blandishments with regard to displays of flamenco as the best troupes have in any case arrangements with the local tourist agencies or hotels. If you accept the services in a *bodega* (bo-dháy-ga) tavern, of a guitarist or singer, do not assume that they will perform for you for hours on end just for the love of the thing or a small tip. As a tourist you will be regarded by the beggars as a soft target; it is up to yourself whether you choose to say once *Perdone hermano* (per-dó-nay er-má-no), "Sorry, brother!" and thereafter ignore any importuning, or get rid of some small change and elicit a *Dios se lo pague* (dee-ós say lo pá-gay), "God reward you".

MADRID	Museo del Prado, main boulevards, Puerta del Sol, the Retiro park, Royal Palace, Plaza Mayor, Excursions to Toledo, the Escorial.
BARCELONA	Main boulevards, the Barrio Gótico (old quarter), the Pueblo Español (exhibition of regional products, etc.). Excursions to Montserrat; Tarragona.
SANTANDER	Excursions to Altamira (prehistoric paintings).
TOLEDO	Cathedral, churches, synagogue; the Alcázar.

CÓRDOBA	Cathedral.
SEVILLA	Cathedral and Giralda; the Alcázar.
GRANADA	The Alhambra palace; the Sacromonte.
SANTIAGO DE COMPOSTELA	Cathedral façade and square.

VOCABULARY

altar-piece, el retablo (ray-táb-lo)
Arab, (el) árabe (á-ra-bay)
avenue, la avenida (a-vay-nēē-dha)
baroque, barroco (ba-ró-ko)
battlements, las almenas (al-máy-nas)
bishop, el obispo (o-bēēs-po)
bridge, el puente (pwén-tay)
building, el edificio (ay-dhee-fēē-thee-o)
buried, enterrado (en-ter-á-dho)
castle, el castillo (kas-tēēl-yo)
catalogue, el catálogo (ka-tá-lo-go)
cathedral, la catedral (ka-tay-drál)
century, el siglo (sēē-glo)
chapel, la capilla (ka-pēēl-ya)
church, la iglesia (ee-glóy-see-a)
Cid, el, Medieval Spanish hero (theed)
Colón, Columbus (ko-lón)
excursion, la excursión (ex-koor-see-ón)
façade, la fachada (fa-chá-dha)
fortress, el alcázar (al-kâ-thar)
gate, ornamental, la reja (ráy-ha)
gipsy, el gitano (hee-tá-no)
Goth, el godo (gó-dho)
guide, guide-book, el guía (gēē-a), la guía (gēē-a)
king, el rey (ráy-ee)
lake, el lago (lá-go)
lake, ornamental, el estanque (es-tán-kay)
library, la biblioteca (beeb-lee-o-táy-ka)
map, el mapa (má-pa)
miracle, el milagro (mee-lá-gro)
Moor, el moro (mó-ro)
Moorish, morisco (mo-rēēs-ko)
mosque, la mezquita (meth-kēē-ta)
mountain, el monte (món-tay), la montaña (mon-tán-ya)
mozárabe, Christian under Moorish rule (moth-á-ra-bay)
outskirts, las afueras (a-fwáy-ras)
painting, la pintura (peen-tōō-ra), el cuadro (kwá-dro), el lienzo (lee-én-tho)
palace, el palacio (pa-lâ-thee-o)
park, el parque (pár-kay)
Parliament, las Cortes (kór-tays)
pilgrimage, la romería (ro-may-rēē-a)

portrait, el retrato (ray-trá-to)
postcard, la tarjeta postal (tar-háy-ta pos-tál)
post office, Correos (ko-ráy-os)
queen, la reina (ráy-ee-na)
relic, la reliquia (ray-lēē-kee-a)
Reyes Católicos, Ferdinand & Isabella, 15th c. (ráy-ays ka-tó-lee-kos)
sculpture, la escultura (es-kool-tōō-ra)
sexton, el sacristán (sa-krees-tán)
square, la plaza (plá-tha)
stained-glass window, la vidriera (veed-ree-áy-ra)
street, la calle (kál-yay)
tomb, la tumba (tōōm-ba)
tower, la torre (tó-ray)
town, la ciudad (thee-oo-dâdh)
town hall, el ayuntamiento (a-yoon-ta-mee-én-to)
university, la universidad (oo-nee-ver-see-dâdh)

Is this the right way to . . . ? ¿ Vamos bien para . . . ?
vá-mos bee-én pá-ra . . .

Would you be so kind as to ¿ Tendría usted la bondad de
direct me to . . . ? decirme dónde está . . . ?
ten-drēē-a oos-táydh la bon-dádh day day-thēēr-may dón-day es-tá . . .

Cross the road. Cruce la calle.
krōō-thay la kál-yay

On the opposite pavement. En la acera de enfrente.
en la a-tháy-ra day en-frén-tay

On the other side of the square. Al otro lado de la plaza.
al ót-ro lá-dho day la plá-tha

The first (opening) on the left La primera (bocacalle) a la
(right). izquierda (derecha).
la pree-máy-ra (bo-ka-kál-yay) a la eeth-kee-áyr-da (day-ráy-cha)

Go straight on. Siga todo derecho.
sēē-ga tó-dho day-ráy-cho

Turn right (left). Tome por la derecha (izquierda).
tó-may por la day-ráy-cha (eeth-kee-áyr-da)

This way. That way. Por aquí. Por allá.
por a-kēē. por al-yá

Have you a map of the town? ¿ Tiene usted un mapa de la
ciudad ?
tee-áy-nay oos-táydh oon má-pa day la thee-oo-dhádh

I want to visit the old quarter. Deseo visitar el barrio viejo.
day-sáy-o vee-see-tár el bá-ree-o vee-áy-ho

Is there a bus? ¿Hay un autobús?
á-ee oon ow-to-bōōs

Where is the bus stop? ¿Dónde está la parada?
dón-day es-tá la pa-rá-dha

Is this the terminus? ¿Es el fin del trayecto?
es el feen del tra-yék-to

Have you a list of excursions? ¿Tiene usted una lista de excursiones?
tee-áy-nay oos-táydh ōō-na lēēs-ta day ex-koor-see-ó-nays

We want to go on a tour to . . . Deseamos hacer una excursión a . . .
dey-say-á-mos a-thér ōō-na ex-koor-see-ón a . . .

We want to be together. Deseamos estar juntos.
day-say-á-mos es-tár hōōn-tos

Is there a guide who speaks English? ¿Hay un guía que hable inglés?
á-ee oon gēē-a kay á-blay een-gláys

Would those who speak English (French) come with me. Por favor, vengan conmigo los de lengua inglesa (francesa).
por fa-vór ven-gán kon-mēē-go los day lén-gwa een-gláy-sa (fran-tháy-sa)

How much is the tour? ¿Qué es el precio de la excursión?
kay es el práy-thee-o day la ex-koor-see-ón

Do we have to pay the guide? ¿Tenemos que pagar al guía?
te-náy-mos kay pa-gár al gēē-a

I am looking for . . . Busco . . .
bōōs-ko

I am lost. Estoy perdido.
es-tóy per-dēē-dho

Can one go on foot? ¿Se puede ir a pie?
say poo-áy-dhay eer a pee-áy

Is it far? ¿Está lejos?
es-tá láy-hos

What is that building? ¿Qué es ese edificio?
kay es é-say ay-dhee-féē-thee-o

Where can I get entrance tickets? ¿Dónde se sacan las entradas?
dón-day say sá-kan las en-trá-dhas

Is it open? ¿Está abierto?
es-tá a-bee-ér-to

When will it open? ¿A qué hora se abre?
a kay ó-ra say á-bray

When does it close? ¿A qué hora se cierra?
a kay ó-ra say thee-áy-ra

Can we go in? ¿Se puede entrar?
say poo-áy-dhay en-trár

We wish to see ... Deseamos ver ...
day-say-á-mos ver ...

Can we take photographs? ¿Se puede sacar fotos?
say poo-áy-dhay sa-kár fó-tos

Follow the guide. Siga al guía.
sēē-ga al gēē-a

Have you postcards showing ¿Tiene usted tarjetas postales
the work of ... ? de la obra de ... ?
tee-áy-nay oos-táydh tar-háy-tas pos-tá-lays day la ó-bra day ...

Painters of the Spanish school. Pintores de la escuela española.
peen-tó-rays day la es-kwáy-la es-pan-yó-la

... dates from the fifteenth ... es del siglo quince.
century.
... es del sēē-glo kēēn-thay

... was built by ... ... fué construido por ...
fway kon-stroo-ēē-dho por ...

I haven't much time. No tengo mucho tiempo.
no tén-go mōō-cho tee-ém-po

How long does it take? ¿Cuánto se tarda?
kwán-to say tár-da

Let us sit down for a while. Sentémonos un rato.
sen-táy-mo-nos oon rá-to

Can we go round alone? ¿Podemos ir solos?
po-dháy-mos eer só-los

When does the next tour start? ¿Cuándo empieza la próxima
excursión (visita)?

kwán-do em-pee-áy-tha la próx-ee-ma ex-koor-see-ón (vee-sée-ta)

It is magnificent (charming). Es magnífico (encantador).

es mag-née-fee-ko (en-kan-ta-dhór)

I am too tired to go farther. Estoy demasiado cansado para
ir más lejos.

es-tóy day-ma-see-á-dho kan-sá-dho pá-ra eer mas láy-hos

I have seen enough for today. He visto bastante para hoy.

ay vées-to bas-tán-tay pá-ra oy

Where can we shelter? ¿Dónde podemos guarecernos?

dón-day po-dháy-mos gwa-ray-thér-nos

Free entry. Entrada gratuita.

en-trá-dha gra-twée-ta

Of what period is it? ¿De qué época es?

day kay áy-po-ka es

Who built it? ¿Quién lo construyó?

kee-én lo kon-stroo-yó

It is open (closed). Está abierto (cerrado).

es-tá a-bee-ér-to (thay-rá-dho)

Come back tomorrow. Vuelva mañana.

voo-áyl-va man-yá-na

AT THE BEACH

Restrictions on beachwear are less severe than formerly, but it must still
be confined to the beach. In many places it is necessary to change in a
bathing-hut, where one's clothes may be left on a coat-hanger under some
sort of supervision although their safety is not guaranteed.

VOCABULARY

air mattress, el colchón de aire (kol-chón day á-ee-ray)
back stroke, la braza de espalda (brá-tha day es-pál-da)
ball, la pelota (pay-ló-ta)
basketball, el baloncesto (ba-lon-tháys-to)
bathing cap, el gorro de baño (gó-ro day bán-yo)
bathing costume, el traje de baño (trá-hay day bán-yo)
bathing costume (two piece), el traje de baño (de dos piezas)
(trá-hay day bán-yo day dos pee-áy-thas)

S.P.B.——D

bathing hut, la caseta de baño (ka-sáy-ta day bán-yo)
bay, la bahía (ba-ēē-a)
beach, la playa (plá-ya)
beach bag, la bolsa de playa (ból-sa day plá-ya)
bikini, el bikini (bee-kēē-nee)
boat, la canoa (ka-nó-a), el bote (bó-tay)
bucket, el cubo (kōō-bo)
buoy, la boya (bó-ya)
canoe, la canoa (ka-nó-a)
chair, folding, la silla plegable (sēēl-ya play-gá-blay)
cliff, el acantilado (a-kan-tee-lá-dho)
clothes, la ropa (ró-pa)
coast, la costa (kós-ta)
crab, el cangrejo (kan-gráy-ho)
cramp, el entumecimiento (en-too-may-thee-mee-én-to)
current, el corriente (ko-ree-én-tay)
dive, to, saltar (sal-tár), zambullirse (tham-bool-yēēr-say)
diving board, la plataforma (pla-ta-fór-ma)
dress, to, vestirse (ves-tēēr-say)
drown, to, ahogarse (a-o-gár-say)
dune, la duna (dōō-na)
fish, el pez (peth)
fish, to, pescar (pes-kár)
flippers, las aletas para nadar (a-láy-tas pá-ra na-dhár)
goggles, las gafas de inmersión (gá-fas day een-mer-see-ón)
harpoon, el arpón (ar-pón)
jelly-fish, la medusa (may-dhōō-sa)
lighthouse, el faro (fá-ro)
motorboat, el deslizador (des-leeth-a-dhór)
oars, los remos (ráy-mos)
outboard motor, el fuera bordo (foo-áy-ra bór-do)
raft, la balsa (bál-sa)
reef, el escollo (es-kól-yo)
rock, la roca (ró-ka), la peña (páyn-ya)
row, to, remar (ray-már)
sail, to, dar un paseo en bote (dar oon pa-sáy-o en bó-tay)
sails, las velas (váy-las)
sand, la arena (a-ráy-na)
sandals, las alpargatas (al-par-gá-tas)
sea, el mar (mar)
shade, la sombra (sóm-bra)
shark, el tiburón (tee-boo-rón)
shell, la concha (kón-cha)
shingle, los guijarros (gee-há-ros)
shiver, to, tiritar (tee-ree-tár)
shower, la ducha (dōō-cha)
spade, la pala (pá-la)
spring-board, el trampolín (tram-po-lēēn)
sun, el sol (sol)
sunbathe, tomar un baño de sol (to-mar oon bán-yo day sol)

sunglasses, las gafas de sol (gá-fas day sol)
sunshade, el quitasol (kee-ta-sól)
sunstroke, la insolación (een-so-la-thee-ón)
sun-tan lotion, la loción para broncear (lo-thee-ón pá-ra bron-thay-ár)
surf, el olaje (o-lá-hay)
surf board, la plancha de deslizamiento (plân-cha day des-leeth-a-mee-én-to)
surf riding, el patinaje sobre las olas (pa-tee-ná-hay so-bray las ó-las)
swimming, la natación (na-ta-thee-ón)
swimming pool, la piscina (pees-thēē-na)
tan, el bronceado (bron-thay-á-dho)
tandem, la bicicleta acuática (bee-thee-cláy-ta a-kwá-tee-ka)
tide (high/low), la marea alta/baja (ma-ráy-a ál-ta/bá-ha)
towel, la toalla (to-ál-ya)
undress, to, desnudarse (des-noo-dhár-say)
water, el agua (á-gwa)
water-skiing, el esquí acuático (es-kēē a-kwá-tee-ko)
wave, la ola (ó-la)
whirlpool, el remolino de agua (ray-mo-lēē-no day á-gwa)

Which is the way to the beach? ¿Por dónde se va a la playa?
por dón-day say va a la plá-ya

Is it far? ¿Está lejos?
es-tá láy-hos

Is there a bus? ¿Hay un autobús?
á-ee oon ow-to-bōōs

Where can we bathe? ¿Dónde podemos bañarnos?
dón-day po-dháy-mos ban-yár-nos

Where does one change? ¿Dónde hay que cambiarse?
dón-day á-ee kay kam-bee-ár-say

Do you have a coat-hanger? ¿Tiene usted una percha?
tee-áy-nay oos-taydh ōō-na pér-cha

What is the number? ¿Qué es el número?
kay es el nōō-may-ro

I want to hire ... Deseo alquilar ...
day-sáy-o al-kee-lár ...

A rowing boat (sailing boat, outboard motorboat). Un bote de remos (de vela, de fuera bordo).
oon bó-tay day ráy-mos (day váy-la, day foo-áy-ra bór-do)

What is the water like?   ¿ Cómo está el agua ?
kó-mo es-tá el á-gwa

Marvellous!   ¡Estupenda!
es-too-pén-da

Is it deep?   ¿ Está honda ?
es-tá ón-da

I cannot swim very well.   No sé nadar muy bien.
no say na-ðhár mwee bee-én

Be careful, there is a strong current.   Cuidado, hay un corriente fuerte.
kwee-dhá-dho á-ee oon ko-ree-én-tay foo-áyr-tay

Watch out for jelly-fish.   Cuidado con las medusas.
kwee-dhá-dho kon las may-dhōō-sas

The water is warm (cold).   El agua está caliente (fría).
el á-gwa es-tá ka-lee-én-tay (frēē-a)

I only want to sunbathe.   No quiero más que tomar un baño de sol.
no kee-áy-ro mas kay to-már oon bán-yo day sol

You will get sunstroke.   Tendrá una insolación.
ten-drá ōō-na een-so-la-thee-ón

How tanned (pale) you are!   ¡Qué bronceado(a) (pálido/a) está usted!
kay bron-thay-á dho (a) (pá-lee-dho/a) es-tá oos-táydh

Is it safe to swim here?   ¿ Se puede bañarse aquí con seguridad ?
say poo-áy-dhay ban-yár-say a-kēē kon say-goo-ree-dádh

Are our things safe here?   ¿ Están seguras nuestras cosas aquí ?
es-tán say-gōō-ras noo-áys-tras kó-sas a-kēē

SPORTS, GAMES AND ENTERTAINMENT

FOOTBALL

This is the favourite sport of most Spaniards and one at which they excel. The following words and phrases may even enable the enthusiast to get the gist of any reported match in a newspaper. Most matches take place on Sunday afternoons. Only a little rugby football is played, mainly in the north.

VOCABULARY

back, el defensa (day-fén-sa)
ball, el balón (ba-lón), la pelota (pay-ló-ta)
centre forward, el delantero centro (day-lan-táy-ro thén-tro)
centre half, el medio centro (máy-dhee-o thén-tro)
championship, el campeonato (kam-pay-on-á-to)
clearance, el despeje (des-páy-hay)
corner, la esquina (es-kēē-na)
corner-kick, el saque de esquina (sá-kay day es-kēē-na)
cross-bar, el larguero (lar-gáy-ro)
draw, el empate (em-pá-tay)
fan, el aficionado (a-fee-thee-o-ná-dho)
football (game), el fútbol (fōōt-bol)
forward, el delantero (day-lan-táy-ro)
foul, la falta (fál-ta)
free-kick, el golpe franco (gól-pay frán-ko), el saque libre (sá-kay lēē-bray)
goal (score), el gol (gol), el tanto (tán-to)
goal (place), la meta (máy-ta), el portal (por-tál), la portería (por-tay-rēē-a), el marco (már-ko), la puerta (poo-áyr-ta)
goal-keeper, el portero (por-táy-ro), el guardametas (gwar-da-máy-tas)
half, first, (second), el primer (segundo) tiempo (pree-mér /say-gōōn-do tee-ém-po)
half back, el medio (máy-dhee-o)
half-time, el descanso (des-kán-so)
header, el remate de cabeza (ray-má-tay day ka-báy-tha), el cabezazo (ka-bay-thá-tho)
inside, interior (een-tay-ree-ór)
kick, la patada (pa-tá-dha)
left, izquierdo(a) (eeth-kee-ér-do/a)
linesman, el juez de banda (línea) (hoo-éth day bán-da /lēē-nay-a), el linier (lee-nee-ér)
line-up, la alineación (a-lee-nay-a-thee-ón)
match, el partido (par-tēē-dho)

off-side, fuera de juego (foo-áy-ra day hoo-áy-go)
pass, el pase (pá-say)
penalty, el penalty (pén-al-tay)
penalty area, el área de castigo (á-ray-a day kas-tēē-go)
player, el jugador (hoo-ga-dhór), el futbolista (foot-bol-ēēs-ta)
referee, el árbitro (ár-bee-tro)
right, derecho(a) (day-ráy-cho/a)
score, la marca (már-ka), el tanto (tán-to)
season, la temporada (tem-po-rá-dha)
shot, el tiro (tēē-ro), el disparo (dees-pá-ro)
stadium, el estadio (es-tá-dhee-o)
stand, la tribuna (tree-bōō-na)
tackle, la entrada (en-trá-dha)
team, el equipo (ay-kēē-po)
terracing, las gradas (grá-dhas)
throw-in, el saque de banda (sá-kay day bán-da)
title-holders, el equipo titular (ay-kēē-po tee-too-lár)
touch-line, la línea de banda (lēē-nay-a day bán-da)
trainer, el entrenador (en-tren-a-dhór)
whistle, el pito (pēē-to)
win, ganar (ga-nár)
wing, el extremo (ex-tráy-mo)

They drew two all.	Han empatado a dos tanto.
	an em-pa-tá-dho a dos tán-to
They won (lost) three one.	Ganaron (perdieron) por tres a uno.
	ga-ná-ron (per-dee-áy-ron) por tres a ōō-no
To score a goal.	Marcar (conseguir) un gol.
	mar-kár (con-say-gēēr) oon gol
Scored by X from a pass by Y.	Marcado por X a pase de Y.
	mar-ká-dho por . . . a pá-say day . . .
One all.	Empate a uno.
	em-pá-tay a ōō-no
Sent off.	Expulsado.
	expool-sá-dho
Four all.	Cuatro tantos.
	kwá-tro tán-tos

BULLFIGHTING

This rather cruel sport is still quite popular in Spain, especially with tourists. Bullfights are held on Sundays and on feast days and sometimes mid-week, in the late afternoon. The most important are to be found in Madrid, Seville and other towns during their fairs. Generally three bullfighters appear with their respective teams and kill two bulls each. They occupy a position in a league table according to points scored. The number of points depends on whether they win an ear, tail, hoof, applause, circuit of the ring, etc. As the tiered seats are of stone one should hire a cushion. As might be expected the seats nearest the ring are dearest, the *contrabarrera* (kon-tra-ba-ráy-ra) and those farthest away are cheapest, the *tendido alto* (ten-dēē-dho ál-to). Medium-priced seats between these are called the *tendido*. The rows of seats are numbered from the front and each section of *tendido* between aisles is given a letter of the alphabet. Seats in the shade *sombra* (sóm-bra) are dearer than those in the sun *sol* (sol). The bull is played with capes, has darts placed in its shoulders and is angered and weakened with a lance. The bullfighter then plays it with a small cape as close as he dares and finally kills it with a sword.

GLOSSARY OF TERMS

el aficionado (a-fee-thee-o-ná-dho) = fan
la almohadilla (al-mo-adh-ēēl-ya) = cushion
el arrastre (a-rás-tray) = dragging out of the carcass by mules
el aviso (a-vēē-so) = warning from the president's box
las banderillas (ban-day-rēēl-yas) = pairs of beribboned darts
el banderillero (ban-day-reel-yáy-ro) = man who places the darts
bravo (brá-vo) = fierce
el brindis (brēēn-dees) = dedication of the bull to someone
el burladero (boor-la-dháy-ro) = wooden refuge
el callejón (kal-yáy-hón) = alley round the ring
la capa (ká-pa) = cape
la corrida (ko-rēē-dha) = bullfight
la cogida (ko-hēē-dha) = toss
la cuadrilla (kwa-drēēl-ya) = bullfighting team
derecho (day-ráy-cho) = a pass with the right arm
el descabello (des-ka-bél-yo) = coup de grâce given with a dagger or special sword
el diestro (dee-és-tro) = bullfighter
embestir(i) (em-bes-tēēr) = to charge
la entera (en-táy-ra) = sword-stroke to the hilt
la espada (es-pá-dha) = sword
el espada (es-pá-dha) = bullfighter
el espontáneo (es-pon-tá-nay-o) = member of public who decides to participate
la estocada (es-to-ká-dha) = sword-thrust made with...
el estoque (es-tó-kay) = bullfighter's sword

estropear (es-tro-pay-ár) =to spoil the bull (often said of the picadores)
la faena (fa-áy-na) =job, task
el farol (fa-ról) =a whirling pass of the cape
el ganado (ga-ná-dho) =livestock: the bulls
hombros, en (en óm-bros) =shoulder high
la manoletina (ma-no-lay-tēē-na) =pass with the cape held from behind the back
manso (mán-so) =tame
el matador (ma-ta-dhór) =bullfighter
el momento de la verdad (mo-mén-to day la ver-dádh) =the kill
el mozo de capa (mó-tho day ká-pa) =assistant bullfighter
la muleta (moo-láy-ta) =small cape on a stick
el natural (na-too-rál) =a common pass
el novillo (no-vēēl-yo) =young bull
el novillero (no-veel-yáy-ro) =apprentice bullfighter
la novillada (no-veel-yá-dha) =bullfight with young bulls
la oreja (o-ráy-ha) =ear
el pase (pá-say) =pass with a cape
el paseo (pa-sáy-o) =preliminary parade
la pata (pá-ta) =hoof
pecho, de (day páy-cho) =pass across the chest
el peso (páy-so) =weight of bull, chalked above the *toril*
el picador (pee-ka-dhór) =mounted man with lance
el pinchazo (peen-chá-tho) =incomplete sword-thrust
pitos (pēē-tos) =whistles of disapproval
la plaza (plá-tha) =the bullring
el quite (kēē-tay) =diverting of the bull's attention
el rabo (rá-bo) =tail
el redondel (ray-dhón-del) =bullring
el rejoneador (ray-hon-ay-a-dhór) =mounted man who places darts
la res (res) =the bull
rodillas, de (day rodh-ēēl-yas) =kneeling
el ruedo (roo-áy-dho) =the ring
la suerte (soo-áyr-tay) =stage of bullfight
el tercio (tér-thee-o) =   ditto
el torero (to-ráy-ro) =bullfighter
el toril (to-rēēl) =bull-pen
el toro de lidia (tó-ro day lēē-dhee-a) =fighting bull
la vara (vá-ra) =lance
la varonica (va-ró-nee-ka) =a pass in which the body revolves contrariwise to the bull's charge.
la vuelta (voo-áyl-ta) =lap of the ring

OTHER SPORTS, GAMES AND ENTERTAINMENT

Spain has other sports to offer: fishing, golf, horse-racing, show jumping, ski-ing, swimming (see *At the Beach*) and pelota which is to be found in the

Basque country and is a ball game played against a wall by two players and which demands agility and stamina. With regard to indoor pastimes it should be noted that although our own French playing cards are used, the Tarot cards are also common in Spain. Cinema tickets as well as those for the theatre are often bought in advance. There is a late cinema session after dinner. Smoking in the auditorium is not usually allowed. Night clubs are an exception to the generally moderate prices of refreshment in Spain, although some good floor shows may be seen for the price of a well-nursed long drink. If you are in Catalonia and feel like dancing you may learn the *sardana* in the street of a fine evening.

VOCABULARY

Fishing, la pesca (páys-ka)
  bait, el cebo (tháy-bo)
  fish, el pez (peth)
  fisherman, el pescador (pays-ka-dhór)
  fly, la mosca (mós-ka)
  hook, el anzuelo (an-thoo-áy-lo)
  line, la línea (leé-nay-a)
  net, la red (red)
  permit, el permiso (per-mēē-so)
  river, el río (rēē-o)
  rod, la caña (kán-ya)
  salmon, el salmón (sal-món)
  stream, el arroyo (a-ró-yo)
  trout, la trucha (trōō-cha)
Golf, el golf
  ball, la pelota (pay-ló-ta)
  bunker, la hoya de arena (ó-ya day a-ráy-na)
  caddie, el caddie
  drive, el golpe de salida (gól-pay day sa-lēē-dha)
  fairway, el fairway
  flag, la bandera (ban-dáy-ra)
  golf bag, la bolsa (ból-sa)
  golf club, el palo (pá-lo)
  golf club (people), el club de golf
  golf course, el campo de golf (kám-po day golf)
  golfer, el jugador de golf (hoo-ga-dhór day golf)
  green, el green
  hole, el hoyo (ó-yo)
  iron, el acero (a-tháy-ro)
  putt, el tiro al hoyo (tēē-ro al ó-yo)
  putter, el putter
  swear word, el taco (tá-ko): a suitable one would be ¡Leche! (láy-chay)
  tee, la salida (sal-lēē-dha)
  wood, el madero (ma-dháy-ro)
Horse-racing, las carreras de caballos (ka-ráy-ras day ka-bál-yos)

Ski-ing, el esquí (es-kēē)
  chair-lift, la telesilla (tay-lay-sēēl-ya)
Tennis, el tenis (tén-ees)
  advantage: in, out, ventaja: dentro, fuera (ven-tá-ha: dén-tro, foo-áy-ra)
  backhand, la devolución de revés (day-vo-loo-thee-ón day ray-vés)
  ball, la pelota (pay-ló-ta)
  court, la pista de tenis (peés-ta day tén-ees)
  deuce, a dos (a dos)
  doubles, el doble (dó-blay)
  forehand, la devolución de derecho (day-vo-loo-thee-ón day day-ráy-cho)
  line, la línea (lēē-nay-a)
  lob, el lob
  love, cero (tháy-ro)
  match, el partido (par-tēē-dho)
  net, la red (red)
  racquet, la raqueta (ra-káy-ta)
  service, el saque (sá-kay)
  singles, el individual (een-dee-vee-dhoo-ál)
  thirty all, treinta tanto (tráy-een-ta tán-to)
  tournament, el torneo (tor-náy-o)
  volley, el golpe de voleo (gól-pay day vo-láy-o)

Can one go fishing here (there)?   ¿Se puede pescar con caña aquí (allí)?
say poo-áy-dhay pays-kár kon kán-ya a-kēē (al-yēē)

What is the fishing like just now?   ¿Cómo está la pesca en este momento?
kó-mo es-tá la páys-ka en és-tay mo-mén-to

Are there any big ones?   ¿Los hay grandes?
los á-ee grán-days

Whose permission does one ask?   ¿A quién se pide permiso?
a kee-én say pēē-dhay per-mēē-so

Is there a golf course?   ¿Hay campo de golf?
á-ee kám-po day golf

How many holes has it?   ¿Cuántos hoyos tiene?
kwán-tos ó-yos tee-áy-nay

Can strangers play?   ¿Pueden jugar los forasteros?
poo-áy-dhen hoo-gár los fo-ras-táy-ros

I have brought my clubs.   He traído mis palos.
                         ay tra-ēē-dho mees pá-los

There are only nine holes.   No hay más que nueve hoyos.
                       no á-ee mas kay noo-áy-vay ó-yos

We are going to the races.   Vamos a las carreras.
                       vámos a las ka-ráy-ras

Is there a car park?   ¿Hay un estacionamiento para los coches?
                       á-ee ōōn es-ta-thee-o-na-mee-én-to pá-ra los kó-chays

We would like to play tennis.   Nos gustaría jugar al tenis.
                       nos goos-ta-rēē-a hoo-gár al ténis

I should like to play in the tournament.   Quisiera jugar en el torneo.
                       kee-see-áy-ra hoo-gár en el tor-náy-o

What is the score?   ¿Qué es el tanto?
                       kay es el tán-to

It is love-fifteen.   Estamos a cero a quince.
                       es-tá-mos a tháy-ro a kēēn-thay

That was a good one!   ¡Vale!
                       vá-lay

Whose service is it?   ¿A quién toca el saque?
                       a kee-én tó-ka el sá-kay

ENTERTAINMENT VOCABULARY

attendant, el(la) encargado(a) (en-kar-gá-dho/a)
ball, el baile de gala (bá-ee-lay day gá-la)
box (theatre), el palco (pál-ko)
box-office, la taquilla (ta-kēēl-ya)
cinema, el cine (thēē-nay)
cloakroom, el guardarropa (gwar-da-ró-pa)
conductor, el director (dee-rek-tór)
dance, el baile (bá-ee-lay)
dancer: male, el bailarín (ba-ee-la-rēēn)
dancer: female, la bailarina (ba-ee-la-rēē-na)
dress circle, el principal (preen-thee-pál)
dubbed version, el doblaje (do-blá-hay)
evening dress, el traje de etiqueta (trá-hay day ay-tee-káy-ta)

exit (emergency), la salida (de urgencia) (sa-leé-dha day oor-hén-thee-a)
film, la película (pay-lēē-koo-la), el film (feelm)
foyer, la sala de descanso (sá-la day des-kán-so)
gallery, el paraíso (pa-ra-ēē-so)
interval, el descanso (des-kán-so)
light opera, la zarzuela (thar-thoo-áy-la)
music, la música (mōō-see-ka)
newsreel, el film de actualidades (ak-too-a-lee-dá-dhays), el "nodo" (nó-dho)
opera, la ópera (ó-pay-ra)
orchestra, la orquesta (or-káys-ta)
orchestra stalls, las butacas de patio (boo-tá-kas day pá-tee-o)
patrons, los concurrentes (kon-koo-rén-tays)
performance, la función (foon-thee-ón)
pit, el patio (pá-tee-o)
play, la pieza (pee-áy-tha), la comedia (ko-máy-dhee-a)
row, la fila (fēē-la)
screen, la pantalla (pan-tál-ya)
seat, la plaza (plá-tha), el sitio (sēē-tee-o)
show, el espectáculo (es-pek-tá-koo-lo)
stage, la escena (es-tháy-na)
stalls, el patio (pá-tee-o)
star, la estrella (es-trél-ya)
theatre, el teatro (tay-á-tro)
ticket, la entrada (en-trá-dha)
upper circle, el anfiteatro (an-fee-tay-á-tro)
usher, el acomodador (a-ko-mo-da-dhór)
waltz, el vals (vals)

Advance bookings.   Venta anticipada.
vén-ta an-tee-thee-pá-dha

Continuous performance.   Sesión continua.
say-see-ón kon-teé-noo-a

Air-conditioned.   Sala refrigerada.
sá-la ray-free-hay-rá-dha

Adults only.   Mayores.
ma-yó-rays

Suitable for all (for children).   Apto todos públicos (menores).
áp-to tó-dhos pōō-blee-kos (may-nó-rays)

Is it a good film?   ¿Es un buen film?
es oon boo-én feelm

I like that actor (actress).	Me gusta aquel actor (aquella actriz).

may gōōs-ta a-kél ak-tór (a-kél-ya ak-trēēth)

When does the next performance start?	¿Cuándo empieza la próxima función?

kwán-do em-pee-áy-tha la próx-ee-ma foon-thee-ón

Enjoy yourselves!	¡Que se diviertan!

kay say dee-vee-áyr-tan

Would you like to dance?	¿Quisiera usted bailar?

kee-see-áy-ra oos-táydh ba-ee-lár

I cannot dance this.	No sé bailar esto.

no say ba-ee-lár és-to

I'll teach you.	Se lo enseñaré.

say lo en-sen-ya-ráy

Should one wear evening dress?	¿Hay que llevar traje de etiqueta?

á-ee kay lyay-vár trá-hay day ay-tee-káy-ta

It is not necessary.	No hace falta.

no á-thay fál-ta

CAMPING AND WEATHER

Camping facilities are not so common in Spain as in France since hotel prices are more competitive and water is not so readily available. There are not as yet reciprocal arrangements for youth hostellers. Hiking and hitch-hiking are not entirely approved of by the police in sparsely patrolled areas.

VOCABULARY

air mattress, el colchón de aire (kol-chón day á-ee-ray)
blanket, la manta (mán-ta)
bucket, el cubo (kōō-bo)
camp, to, acampar (a-kam-pár)
camp bed, la cama tijera (ká-ma tee-háy-ra)
camping site, el terreno de camping (tay-ráy-no day kám-ping)
candle, la bujía (boo-hēē-a)
cloud, la nube (nōō-bay)
cold, el frío (frēē-o)
compass, la brújula (brōō-hoo-la)

cork-screw, el sacacorchos (sa-ka-kór-chos)
cup, la taza (tá-tha)
dawn, el amanecer (a-ma-nay-thér), el alba (ál-ba)
drinking water, el agua potable (á-gwa po-tá-blay)
dusk, el anochecer (a-no-chay-thér)
fire, el fuego (foo-áy-go), la lumbre (lōōm-bray)
firewood, la leña (láyn-ya)
first aid kit, el botiquín (bo-tee-kēēn)
fog, la niebla
frying pan. la sartén (sar-tén)
groundsheet, la alfombra (al-fóm-bra)
hail, el granizo (gra-nēē-tho)
heat, el calor (ka-lór)
hike, to, viajar a pie (vee-a-hár a pee-áy)
hitch-hike, to, viajar pidiendo ser llevado (vee-a-hár pee-dhee-én-do ser lyay-vá-dho)
ice, el hielo (ee-áy-lo)
lamp, la lámpara (lám-pa-ra)
latrine, la letrina (lay-trēē-na)
lightning, el relámpago (re-lám-pa-go)
matches, las cerillas (thay-rēēl-yas)
meadow, el prado (prá-dho)
methylated spirit, el alcohol para quemar (al-ko-ól pá-ra kay-már)
mist, la neblina (nay-blēē-na)
mud, el barro (bá-ro), el lodo (ló-dho)
paraffin, el petróleo (pay-tró-lay-o)
path, la senda (sáyn-da)
picnic, la comida campestre (ko-mēē-dha kam-páys-tray)
pillow, la almohada (al-mo-á-dha)
plate, el plato (plá-to)
pocket knife, la navaja de bolsillo (na-vá-ha day bol-sēēl-yo)
rain, la lluvia (lyōō-vee-a)
rubbish, la basura (ba-sōō-ra)
rucksack, la mochila (mo-chēē-la)
saucepan, la cacerola (ka-thay-ró-la)
shorts, el pantalón corto (pan-ta-lón kór-to)
shower, el chubasco (choo-bás-ko), el aguacero (a-gwa-tháy-ro)
sleeping bag, el saco de dormir (sá-ko day dor-mēēr)
snow, la nieve (nee-áy-vay)
storm, la tormenta (tor-mén-ta), la tempestad (tem-pes-tádh)
stove, el anafe (a-náf-ay)
sun (shine), el sol (sol)
tent, la tienda (tee-áyn-da)
tent peg, el piquete (pee-káy-tay)
tent pole, el mastil (mas-tēēl)
tent rope, el cordón (kor-dón)
thunder, el trueno (troo-áy-no)
tin-opener, el abrelatas (a-bray-lá-tas)
toilet bag, el neceser (nay-thay-sér)
torch, la lámpara de bolsillo (lám-pa-ra day bol-sēēl-yo)

transistor radio, la radio portátil (rá-dhee-o por-tá-teel)
vacuum flask, la botella de vacío (bo-táyl-ya day va-thēē-o)
water bottle, la cantimplora (kam-teem-pló-ra)
waterproof, impermeable (eem-per-may-á-blay)
weather, el tiempo (tee-ém-po)
wind, el viento (vee-én-to)

What is the weather like? ¿Qué tiempo hace?
kay tee-áym-po á-thay

The weather is good (bad). Hace buen (mal) tiempo.
á-thay boo-én (mal) tee-áym-po

It is clear (cloudy). Está claro (nublado).
es-tá klá-ro (noo-blá-dho)

The sun is shining. Hace sol.
á-thay sol

It is warm (cold, windy). Hace calor (frío, viento).
á-thay ka-lór (frēē-o, vee-áyn-to)

It is raining (drizzling, freezing, Llueve (llovizna, hiela, nieva).
snowing).
lyoo-áy-vay (lyo-vēēth-na, ee-áy-la, nee-áy-va)

It is pouring with rain. Llueve a cántaros.
lyoo-áy-vay a kán-ta-ros

The sun is getting hot. El sol empieza a picar.
el sol em-pee-áy-tha a pee-kár

I can't stand the heat. No aguanto el calor.
no a-gwán-to el ka-lór

There is thunder (lightning). Truena (relampaguea).
troo-áy-na (ray-lam-pa-gáy-a)

It is getting light (dark). Amanece (oscurece).
a-ma-náy-thay (os-koo-ráy-thay)

Let's take shelter. Si nos ponemos al abrigo.
see nos po-náy-mos al a-brēē-go

Let's go into the shade. Vamos a la sombra.
vá-mos a la sóm-bra

I'm soaked. Estoy mojado hasta los huesos.
es-tóy mo-há-dho á-sta los wáy-sos

I'm sweating.   Estoy sudando.
es-tóy soo-dán-do

The temperature is . . . degrees   La temperatura es de . . . grados
above (below) zero.   sobre (bajo) cero.
la tem-pay-ra-tōō-ra es day . . . grá-dhos só-bray (bá-ho) tháy-ro

What is the weather forecast?   ¿Qúe es el pronóstico meteorológico?
kay es el pro-nós-tee-ko may-tay-o-ro-ló-hee-ko

It is going to rain.   Va a llover.
va a lyo-vér

It will be a fine day.   El día se promete bien.
el dēē-a say pro-máy-tay bee-én

It will be a wet (dull) day.   Será un día lluvioso (cubierto).
say-rá oon dēē-a lyoo-vee-ó-so (koo-bee-áyr-to)

Is there drinking water?   ¿Hay agua potable?
á-ee á-gwa po-tá-blay

We are looking for a camping   Buscamos un terreno de
site.   camping.
boos-ká-mos oon tay-ráy-no day kám-ping

Is camping allowed?   ¿Está autorizado el camping?
es-tá ow-to-ree-thá-dho el kám-ping

Can we camp here?   ¿Se permite acampar aquí?
say per-mēē-tay a-kam-pár a-kēē

Who is in charge of the site?   ¿Quién es el encargado del
terreno?
kee-én es el en-kar-gá-dho del tay-ráy-no

Whose permission must we ask?   ¿A quién debemos pedir
permiso?
a kee-én day-báy-mos pay-dhēēr per-mēē-so

May we light a fire?   ¿Se puede hacer un fuego?
say poo-áy-dhay a-thér oon foo-áy-go

How much do you charge a day?   ¿Cuánto cobra usted al día?
kwán-to kó-bra oos-táydh al dēē-a

Where can I buy . . . ?   ¿Dónde puedo comprar . . . ?
dón-day poo-áy-dho kom-prár . . .

Where can I put this rubbish?   ¿Dónde puedo echar esta
                                            basura?
dón-day poo-áy-dho ay-chár és-ta ba-sŏŏ-ra

We shall be leaving early.   Nos marcharemos temprano.
nos mar-char-áy-mos tem-prá-no

Can we pay now?   ¿Cobrará usted ahora?
ko-bra-rá oos-táydh a-ó-ra

SHOPPING

Shops are open from about 9 a.m. to 1 p.m. and from about 3.30 p.m. to about 8 p.m. Opening hours generally depend on the time of year, so that from May to October; when the *horario de verano* (o-rá-ree-o day vay-rá-no) or summer time-table is in operation, the afternoon break is longer and the evening closing hour correspondingly later. As a rule only food shops are open on Sundays. Sizes and measurements differ from those in use in Britain and the U.S.A. Tables of these continental sizes will be found in the appendix. Fruit and vegetables are sold by the *kilo* (kēē-lo), or *kilogramo*, which is about 2 lb. weight. Prices are normally given in pesetas but the following terms are also used; *un duro* (oon dŏŏ-ro) = 5 *pesetas*; *un real* (oon ray-ál) = ¼ peseta or 25 *céntimos* (thén-tee-mos). Good value will be found among the following types of goods: leatherwork, basket work, wrought iron work, lace, filigree work, sherries and liqueurs.

Shops: *Las tiendas* (tee-én-das)

baker, la panadería (pa-na-dhay-rēē-a)
       la pastelería (pas-tel-ay-rēē-a)
barber, la barbería (bar-bay-rēē-a)
bookshop, la librería (lee-bray-rēē-a)
chemist, la farmacia (far-má-thee-a)
cleaner, dyer, la tintorería (teen-to-ray-rēē-a)
confectioner, la confitería (kon-fee-tay-rēē-a)
dairy, la lechería (lay-chay-rēē-a)
department store, el almacén (al-ma-thén)
draper, tejidos y confecciones (tay-hēē-dos ee kon-fek-thee-ó-nays)
dressmaker, la modista (mo-dhēēs-ta)
fancy leather goods, artículos de cuero (ar-tēē-koo-los day kwáy-ro)
fishmonger, la pescadería (pes-ca-dhay-rēē-a)
fruiterer, la frutería (froo-tay-rēē-a)

grocer, alimentación (a-lee-men-ta-thee-ón)
      comestibles (ko-mes-tēē-blays)
      ultramarinos (ool-tra-ma-rēē-nos)
hairdresser, la peluquería (pay-loo-kay-rēē-a)
ironmonger, la ferretería (fay-ray-tay-rēē-a)
jeweller, la joyería (ho-yay-rēē-a)
laundry, el lavado de ropa (la-vá-dho day ró-pa)
newsagent, el estanco (es-tán-ko), el puesto de periódicos
    (poo-áys-to day pay-ree-ó-dhee-kos)
optician, el óptico (óp-tee-ko)
perfumery, la perfumería (per-foo-may-rēē-a)
photographic dealer, la fotografía (fo-to-gra-fēē-a)
pork-butcher, la salchichería (sal-chee-chay-rēē-a)
shirtmaker, la camisería (ka-mee-say-rēē-a)
shoemaker (repairs), salón de limpiabotas (sa-lón day lēēm-
    pee-a-bó-tas) zapatero remendón (tha-pa-táy-ro ray-
    men-dón)
shoe-shop, calzado (kal-thá-dho), la zapatería (tha-pa-
    tay-rēē-a)
stationer, la papelería (pa-pay-lay-rēē-a)
tailor, la sastrería (sas-tray-rēē-a)
tobacconist, el estanco (es-tán-ko)

VOCABULARY

battery, la batería (ba-tay-rēē-a)
book, el libro (lēē-bro)
cheap, barato (ba-rá-to)
cigarette, el cigarillo (thee-ga-rēēl-yo), el pitillo (pee-tēēl-yo)
counter, el mostrador (mos-tra-dhór)
dear, caro (ká-ro)
dictionary, el diccionario (deek-thee-on-á-ree-o)
discount, la rebaja (ray-bá-ha)
doll, el muñeco (la muñeca) (moon-yáy-ko/ka)
elastic, elástico (ay-lás-tee-ko)
envelope, el sobre (só-bray)
gramophone record, el disco (dēēs-ko)
guide book, la guía (gēē-a)
handbag, el bolso (ból-so)
ink, la tinta (tēēn-ta)
label, la etiqueta (ay-tee-káy-ta)
magazine, la revista (ray-vēēs-ta)
map, el mapa (má-pa)
market, el mercado (mayr-ká-dho)
matches, las cerillas (thay-rēēl-yas)
nail-file, la lima de uñas (lēē-ma day ōōn-yas)
needle, la aguja (a-gōō-ha)
newspaper, el periódico (pay-ree-ó-dhee-ko), el diario
    (dee-á-ree-o)

pen, ball-point, el bolígrafo (bo-lēē-gra-fo)
pencil, el lápiz (lá-peeth)
pin, el alfiler (al-fee-lér)
pin, safety, el imperdible (eem-per-dēē-blay)
purse, el portamonedas (por-ta-mo-náy-dhas)
ring, la sortija (sor-tēē-ha)
sale, la venta (váyn-ta)
scissors, las tijeras (tee-háy-ras)
shoe-laces, los cordones para zapatos (kor-dó-nays pá-ra tha-pá-tos)
shopkeeper, el tendero (tayn-dáy-ro)
string, el bramante (bra-mán-tay)
sweets, los caramelos (ka-ra-máy-los)
thread, el hilo (ēē-lo)
toy, el juguete (hoo-gáy-tay)
umbrella, el paraguas (pa-rá-gwas)
wallet, la cartera (car-táy-ra)
watch, el reloj (ray-lóh)
writing-paper, el papel de escribir (pa-pél day es-kree-bēēr)

Where can I buy . . . ? ¿Dónde puedo comprar . . . ?
dón-day poo-áy-dho kom-prár . . .

Have you any . . . ? ¿Tiene usted . . . ?
tee-áy-nay oos-táydh

Have you any British (American) cigarettes? ¿Tiene usted cigarillos ingleses (americanos)?
tee-áy-nay oos-táydh thee-ga-rēēl-yos een-gláy-says (a-may-ree-ká-nos)

At what time do the shops open? ¿A qué hora se abren las tiendas?
a kay ó-ra say á-bren las tee-én-das

Where are the best shops? ¿Dónde están las mejores tiendas?
dón-day es-tán las may-hó-rays tee-én-das

How much is it? ¿Cuánto es?
kwán-to es

Would you write down the price? ¿Sírvase escribir el precio?
sēēr-va-say es-kree-bēēr el práy-thee-o

How much (how many) do you want? ¿Cuánto (cuántos) quiere usted?
kwán-to(s) kee-áy-ray oos-táydh

A pound of grapes please.	Medio kilo de uvas, por favor.
	máy-dhee-o kēē-lo day ōō-vas por fa-vór
Do you have change?	¿Tiene usted el cambio?
	tee-áy-nay oos-táydh el kám-bee-o
Have you anything cheaper?	¿Tiene usted algo más barato?
	tee-áy-nay oos-táydh ál-go mas ba-rá-to
It is too expensive.	Es demasiado caro.
	es day-ma-see-á-dho ká-ro
Have you something of better quality?	¿Tiene usted algo de mejor calidad?
	tee-áy-nay oos-táydh ál-go day may-hór ka-lee-dhádh
Pay at the cash-desk, please.	Sírvase pagar a la caja.
	sēēr-va-say pa-gár a la ká-ha
You have given me the wrong change.	Se ha equivocado con el cambio.
	say a ay-kee-vo-ká-dho kon el kám-bee-o
I bought this yesterday.	Compré esto ayer.
	kom-práy és-to a-yér
It doesn't work.	No funciona.
	no foon-thee-ó-na
Can you change it?	¿Puede usted darme otro?
	poo-áy-dhay oos-táydh dár-may ó-tro
Can you refund my money?	¿Puede usted reintegrármelo?
	poo-áy-dhay oos-táydh ray-een-tay-grár-may-lo
Can you send it?	¿Puede usted mandarlo?
	poo-áy-dhay oos-táydh man-dár-lo
Will you accept a traveller's cheque?	¿Aceptará usted un cheque de viajero?
	a-thayp-ta-rá oos-táydh oon cháy-kay day vee-a-háy-ro
Do you sell . . . ?	¿Vende usted . . . ?
	váyn-day oos-táydh . . .
May I come back and collect it?	¿Puedo volver a recogerlo?
	poo-áy-dho vol-vér a ray-ko-hér-lo
I want something similar to this,	Deseo algo parecido a esto.
	day-sáy-o ál-go pa-ráy-thēē-dho a és-to

Have you anything bigger (smaller, thicker, thinner)? ¿Tiene usted algo más grande (pequeño, grueso, delgado)?

tee-áy-nay oos-táydh ál-go mas grán-day (pay-káyn-yo, groo-áy-so, del-gá-dho)

Can you wrap it up? ¿Puede usted envolverlo?

poo-áy-dhay oos-táydh en-vol-vér-lo

Have you a paper bag? ¿Tiene usted un saco de papel?

tee-áy-nay oos-táydh oon sá-ko day pa-pél

I need . . . Necesito . . .

nay-thay-sēē-to . . .

I (do not) like it. (No) me gusta.

(no) may gōōs-ta

You have not sent . . . No ha mandado . . .

no a man-dá-dho . . .

Here is my address. He aquí mis señas.

ay a-kēē mees sáyn-yas

Do you sell long-playing records? ¿Vende usted discos de larga duración?

vén-day oos-táydh dēēs-kos day lár-ga doo-ra-thee-ón

POST OFFICE

Tobacconists' kiosks which sell postage stamps and receive mail for posting are painted red and yellow, as are pillar and post boxes. Other business has to be transacted at a main post office. When posting mail abroad use the box marked *extranjero* (ex-tran-háy-ro), foreign mail.

Current postage rates are: letters abroad: 5 pesetas; postcards abroad with more than five words: 3 pesetas; postcards with five words or less: 2 pesetas; internal mail: letters 1 peseta; postcards 70 céntimos.

VOCABULARY

address, la dirección (dee-rek-thee-ón), las señas (sáyn-yas)
airmail, el correo aéreo (ko-ráy-o a-áy-ray-o)
cablegram, el cablegrama (ka-blay-grá-ma)
collection, la recogida (ray-ko-hēē-dha)
delivery, la distribución (dees-tree-boo-thee-ón)
express, urgente (oor-hén-tay)
letter, la carta (kár-ta)
mail, el correo (ko-ráy-o)
parcel, el paquete (pa-káy-tay)

post box, el buzón (boo-thón)
post office, la casa de correos (ká-sa day ko-ráy-os)
postal order, el giro postal (hēē-ro pos-tál)
postcard, la tarjeta postal (tar-háy-ta pos-tál)
postman, el cartero (kar-táy-ro)
reply coupon, el cupón de respuesta (koo-pón day res-poo-áys-ta)
sign, to, firmar (feer-már)
telegram, el telegrama (tay-lay-grá-ma)

Where is the Post Office?   ¿Dónde está la Casa de Correos?
dón-day es-tá la ká-sa day ko-ráy-os

I want some stamps.   Quiero sellos.
kee-áy-ro sáyl-yos

How much is it to send a letter (postcard) abroad?   ¿Cuánto es una carta (una postal) al extranjero?
kwán-to es ōō-na kár-ta (ōō-na pos-tál) al ex-tran-háy-ro

Will this go tonight?   ¿Saldrá esta noche?
sal-drá és-ta nó-chay

I want to send this parcel.   Quiero mandar este paquete.
kee-áy-ro man-dár és-tay pa-káy-tay

I want to register it.   Quiero certificarlo.
kee-áy-ro ther-tee-fee-kár-lo

Where are there telegraph forms?   ¿Dónde hay impresos de telegrama?
dón-day á-ee eem-práy-sos day tay-lay-grá-ma

Where can I cash a postal order?   ¿Dónde se cobran los giros?
dón-day say kó-bran los hēē-ros

Where is the Poste Restante?   ¿Dónde está la Lista de Correos?
dón-day es-tá la lēēs-ta day ko-ráy-os

Is there a letter for me?   ¿Hay una carta para mí?
á-ee ōō-na kár-ta pá-ra mēē

Have you any identification papers?   ¿Tiene usted alguna pieza de identificación?
tee-áy-nay oos-táydh al-gōō-na pee-áy-tha day ee-dhen-tee-fee-ka-thee-ón

I want to send a telegram.   Quiero poner un telegrama.

kee-áy-ro po-nér oon tay-lay-grá-ma

How much is it per word?   ¿Cuánto es por palabra?

kwán-to es por pa-lá-bra

THE TELEPHONE

Numbers should be stated individually, e.g. 707 =*siete, cero, siete*. The telephone and postal buildings are often separate. One may telephone from a bar on buying a jeton, *ficha* (fee-cha), which is put in the slot to pay for a call. Some delay may be experienced in having a trunk call put through.

VOCABULARY

call, la comunicación (ko-moo-nee-ka-thee-ón), la llamada (lya-má-dha)

dial, to, marcar (mar-kár)

directory, la guía de teléfonos (gēē-a day tay-láy-fo-nos)

exchange, la central (then-trál)

number, el número (nōō-may-ro)

operator, la señorita (sayn-yo-rēē-ta)

receiver, el auricular (ow-ree-koo-lár)

telephone, el teléfono (tay-láy-fo-no)

trunk call, la conferencia (kon-fay-rén-thee-a)

Where may I telephone?   ¿Dónde puedo telefonear?

dón-day poo-áy-dho tay-lay-fo-nay-ár

Is there a telephone?   ¿Hay el teléfono?

á-ee el tay-láy-fo-no

Operator, get me ...   Señorita, por favor póngame...

sayn-yo-rēē-ta, por fav-ór pón-ga-may ...

I should like to make a trunk   Quisiera una conferencia

call to ...   con ...

kee-see-áy-ra ōō-na kon-fay-rén-thee-a kon ...

Hullo! (making the call) (taking   ¡Oiga! ¡Dígame!

the call).

óy-ga, dēē-ga-may

There is no answer.   No contestan.

no kon-táys-tan

The line is engaged.   Está comunicando.
                                es-tá ko-moo-nee-kán-do

This is Mr. Smith.   Es el Señor Smith.
                                el el sayn-yór Smith

Is Mr. Quevedo at home?   ¿ Está el Señor Quevedo ?
                                es-tá el sayn-yór Quevedo

He is not at home.   No está.
                                no es-tá

Will you take a message?   ¿ Quiere usted tomar un
                                          mensaje ?
                          kee-áy-ray oos-táydh to-már oon men-sá-hay

Ask him to ring me.   Dígale que me llame.
                              dēē-ga-lay kay may lyá-may

CHEMIST

Chemists do not sell such a wide range of articles as in Britain and for
perfumes and soap, for instance, one would go to a *perfumería*. The
newspapers indicate which chemists' shops are open all night on a particular
date; these are called the *farmacias de guardia* (day gwár-dee-a).

VOCABULARY

adhesive dressing, las tiritas (tee-rēē-tas)
aspirin, la aspirina (as-pee-rēē-na)
bandage, la venda (váyn-da)
chemist, la farmacia (far-má-thee-a)
cosmetics, los artículos de tocada (ar-tēē-koo-los day to-kâ-dha)
cough sweets, las pastillas para la tos (pas-tēēl-yas pá-ra la tos)
disinfectant, el desinfectante (days-een-fek-tán-tay)
gargle, las gárgaras (gár-gar-as)
laxative, el laxante (lax-án-tay)
lint, las hilas (ēē-las)
lipstick, el lápiz de labios (lá-peeth day lá-bee-os)
medicine, el remedio (ray-máy-dhee-o), el medicamento (may-dhee-ka-mén-to)
nail brush, el cepillo de uñas (thay-pēēl-yo day ōōn-yas)
ointment, el ungüento (oon-gwén-to)
perfume, el perfume (per-fōō-may)
pill, la píldora (pēēl-do-ra)
powder, los polvos (pól-vos)
prescription, la receta (ray-tháy-ta)

quinine, la quinina (kee-nēē-na)
sanitary towels, las compresas higiénicas (kom-práy-sas ee-hee-áy-nee-kas)
sleeping pill, un somnífero (som-nēē-fay-ro)
soap, el jabón (ha-bón)
sponge, la esponja (es-pón-ha)
sunburn cream, la crema contra el sol (kráy-ma kón-tra el sol)
suntan lotion, el aceite para broncear (a-tháy-ee-tay pá-ra bron-thay-ár)
tablet, el comprimido (kom-pree-mēē-dho)
toilet paper, el papel higiénico (pa-pél ee-hee-áy-nee-ko)
tooth brush, el cepillo de dientes (thay-pēēl-yo day dee-én-tays)
toothpaste, el dentífrico (den-tēē-free-ko)

Can you make up this pre-scription?
poo-áy-dhay oos-táydh a-thér és-ta ray-tháy-ta

¿Puede usted hacer esta receta?

I shall call for it later.
vol-vay-ráy a ray-ko-háyr-la

Volveré a recogerla.

Can you read an English pre-scription?
sá-bay oos-táydh lay-ér ōō-na ray-tháy-ta een-gláy-sa

¿Sabe usted leer una receta inglesa?

My back is badly sunburnt.
tén-go la es-pál-da mwee kay-má-dha del sol

Tengo la espalda muy quemada del sol.

Give me something for mosquito bites.
dáy-may ál-go kón-tra las pee-ka-dhōō-ras day mos-kēē-to

Déme algo contra las picaduras de mosquito.

Can you give me something for constipation (diarrhoea, hay fever)?
poo-áy-dhay oos-táydh dár-may ál-go kón-tra el es-tren-yee-mee-én-to (la dee-a-ráy-a, la fee-áy-bray del áy-no)

¿Puede usted darme algo contra el estreñimiento (la diarrea, la fiebre del heno)?

Three times a day. In a glass of water.
trays váy-thays al dēē-a. en oon vá-so day á-gwa

Tres veces al día. En un vaso de agua.

After meals.
days-poo-áys day ko-mér

Después de comer.

Directions for use.	Modo de usar.
	mó-dho day oo-sár

For external use.	Para el uso externo.
	pá-ra el ōō-so ex-tér-no

HAIRDRESSER

VOCABULARY

MEN

after shave lotion, la loción de después del afeitado (lo-thee-ón day des-poo-áys del a-fay-ee-tá-dho)
barber's shop, la barbería (bar-bay-rēē-a)
beard, la barba (bár-ba)
comb, el peine (páy-ee-nay)
eau de Cologne, la colonia (ko-ló-nee-a)
hair, el pelo (páy-lo), los cabellos (ka-bél-yos)
hair cream, la crema para el pelo (kráy-ma pá-ra el páy-lo)
hair oil, la brillantina (breel-yan-tēē-na)
haircut, el corte de pelo (kór-tay day páy-lo)
hairdresser (men's), la barbería (bar-bay-rēē-a)
parting, la raya (rá-ya)
razor (safety), la máquina de afeitar (má-kee-na day a-fay-ee-tár)
razor blade, la hoja de afeitar (ó-ha day a-fay-ee-tár)
shampoo, el lavado de la cabeza (la-vá-dho day la ka-báy-tha)
shaver, electric, la máquina eléctrica de afeitarse (má-kee-na ay-lék-tree-ka day a-fay-ee-tár-say)
shaving brush, la brocha de afeitar (bró-cha day a-fay-ee-tár)
shaving cream, la crema de afeitar (kráy-ma day a-fay-ee-tár)
shaving stick, el jabón de afeitar (ha-bón day a-fay-ee-tár)

Shave please.	Sírvase afeitarme.
	sēēr-va-say a-fay-ee-tár-may

Haircut please.	Sírvase cortarme el pelo.
	sēēr-va-say kor-tár-may el páy-lo

Short back and sides.	Corto por detrás y al lado.
	kór-to por day-trás ee al lá-dho

A trim please.	Recórtelo por favor.
	ray-kór-tay-lo por fa-vór

A shampoo please.	Sírvase lavarme la cabeza.
	sēēr-va-say la-vár-may la ka-báy-tha

Shall I put anything on it?   ¿ Le pongo algo?

lay pón-go ál-go

A little cologne.   Un poco de colonia.

oon pó-ko day ko-ló-nee-a

That's you then, sir.   ¡ Servido, caballero!

ser-vēē-dho, ka-bal-yáy-ro

Something else? Nothing else. ¿ Algo más? Nada más.

ál-go mas. ná-dha mas

WOMEN

appointment, la cita (thēē-ta)
comb, el peine (páy-ee-nay)
curl, el rizo (rēē-tho)
curler, el rizador (ree-tha-dhór)
dryer, el secador (say-ka-dhór)
dye, el tinte para el pelo (tēēn-tay pá-ra el páy-lo)
hair, el pelo (páy-lo), los cabellos (ka-bél-yos)
hairdresser, el(la) peluquero(a) (pay-loo-káy-ro/ra)
hairnet, la redecilla (ray-dhay-thēēl-ya)
hairpin, la horquilla (or-kēēl-ya)
lacquer, la laca (lá-ka)
permanent wave, la permanente (per-ma-nén-tay)
wave, la onda (ón-da)
wig, la peluca (pay-lōō-ka)

May I make an appointment?   ¿ Puede usted darme cita?

poo-áy-dhay oos-táydh dár-may thēē-ta

I want my hair trimmed.   Córteme un poco el pelo.

cór-tay-may oon pó-ko el páy-lo

Not too short.   No demasiado corto.

no day-ma-see-á-dho kór-to

Quite short.   Bastante corto.

bas-tán-tay kór-to

Don't take any off the top.   No corte nada de arriba.

no kór-tay ná-dha day a-rēē-ba

I want a manicure.   Deseo una manicura.

day-sáy-o ōō-na ma-nee-kōō-ra

I want my hair tinted.   Deseo teñirme el pelo.

day-sáy-o ten-yēēr-may el páy-lo

The same colour (darker, lighter).	El mismo color (más oscuro, más claro).

el mēēs-mo ko-lór (mas os-kōō-ro, mas klá-ro)

A shampoo and set, please.	Lavar y marcar, por favor.

la-vár ee mar-kár, por fa-vór

It is too hot.	Está demasiado caliente.

es-tá day-ma-see-á-dho ka-lee-én-tay

I have dry (greasy) hair.	Tengo el pelo seco (grasiento).

tén-go el páy-lo sáy-ko (gra-see-én-to)

I would like a cold (hot) perm.	Quisiera una permanente en frío (caliente).

kee-see-áy-ra ōō-na per-ma-nén-tay en frēē-o (ka-lee-én-tay)

PHOTOGRAPHY

VOCABULARY

camera, el aparato fotográfico (a-pa-rá-to fo-to-grá-fee-ko)
enlargement, la ampliación (am-plee-a-thee-ón)
film (colour), la cinta de color (thēēn-ta day ko-lór)
film (miniature), la cinta en miniatura (thēēn-ta en mee-nee-a-tōō-ra)
filter, el filtro de luz (fēēl-tro day looth)
flash bulb, la bombilla relámpago (bom-bēēl-ya ray-lám-pa-go)
lens, el objetivo (ob-hay-tēē-vo)
lens hood, el capuchón (ka-poo-chón)
light meter, el exposímetro (ex-po-sēē-may-tro)
negative, la prueba negativa (proo-áy-ba nay-ga-tēē-va)
photograph, la fotografía (fo-to-gra-fēē-a)
print, la copia (kó-pee-a)
range finder, el telémetro (tay-láy-may-tro)
shutter, el obturador (ob-too-ra-dhór)
slide, la diapositiva (dee-a-po-see-tēē-va)
snapshot, la instantánea (een-stan-tá-nay-a)
stereoscope, el estereoscopio (es-tay-ray-o-skó-pee-o)
view finder, el visór (vee-sór)
winder, el enrollador (en-rol-ya-dhór)

Have you a fast (colour) film?	¿Tiene usted una película rápida de color)?

tee-áy-nay oos-taydh ōō-na pay-lēē-koo-la rá-pee-dha (day co-lór)

What size do you want? ¿Qúe tamaño quiere?
kay ta-mán-yo kee-áy-ray

Will you develop this film please. Haga el favor de revelar esta película.
á-ga el fa-vór day ray-vay-lár és-ta pay-lēē-koo-la

When will it be ready? ¿Cuándo estará?
kwán-do es-ta-rá

I want two prints of each negative. Deseo dos copias de cada prueba.
day-sáy-o dos kó-pee-as day ká-dha proo-áy-ba

Please enlarge this. Amplíe esto, por favor.
am-plēē-ay és-to por fa-vór

They are under-exposed. No las ha revelado bastante.
no las a ray-vay-lá-dho bas-tán-tay

They are over-exposed. Las ha revelado demasiado.
las a ray-vay-lá-dho day-mas-ee-á-dho

The film is jammed. La cinta está atascada.
la thēēn-ta es-tá a-tas-ká-dha

The winder isn't working. El enrollador no funciona.
el en-rol-ya-dhór no foon-thee-ó-na

CLOTHING

VOCABULARY

MEN

belt, el cinturón (theen-too-rón)
bow-tie, la corbata de lazo (kor-bá-ta day lá-tho)
braces, los tirantes de pantalón (tee-rán-tays day pan-ta-lón)
button, el botón (bo-tón)
cap, la gorra (gó-ra)
collar, el cuello (koo-él-yo)
collar stud, el pasador (pa-sa-dhór)
cuff links, las gemelas (hay-máy-las)
dinner jacket, el smoking
dressing gown, la bata (bá-ta)
evening dress, el traje de etiqueta (trá-hay day ay-tee-káy-ta)
gloves, los guantes (goo-án-tays)
handkerchief, el pañuelo (pan-yoo-áy-lo)
hat, el sombrero (som-bráy-ro)
jacket, la chaqueta (cha-káy-ta)

jersey, el jersey (her-sáy)
overcoat, el abrigo (a-brēē-go)
pyjamas, el pijama (pee-há-ma)
raincoat, el impermeable (eem-per-may-á-blay), la gabardina (ga-bar-dēē-na)
sandals, las sandalias (san-dá-lee-as), las alpargatas (al-par-gá-tas)
shirt, la camisa (ka-mēē-sa)
shoes, los zapatos (tha-pá-tos), el calzado (kal-thá-dho)
slippers, las zapatillas (tha-pa-tēēl-yas)
socks, los calcetines (kal-thay-tēē-nays)
suit, el traje (trá-hay)
tie, la corbata (kor-bá-ta)
trousers, el pantalón (pan-ta-lón)
underpants, el calzoncillo (kal-thon-thēēl-yo)
vest, la camiseta (ka-mee-sáy-ta)
waistcoat, el chaleco (cha-láy-ko)

WOMEN

belt, el cinturón (theen-too-rón)
blouse, la blusa (blōō-sa)
bracelet, el brazalete (bra-tha-láy-tay)
brassiere, el sostén (sos-tén)
brooch, el broche (bró-chay)
button, el botón (bo-tón)
cloth, el paño (pán-yo)
coat, la chaqueta (cha-káy-ta)
corset, el corsé (kor-sáy)
cotton, el algodón (al-go-dhón)
dress, el vestido (ves-tēē-dho), el traje (trá-hay)
dressing-gown, la bata (bá-ta)
ear-rings, los pendientes (pen-dee-én-tays)
fine, fino (fēē-no)
frock, el vestido (ves-tēē-dho)
girdle, la faja (fá-ha)
gloves, las guantes (goo-án-tays)
gown, el traje de tarde (trá-hay day tár-day)
handkerchief, el pañuelo (pan-yoo-áy-lo)
hat, el sombrero (som-bráy-ro)
headscarf, el pañuelo de cabeza (pan-yoo-áy-lo day ka-báy-tha)
jacket, la chaqueta (cha-káy-ta)
jumper, el jersey (her-sáy)
lace, el encaje (en-ká-hay)
lingerie, la ropa interior (ró-pa een-tay-ree-ór)
loose, holgado (ol-gá-dho), flotante (flo-tán-tay)
low neck, el escote (es-kó-tay)
necklace, el collar (kol-yár)
nightdress, la camisa de dormir (ka-mēē-sa day dor-mēēr)
nylon, el nilón (nee-lón)

panties, las bragas (brá-gas)
petticoat, el enaguas (en-á-gwas)
pyjamas, el pijama (pee-há-ma)
rayon, el rayón (ray-ón)
scarf, la bufanda (boo-fán-da)
shawl, el mantón (man-tón)
shoes, los zapatos (tha-pá-tos)
skirt, la falda (fál-da)
silk, la seda (sáy-dha)
slip, la combinación (kom-bee-na-thee-ón)
stockings, las medias (máy-dhee-as)
suit, el traje (trá-hay)
suspender, el tirante de media (tee-rán-tay day máy-dhee-a)
suspender-belt, el porta-ligas (pór-ta-lēē-gas)
wool, la lana (lá-na)
zip, el cierre relámpago (thee-áy-ray ray-lám-pa-go)

What is your size? ¿Cuál es su tamaño?
kwal es soo ta-mán-yo

The English size is . . . La medida inglesa es de . . .
la may-dhēē-dha een-glày-sa es day

Can you match this colour? ¿Puede usted aparear este color?
poo-áy-dhay oos-táydh a-pa-ray-ár és-tay ko-lór

May I see this by daylight? ¿Puedo verlo a la luz del día?
poo-áy-dho vér-lo a la looth del dēē-a

I (do not) like this colour. (No) me gusta este color.
(no) may gōōs-ta és-tay ko-lór

I prefer that one. Me gusta más ése.
may gōōs-ta mas áy-say

I prefer a lighter (darker) colour. Prefiero un color más claro (más oscuro).
pray-fee-áy-ro oon ko-lór mas klá-ro (mas os-kōō-ro)

Will it fade? ¿Se perderá el color?
say per-day-rá el ko-lór

Will it shrink? ¿Se encogerá?
say en-ko-hay-rá

May I try it on? ¿Puedo probármelo?
poo-áy-dho pro-bár-may-lo

It is too big (small, loose, tight, long, short).

Es demasiado grande (pequeño, holgado, justo, largo, corto).

es day-ma-see-á-dho grán-day (pay-káyn-yø, ol-gá-dho, hōōs-to, lár-go, kór-to)

How long would you take to make me a suit?

¿Cuánto tardaría en hacerme un traje?

kwán-to tar-da-rēē-a en a-thér-may oon trá-hay

It does not fit me.

No me sienta bien.

no may see-áyn-ta bee-én

Can you alter it?

¿Puede usted modificarlo?

poo-áy-dhay oos-táydh mo-dhee-fee-kár-lo

REPAIRS

VOCABULARY

heel, el tacón (ta-kón)
key, la llave (lyá-vay)
lock, la cerradura (thay-ra-dhōō-ra)
sole, la suela (soo-áy-la)
spring, la cuerda (kwér-da)
strap, la correa (ko-ráy-a)
watch, el reloj (ray-ló)

I have broken, torn . . .

He roto . . .

ay ró-to . . .

I dropped it.

Se me cayó.

say may ka-yó

Can you repair . . . ?

¿Puede usted arreglar . . . ?

poo-áy-dhay oos-táydh a-ray-glár . . .

How long will it take?

¿Cuánto tardará?

kwán-to tar-da-rá

Will it be expensive?

¿Costará mucho?

kos-ta-rá mōō-cho

I need new lenses (frame)

Necesito nuevos cristales (una nueva montura).

nay-thay-sēē-to noo-áy-vos krees-tá-lays (noo-áy-va mon-tōō-ra)

My watch won't go.

Mi reloj no anda.

mee ray-ló no án-da

It gains (loses).	Adelanta (retrasa).
	a-dhay-lán-ta (ray-trá-sa)
Can you let me have it back by . . . ?	¿Puede usted devolvérmelo para . . . ?
	poo-áy-dhay oos-táydh de-vol-vér-may-lo pá-ra . . .
I need new soles (heels)	Necisito suelas nuevas (tacones nuevos).
	nay-thay-sēē-to soo-áy-las noo-áy-vas (ta-kó-nays noo-áy-vos)
Can you patch it?	¿Puede ponerlo un remiendo?
	poo-áy-dhay po-nér-lo oon ray-mee-én-do
Can you sew it?	¿Puede coserlo?
	poo-áy-dhay ko-sér-lo

ACCIDENTS AND ILLNESS

Most drugs except morphia, etc., can be obtained from chemists without a prescription. It is useful to take with one a bottle of Mist. kaolin et Morph. (no prescription needed in Great Britain) as it is the best first aid for summer diarrhoea. Chemists often give good advice as well as first aid if needed. The fees of G.P.'s and specialists are reasonable but not many speak English. Dentists in Spain are also qualified doctors. Many small towns are served by non-resident dentists who visit the town two or three days a week. If you are not a regular patient the doctor or dentist will expect his fee on the spot.

VOCABULARY

PARTS OF THE BODY

ankle, el tobillo (to-bēēl-yo)
arm, el brazo (brá-tho)
back, la espalda (es-pál-da)
blood, la sangre (sán-gray)
bone, el hueso (wáy-so)
bowel, los intestinos (een-tes-tēē-nos)
cheek, la mejilla (may-hēēl-ya)
chest, el pecho (páy-cho)
chin, la barbilla (bar-bēēl-ya)
dentures, la dentadura (dayn-ta-dhōō-ra)
ear, la oreja (o-ráy-ha)
elbow, el codo (kó-dho)
eye, el ojo (ó-ho)
eyelid, el párpado (pár-pa-dho)
face, la cara (ká-ra)
finger, el dedo (dáy-dho)

S.P.B.---E

foot, el pie (pee-áy)
gum, la encía (en-thēē-a)
hand, la mano (má-no)
head, la cabeza (ka-báy-tha)
heart, el corazón (ko-ra-thón)
heel, el talón (ta-lón)
hip, la cadera (ka-dháy-ra)
joint, la articulación (ar-tee-koo-la-thee-ón)
kidney, el riñón (reen-yón)
knee, la rodilla (ro-dhēēl-ya)
knee-cap, la rodillera (ro-dheel-yáy-ra)
leg, la pierna (pee-áyr-na)
lip, el labio (lá-bee-o)
liver, el hígado (ēē-ga-dho)
lung, el pulmón (pool-món)
mouth, la boca (bó-ka)
neck, el cuello (koo-áyl-yo)
nerve, el nervio (náyr-vee-o)
nose, la nariz (na-rēēth)
shoulder, el hombro (óm-bro)
stomach, el estómago (es-tó-ma-go), el vientre (vee-áyn-tray)
throat, la garganta (gar-gán-ta)
toe, el dedo del pie (dáy-dho del pee-áy)
tongue, la lengua (lén-gwa)
tooth, el diente (dee-én-tay), la muela (moo-áy-la)
wrist, la muñeca (moon-yáy-ka)

GENERAL

abscess, el absceso (abs-tháy-so)
accident, el accidente (ak-thee-dháyn-tay)
ambulance, la ambulancia (am-boo-lán-thee-a)
appendicitis, la apendecitis (a-pen-day-thēē-tees)
bandage, la venda (váyn-da)
bite, el mordisco (mor-dēēs-ko)
blister, la ampolla (am-pól-ya)
boil, el furúnculo (foo-rōōn-koo-lo)
bruise, la contusión (kon-too-see-ón)
burn, la quemadura (kay-ma-dhōō-ra)
    heart-burn, la acedía (a-thay-dhēē-a)
    sun-burn, la quemadura del sol (kay-ma-dhōō-ra del sol)
chill, el resfriado (rays-free-á-dho)
chiropodist, el callista (kal-yēēs-ta)
cold, el constipado (kon-stee-pá-dho)
constipation, el estreñimiento (es-tren-yee-mee-én-to)
convalescence, la convalecencia (kon-va-lay-thén-thee-a)
cough, la tos (tos)
cramp, el entumecimiento (en-too-may-thee-mee-én-to)
cure, la cura (kōō-ra), el remedio (ray-máy-dhee-o)
cut, la cuchillada (koo-cheel-yá-dha)

dentist, el dentista (dayn-tēēs-ta)
diarrhoea, la diarrea (dee-a-ráy-a)
doctor, el médico (máy-dhee-ko)
emergency service, el servicio de urgencia (sayr-vēē-thee-o day oor-hén-thee-a)
epidemic, el epidémico (ay-pee-dháy-mee-ko)
faint, el desmayo (days-má-yo)
fever, la fiebre (fee-áy-bray)
filling, la orificación (o-ree-fee-ka-thee-ón)
la empastadura (em-pas-ta-dhōō-ra)
fracture, la fractura (frak-tōō-ra)
hay-fever, el romadizo (ro-ma-dhēē-tho)
hospital, el hospital (os-pee-tál)
illness, la enfermedad (en-fer-may-dhádh)
indigestion, la indigestión (een-dee-hes-tee-ón)
influenza, la gripe (grēē-pay)
injection, la inyección (een-yek-thee-ón)
insomnia, el insomnio (een-sóm-nee-o)
nausea, el asco (ás-ko)
nurse, la enfermera (en-fer-máy-ra)
operation, la operación (o-pay-ra-thee-ón)
pain, el dolor (do-lór)
patient, el enfermo (en-fér-mo)
poison, el veneno (vay-náy-no)
policeman, el guardia (gwár-dee-a)
remedy, el remedio (ray-máy-dhee-o)
spot, la maca (má-ka)
sprain, la torcedura (tor-thay-dhōō-ra)
sting, la picadura (pee-ka-dhōō-ra)
stomach ache, el dolor de estómago (do-lór day es-tó-ma-go)
stye, el orzuelo (or-thoo-áy-lo)
sunstroke, la insolación (een-so-la-thee-ón)
surgeon, el cirujano (thee-roo-há-no)
surgery, el consultorio (kon-sool-tó-ree-o)
swelling, la tumefacción (too-may-fak-thee-ón)
temperature, la temperatura (taym-payr-a-tōō-ra)
toothache, el dolor de muelas (do-lór day moo-áy-las)
treatment, el tratamiento (tra-ta-mee-én-to)
wound, la herida (ay-rēē-dha)
X-ray, la radiografía (ra-dhee-o-gra-fēē-a)

There has been an accident.   Ha habido un accidente.
a a-bēē-dho oon ak-thee-dhén-tay

Call a policeman quickly.   Llame rápido un guardia.
lyá-may rá-pee-dho oon gwár-dee-a

Call an ambulance (the emergency service).
Haga mandar una ambulancia (el servicio de urgencia).
á-ga man-dár ōō-na am-boo-lán-thee-a (ser-vēē-thee-o day oor-hén-thee-a)

Is there a doctor near here?
¿Hay un médico cerca de aquí?
á-ee oon máy-dhee-ko thér-ka day a-kēē

Someone has fallen in the water.
Alguien ha caído al agua.
ál-gee-en a ka-ēē-dho al á-gwa

He (she) is seriously injured.
Está gravemente herido(a).
es-tá gra-vay-mén-tay ay-rēē-dho(a)

He (she) has been run over.
Ha sido atropellado(a).
a sēē-dho a-tro-payl-yá-dho(a)

He (she) is losing blood.
Pierde la sangre.
pee-áyr-day la sán-gray

He has lost consciousness.
Ha perdido el sentido.
a per-dēē-dho el sen-tēē-dho

He has fainted.
Se ha desmayado.
say a des-ma-yá-dho

He has burnt (cut) his face.
Se ha quemado (cortado) la cara.
say a kay-má-dho (kor-tá-dho) la ká-ra

It is bleeding.
Echa sangre.
áy-cha sán-gray

It is swollen.
Está entumecido.
es-tá en-too-may-thēē-dho

Who is responsible for the accident?
¿Quién ha causado el accidente?
kee-én a kow-sá-dho el ak-thee-dén-tay

Have you any bandages?
¿Tiene usted vendas?
tee-áy-nay oos-taydh vén-das

Can you dress this wound?
¿Puede usted curar esta herida?
poo-áy-dhay oos-táydh koo-rár és-ta ay-rēē-dha

Can you make a splint?
¿Sabe usted hacer una tablilla?
sá-bay oos-táydh a-thér ōō-na ta-blēēl-ya

Bring hot (cold) water (a blanket).
Traiga agua caliente (fría) (una manta).
trá-ee-ga á-gwa ka-lee-én-tay (frēē-a) (ōō-na mán-ta)

He (she) ought to be X-rayed.
Deberían hacerle una radiografía.
deb-ay-rēē-an a-thér-lay ōō-na ra-dhee-o-gra-fēē-a

Help me to carry him (her).
Ayúdeme a llevarle (la).
a-yōō-dhay-may a lyay-vár-le(la)

Don't move the injured.
No mueva al (a la) herido(a).
no moo-áy-va al (a la) ay-rēē-dho(a)

He (she) is not well.
No está bien.
no es-tá bee-én

I am feeling very ill. Please send for the doctor.
Me siento muy enfermo(a). Mande buscar al médico, por favor.
may see-én-to mwee en-fér-mo(a). mán-day boos-kár al máy-dhee-ko por fa-vór

I have a pain in . . .
Me duele . . .
may doo-áy-lay . . .

Do you feel any pain here?
¿ Le duele aquí?
lay doo-áy-lay a-kēē

Show me your tongue.
Enséñeme la lengua.
en-sáyn-yay-may la lén-gwa

I am not sleeping well.
No duermo.
no doo-ér-mo

I cannot eat.
No puedo comer.
no poo-áy-dho ko-mér

I have no appetite.
No tengo apetito.
no tén-go a-pay-tēē-to

I have a stomach ache.
Tengo dolor de estómago.
tén-go do-lór day es-tó-ma-go

I feel giddy.
La cabeza se me vuelve.
la ka-báy-tha say may voo-áyl-vay

I think I have food poisoning.
Creo haber comido algo en malas condiciones.
kráy-o a-bér ko-mēē-dho ál-go en má-las kon-dee-thee-ó-nays

Will you give me a prescription? ¿Quiere usted darme una receta?

kee-áy-ray oos-táydh dár-may ŏŏ-na ray-tháy-ta

What must I do? ¿Qué debo hacer?

kay dáy-bo a-thér

Should I stay in bed? ¿Guardo la cama?

gwár-do la ká-ma

I feel better. Me siento mejor.

may see-én-to may-hór

When will you come and see me again? ¿Cuándo volverá usted a verme?

kwán-do vol-vay-rá oos-táydh a vér-may

How much is your fee, doctor? ¿Cuánto es su honorario, doctor?

kwán-to es soo o-no-rá-ree-o, dok-tór

Where is there a chemist who will make up this prescription? ¿Dónde hay una farmacia que me haga esta receta?

dón-day á-ee ŏŏ-na far-má-thee-a kay may á-ga és-ta ray-tháy-ta

Can you recommend a dentist? ¿Puede usted recomendarme un dentista?

poo-áy-dhay oos-táydh ray-ko-men-dhár-may oon den-tēēs-ta

Can you give me an appointment for Monday? ¿Puede usted darme cita para el lunes?

poo-áy-dhay oos-táydh dár-may thēē-ta pá-ra el lŏŏ-nays

I have toothache. Tengo dolor de muelas.

tén-go do-lór day moo-áy-las

It aches a lot; I cannot wait. Duele mucho; no puedo esperar.

doo-áy-lay mŏŏ-cho; no poo-áy-dho es-pay-rár

Will you extract it? ¿Quiere usted sacármelo?

kee-áy-ray oos-táydh sa-kár-may-lo

Can you save it? ¿Puede salvarlo?

poo-áy-dhay sal-vár-lo

I have lost a filling. He perdido una empastadura.

ay per-dēē-dho ŏŏ-na em-pas-ta-dhŏŏ-ra

I am going to fill it.	Voy a empastarlo.
	voy a em-pas-tár-lo
You are hurting me.	Me hace daño.
	may á-thay dán-yo
I prefer gas (an injection).	Prefiero el gas (una inyección).
	pray-fee-áy-ro el gas (ōō-na een-yek-thee-ón)
My gums are swollen (are bleeding).	Mis encías están hinchadas (echan sangre).
	mees en-thēē-as es-tán een-chá-dhas (áy-chan sán-gray)
I have broken my dentures.	He roto mi dentadura.
	ay ró-to mee den-ta-dhōō-ra
Can you repair it quickly?	¿ Puede arreglarla rápido ?
	poo-áy-dhay a-ray-glár-la rá-pee-dho

PLACES AND INHABITANTS

Africa, Africa, africano (á-free-ka, a-free-ká-no)
Andalusia, Andalucía, andaluz (an-da-loo-thēē-a, an-da-lúth)
Aragon, Aragón, aragonés (a-ra-gón, a-ra-go-nés)
Argentina, la Argentina, argentino (ar-hen-tēē-na, ar-hen-tēē-no)
Asturias, Asturias, asturiano (as-tōō-ree-as, as-too-ree-á-no)
Australia, Australia, australiano (ows-trá-lee-a, ows-tra-lee-á-no)
Austria, Austria, austríaco (óws-tree-a, ows-trēē-a-ko)
Basque provinces, Vascongadas, vasco, vascuence (vas-kon-gá-das, vás-ko, vas-kwén-thay)
Belgium, Bélgica, belga (bél-hee-ka, bél-ga)
Bolivia, Bolivia, boliviano (bo-lēē-vee-a, bo-lee-vee-á-no)
Brazil, el Brasil, brasileño (bra-sēēl, bra-see-láyn-yo)
Canada, el Canadá, canadiense (ka-na-dhá, ka-na-dhee-én-say)
Castile, Castilla, castillano (kas-tēēl-ya, kas-teel-yá-no)
Catalonia, Cataluña, catalán (ka-ta-lōōn-ya, ka-ta-lán)
Chile, Chile, chileno (chēē-lay, chee-láy-no)
Colombia, Colombia, colombiano (ko-lóm-bee-a, ko-lom-bee-á-no)
Ecuador, el Ecuador, ecuatoriano (ay-kwa-dhór, ay-kwa-to-ree-á-no)
England, Inglaterra, inglés (een-gla-táy-ra, een-gláys)
Extremadura, Extremadura, extremeño (ex-tray-ma-dhōō-ra, ex-tray-máyn-yo)
France, Francia, francés (frán-thee-a, fran-thés)
Galicia, Galicia, gallego (ga-lēē-thee-a, gal-yáy-go)
Germany, Alemania, alemán (a-lay-má-nee-a, a-lay-mán)
Great Britain, la Gran Bretaña, británico (gran bray-tán-ya, bree-tá-nee-ko)
Greece, Grecia, griego (gráy-thee-a, gree-áy-go)
India, la India, indio (ēēn-dee-a, ēēn-dee-o)
Ireland, Irlanda, irlandés (eer-lán-da, eer-lan-dés)

Israel, Israel, judío (ees-ra-él, hoo-dēē-o)
Italy, Italia, italiano (ee-tá-lee-a, ee-ta-lee-á-no)
Majorca, Mallorca, mallorquin (mal-yór-ka, mal-yor-kēēn)
Malaga, Málaga, malagueño (má-la-ga, ma-la-gáyn-yo)
Mexico, Méjico, mejicano (máy-hee-ko, may-hee-ká-no)
Morocco, Marruecos, marroquí (mar-wáy-kos, ma-ro-kēē)
Navarre, Navarra, navarrés (na-vá-ra, na-va-rés)
Netherlands, los Países Bajos, holandés (pa-ēē-says bá-hos, o-lan-dés)
New Zealand, la Nueva Zelanda, nuevazelandés (noo-áy-va thay-lán-da, noo-áy-va-thay-lan-dés)
Norway, Noruega, noruego (nor-wáy-ga, nor-wáy-go)
Panama, el Panamá, panameño (pa-na-má, pa-na-máyn-yo)
Paraguay, el Paraguay, paraguayo (pa-ra-goo-á-ee, pa-ra-goo-á-yo)
Peru, el Perú, peruviano (pay-rōō, pay-roo-vee-á-no)
Porto Rico, Puerto Rico, puertoriqueño (pwáyr-to rēē-ko, pwayr-to-ree-káyn-yo)
Portugal, Portugal, portugués (por-too-gál, por-too-gáys)
Russia, la Unión Soviética, ruso (oo-nee-ón so-vee-áy-tee-ka, rōō-so)
Scotland, Escocia, escocés (es-kó-thee-a, es-ko-thés)
Seville, Sevilla, sevillano (say-vēēl-ya, say-veel-yá-no)
South America, la América del sur, suramericano (a-máy-ree-ka del soor, soor-a-may-ree-ká-no)
Spain, España, español (es-pán-ya, es-pan-yól)
Sweden, Suecia, sueco (swáy-thee-a, swáy-ko)
Switzerland, Suiza, suizo (swēē-tha, swēē-tho)
Tangiers, Tánger (tán-her)
Uruguay, el Uruguay, uruguayo (oo-roo-gwá-ee, oo-roo-gwá-yo)
U.S.A., los Estados Unidos, norteamericano (es-tá-dhos oo-nēē-dos, nor-tay-a-may-ree-ká-no)
Venezuela, Venezuela, venezolano (vay-nay-thoo-áy-la, vay-nay-tho-lá-no)
Wales, El País de Gales, galés (pa-ēēs day gá-lays, ga-láys)

STUDENT LIFE AND AU PAIR

VOCABULARY

bursary, la beca (báy-ka)
certificate, el diploma (dee-pló-ma)
class, la clase (klá-say)
course, el curso (kōōr-so)
examination, el examen (ex-á-men)
excellent, sobresaliente (so-bray-sa-lee-én-tay)
fee, la matrícula (ma-trēē-koo-la)
homesickness, la añoranza (an-yo-rán-tha)
housework, los quehaceres domésticos (kay-a-tháy-rays do-máys-tee-kos)
lecture, la conferencia (kon-fay-rén-thee-a)
lecturer, el(la) conferenciante (kon-fay-ren-thee-án-tay)

lodging, el alojamiento (a-lo-ha-mee-én-to)
note, to, apuntar (a-poon-tár)
notebook, el cuaderno (kwa-dáyr-no)
pocket money, el dinero para gastos pequeños (dee-náy-ro pá-ra gás-tos pay-káyn-yos)
professor, el catedrático (ka-tay-drá-tee-ko)
student, el(la) estudiante (es-too-dhee-án-tay)
term, el trimestre (tree-máys-tray)
thesis, la tesis (táy-sees)
tutor, el tutor (too-tór)
university, la universidad (oo-nee ver-see-dádh)

Welcome to ...   Sea el(la) bienvenido(a) a ...
  sáy-a el (la) bee-en-vay-nēē-dho (dha) a ...

Did you have a good journey?   ¿Ha hecho un buen viaje?
  a áy-cho oon boo-én vee-á-hay

Do you need anything?   ¿Le hace falta algo?
  lay á-thay fál-ta ál-go

Is there anything you don't eat? ¿Hay algo que no come?
  á-ee ál-go kay no kó-may

I can't eat ...   No puedo comer ...
  no poo-áy-dho ko-mér ...

I shall give you ... per week   Le daré ... por semana para
pocket-money.   sus gastos pequeños.
  lay da-ray ... por say-má-na pá-ra soos gás-tos pay-káyn-yos

Will you help with the house-   ¿Quiere usted ayudar con los
work (shopping, washing-up,   quehaceres domésticos (a
to look after the children)?   hacer las compras, a lavar la
                                        vajilla, a cuidar a los niños)?
  kee-áy-ray oes-táydh a-yoo-dhár kon los kay-a-thér-ays do-máys-tee-kos (a a-thér
    las kóm-pras, a la-vár la va-hēēl-ya, a kwee-dhár a los nēēn-yos)

Could you take the children to   ¿Quiere usted llevar a los
school?   niños a la escuela?
  kee-áy-ray oos-táydh lyay-vár a los nēēn-yos a la es-kwáy-la

May I go out?   ¿Puedo salir?
  pwáy-dho sa-lēēr

Where is the Catholic (Protes- ¿Dónde está la iglesia católica
tant) church? (protestante)?
dón-day es-tá la ee-gláy-see-a ka-tó-lee-ka (pro-tays-tán-tay)

At what time is mass? ¿A qúe hora se dice la misa?
a kay ó-ra say dēē-thay la mēē-sa

I want to go to confession. Quiero confesarme.
kee-áy-ro kon-fay-sár-may

Have you written to your ¿Ha escrito a sus padres?
parents?
a es-krēē-to a soos pá-drays

Where is the faculty of arts ¿Dónde está la facultad de
(law, science, medicine)? letras (derecho, ciencias,
medicina)?
dón-day es-tá la fa-kool-tádh day láy-tras (day-ráy-cho, thee-én-thee-as, may-dhay-
thēē-na)

Where can I enrol for . . . ? ¿Dónde puedo matricularme
para . . . ?
dón-day poo-áy-dho ma-tree-koo-lár-may pá-ra . . .

Are there any courses for ¿Hay cursos para extranjeros?
foreigners?
á-ee kōōr-sos pá-ra ex-tran-háy-ros

Does one get a certificate? ¿Se otorga un diploma?
say o-tór-ga oon dee-pló-ma

A course not leading to a Un curso sin efectos acadé-
certificate or degree. micos.
oon kōōr-so seen ay-fék-tos a-ka-dháy-mee-kos

Where can I pay the fee? ¿Dónde puedo pagar la matrícula?
dón-day poo-áy-dho pa-gár la ma-trēē-koo-la

I am looking for lodgings. Busco alojamiento.
bōōs-ko a-lo-ha-mee-én-to

Where is the library (reading ¿Dónde está la biblioteca (sala
room)? de lectura)?
dón-day es-tá la bee-blee-o-táy-ka (sá-la day lek-tōō-ra)

Is there a students' club (restaurant)?

¿Hay un club (restaurante) para estudiantes?

á-ee oon kloob (res-tow-rán-tay) pá-ra es-too-dhee-án-tays

Is there a reduction in price for students?

¿Hay una rebaja para los estudiantes?

á-ee ōō-na ray-bá-ha pá-ra los es-too-dhee-án-tays

Here is my student's card.

Aquí tiene usted mi tarjeta de estudiante.

a-kēē tee-áy-nay oos-táydh mee tar-háy-ta day es-too-dhee-án-tay

MONEY

Banks are open from about 9 a.m. to 1 p.m. and for a time in the afternoon. Like shops they have a longer break in the middle of the day from May to October. Only the cashier pays out money and this only on surrender of a numbered ticket obtained from the window where one has done business. A quarter of an hour often elapses between obtaining a ticket and the cashier calling one's number. When cashing a traveller's cheque one is required to show one's passport and give an address. There is a charge (not everywhere the same) of a few pesetas for cashing a cheque and stamp duty of a few cents.

VOCABULARY

bank, el banco (bán-ko)
cashier's window, pagos (pá-gos)
cheque, el cheque (cháy-kay)
dollars, dólares (dó-la-rays)
exchange, el cambio (kám-bee-o)
francs, francos (frán-kos)
letter of credit, la carta de crédito (kár-ta day kráy-dhee-to)
note, el billete (beel-yáy-tay)
pound sterling, la libra esterlina (lēē-bra es-ter-lēē-na)
rate of exchange, el cambio (kám-bee-o)
traveller's cheque, el cheque de viajero (cháy-kay day vee-a-háy-ro)
window, la ventanilla (vayn-ta-nēēl-ya)

Is there a bank near here?

¿Hay un banco cerca de aquí?

á-ee oon bán-ko tháyr-ka day a-kēē

At what time does the bank open?	¿A qué hora se abre el banco?
	a kay ó-ra say á-bray el bán-ko

I should like to cash a cheque.	Deseo cambiar un cheque.
	day-sáy-o kam-bee-ár oon cháy-kay

What is the pound at?	¿A cuánto está la libra?
	a kwán-to es-tá la lēē-bra

Sign here please.	Firme aquí por favor.
	fēēr-may a-kēē por fa-vór

How would you like it?	¿Cómo lo quiere usted?
	kó-mo lo kee-áy-ray oos-táydh

One large note and the rest small.	Un billete grande y los demás pequeños.
	oon beel-yáy-tay grán-day ee los day-más pay-káyn-yos

TABLES

The following units of currency are used. The traveller should work out for himself or herself a few useful equivalents at the prevailing rate and note them in the space provided.

SPAIN

100 céntimos (tháyn-tee-mos)=1 peseta (pay-sáy-ta)

£1	=	10s.	=	5s.	=	1s.	=
5 dollars	=	2 dollars	=	1 dollar	=	50 cents	=

ARGENTINA, MEXICO

100 centavos (thayn-tá-vos)=1 peso (páy-so)

£1	=	10s.	=	5s.	=	1s.	=
5 dollars	=	2 dollars	=	1 dollar	=	50 cents	=

NUMBERS

1 = uno (ōō-no) [un, una (oon, ōō-na) before a noun]
2 = dos (dos)
3 = tres (trays)
4 = cuatro (kwá-tro)
5 = cinco (thēēn-ko)
6 = seis (sáy-ees)
7 = siete (see-áy-tay)
8 = ocho (ó-cho)
9 = nueve (noo-áy-vay)
10 = diez (dee-áyth)
11 = once (ón-thay)
12 = doce (dó-thay)
13 = trece (tráy-thay)
14 = catorce (ka-tór-thay)
15 = quince (kēēn-thay)
16 = dieciseis (dee-ayth-ee-sáy-ees)
17 = diecisiete (dee-ayth-ee-see-áy-tay)
18 = dieciocho (dee-ayth-ee-ó-cho)
19 = diecinueve (dee-ayth-ee-noo-áy-vay)
20 = veinte (váy-een-tay)
21 = veintiuno (*see* uno) (vay-een-tee-ōō-no)
22 = veintidos (vay-een-tee-dhós)
30 = treinta (tráy-een-ta)
31 = treinta y uno (tray-een-ta ee ōō-no)
32 = treinta y dos (tray-een-ta ee dós)
40 = cuarenta (kwa-rén-ta)
41 = cuarenta y uno (kwa-rén-ta ee ōō-no)
50 = cincuenta (theen-kwáyn-ta)
51 = cincuenta y uno (thee-kwáyn-ta ee ōō-no)
60 = sesenta (say-sáyn-ta)
61 = sesenta y uno (say-sáyn-ta ee ōō-no)
70 = setenta (say-tén-ta)
71 = setenta y uno (say-ten-ta ee ōō-no)
80 = ochenta (o-cháyn-ta)
81 = ochenta y uno (o-cháyn-ta ee ōō-no)
90 = noventa (no-váyn-ta)
91 = noventa y uno (no-váyn-ta ee ōō-no)
100 = ciento (thee-áyn-to) [cien (thee-áyn) before a noun]
200 = doscientos(as) (dos-thee-áyn-tos/as)
300 = trescientos(as) (trays-thee-áyn-tos/as)
1,000 = mil (meel)
2,000 = dos mil (dos meel)
1 million = un millón (oon meel-yón)

    1st = primero (pree-máy-ro)
    2nd = segundo (say-gōōn-do)
    3rd = tercero (tayr-tháy-ro)
    4th = cuarto (kwár-to)
    5th = quinto (kēēn-to)
    6th = sexto (sáys-to)
    7th = septimo (sáy-tee-mo)
    8th = octavo (ok-tá-vo)
    9th = noveno (no-váy-no)
    10th = décimo (dáy-thee-mo)

From here on one uses the cardinal numbers *uno*, *dos*, etc., with the exceptions of *vigésimo* (vee-háy-see-mo), 20th; and *centésimo* (thayn-táy-see-mo), 100th.

    half, la mitad (mee-tádh), but ½ **kilo** = medio kilo (máy-dhee-o)
    half asleep, medio dormido (máy-dhee-o dor-mēē-do)
    a quarter, un cuarto (kwár-to)
    a third, un tercio (táyr-thee-o)
    two thirds, los dos tercios (dos táyr-thee-os)
    a fifth, la quinta parte (kēēn-ta pár-tay)

CONVERSION TABLES

DISTANCE

Kilómetros		Miles	Miles		Kilómetros
1	approx.	$\frac{5}{8}$	1	approx.	1·6
2	,,	$1\frac{1}{4}$	2	,,	3·2
3	,,	$1\frac{7}{8}$	3	,,	4·8
4	,,	$2\frac{1}{2}$	4	,,	6·4
5	,,	$3\frac{1}{8}$	5	,,	8
6	,,	$3\frac{3}{4}$	6	,,	9·6
7	,,	$4\frac{3}{8}$	7	,,	11·3
8	,,	5	8	,,	12·9
9	,,	$5\frac{5}{8}$	9	,,	14·5
10	,,	$6\frac{1}{4}$	10	,,	16·1
15	,,	$9\frac{3}{8}$	15	,,	24·1
20	,,	$12\frac{1}{2}$	20	,,	32·2
25	,,	$15\frac{5}{8}$	25	,,	40·2
30	,,	$18\frac{3}{4}$	30	,,	48·3
35	,,	$21\frac{7}{8}$	35	,,	56·3
40	,,	25	40	,,	64·4
45	,,	$28\frac{1}{8}$	45	,,	72·4
50	,,	$31\frac{3}{8}$	50	,,	80·5
55	,,	$34\frac{3}{8}$	55	,,	88·5
60	,,	$37\frac{1}{2}$	60	,,	96·6
65	,,	$40\frac{5}{8}$	65	,,	104·6
70	,,	$43\frac{3}{4}$	70	,,	112·7
75	,,	$46\frac{7}{8}$	75	,,	120·7
80	,,	50	80	,,	128·7
85	,,	$53\frac{1}{8}$	85	,,	136·8
90	,,	$56\frac{1}{4}$	90	,,	144·8
95	,,	$59\frac{3}{8}$	95	,,	152·9
100	,,	$62\frac{1}{2}$	100	,,	161

N.B. A rough way to convert kilometres to miles: divide the kilometres by 8 and multiply by 5. E.g. 32 kms. $\div 8 = 4 \times 5 = 20$ miles.

Vice versa, to convert miles to kilometres divide by 5 and multiply by 8. E.g. 35 miles $\div 5 = 7 \times 8 = 56$ kms.

LENGTH

Centímetros		Feet	Inches	Feet	Inches		Centímetros
1	approx.		2/5"		1"	approx.	2·5
5	,,		2"		3"	,,	7·5
10	,,		4"		6"	,,	15
15	,,		6"		9"	,,	22·5
20	,,		8"	1'		,,	30·5
25	,,		10"	1'	6"	,,	45·5
50	,,	1'	8"	2'		,,	61
75	,,	2'	6"	2'	6"	,,	75
100 (1 metro)		3'	3"	3'		,,	91·5

ALTITUDE

Metros		Feet	Feet		Metros
25	approx.	82	50	approx.	15
50	,,	164	75	,,	23
75	,,	246	100	,,	31
100	,,	328	250	,,	76
250	,,	820	500	,,	152
500	,,	1,640	1,000	,,	305
1,000	,,	3,281	2,000	,,	610
2,000	,,	6,562	3,000	,,	915
3,000	,,	9,843	4,000	,,	1,220
4,000	,,	13,124	5,000	,,	1,525

N.B. To convert metres roughly to yards multiply by 12 and divide by 11.
E.g. 100 metres × 12 = 1,200 ÷ 11 = 109 yards.

LIQUID MEASURES

Litros		Pints and Gallons	Gallons		Litros
1	approx.	1¾ pints	⅛ (1 pint)	approx.	0·57
2	,,	3½ ,,	¼ (2 pints)	,,	1·15
3	,,	5¼ ,,	½ (4 pints)	,,	2·3
4	,,	7 ,,	¾ (6 pints)	,,	3·42
5	,,	1·1 gallons	1	,,	4·5
6	,,	1·3 ,,	2	,,	9·1
7	,,	1·5 ,,	3	,,	13·6
8	,,	1·8 ,,	4	,,	18·2
9	,,	2·0 ,,	5	,,	22·7